KINETIC THEORY OF GASES

INTERNATIONAL SERIES IN PURE AND APPLIED PHYSICS

LEONARD I. SCHIFF, *Consulting Editor*

The late F. K. Richtmyer was Consulting Editor of the series from its inception in 1929 to his death in 1939.   Lee A. DuBridge was Consulting Editor from 1939 to 1946, and G. P. Harnwell from 1947 to 1954.

KINETIC THEORY
OF GASES

R. D. Present

Professor of Physics
University of Tennessee

McGRAW-HILL BOOK COMPANY, INC.

New York   Toronto   London

1958

KINETIC THEORY OF GASES

Library of Congress Catalog Card Number 58-6694

III

50730

THE MAPLE PRESS COMPANY, YORK, PA.

To the memory of:

J. F. Carlson
H. H. Goldsmith
I. S. Lowen

PREFACE

The purpose of this text is to provide an introduction to the kinetic theory of gases for students of physics which will also be useful to students of chemistry and of the engineering sciences. The book is an outgrowth of a lecture course for advanced undergraduate and beginning graduate students. The author feels that a brief course in kinetic theory at this level furnishes important physical concepts and elementary mathematical techniques which should enter early into the training of a physicist. The customarily prescribed undergraduate courses deal mainly with phenomenological physics: the formulas relate directly observable quantities, and neither in the theory nor in the applications does the development stray far from the macroscopic world of experience. The study of a nonphenomenological subject like the kinetic theory of gases introduces the student to a hypothetical, speculative approach to complex phenomena which stimulates the imagination. In the development of kinetic theory we introduce a scaffolding of hypothetical elements such as "billiard-ball" molecules and "perfectly smooth" walls, and then later we abstract their essential properties and find that our results still stand when we knock away the cruder elements—e.g., when we replace the billiard ball by the central field of force. Although the atomistic approach is, of course, exemplified in the quantum theory of the atom and in nuclear and solid-state physics, the introductory courses in these subjects either are largely descriptive or make premature use of concepts and methods which require a good deal of mathematical physics to be properly understood. Thus many things have to be taken on faith in such courses. Kinetic theory, on the other hand, requires of the student only a degree of familiarity with introductory mechanics and a working knowledge of calculus.

Kinetic theory provides the simplest and most natural approach to many working concepts and methods of modern physics. The statistical description of physical phenomena, which is at the root of quantum physics, is first encountered in the theory of gases, where the student learns to work with distribution functions. The concepts of cross section, e.g., the differential scattering cross section and the transport cross section, which play so important a role in atomic and nuclear

vii

physics, are introduced in kinetic theory. The theory of diffusion and the Boltzmann equation can be applied to neutrons as well as to gas molecules. A course in kinetic theory not only has methodological value but provides a background for current physicochemical research on the forces between molecules. The quantitative determination of inter-molecular forces is one of the foremost problems of molecular physics, and the kinetic theory of the transport phenomena is an important tool in such investigations. There are also increasingly numerous practical applications of the subject, e.g., to isotope separation and to flow problems in aerodynamics.

The present text is strictly limited in its subject matter, and, far from being a treatise, it is intended only as a concise, reasonably up-to-date introduction to the subject which will provide at the same time some preliminary training in the methods of theoretical physics. The book is designed for a one-semester course, since it is unrealistic to expect that more time could be devoted to this subject in the overcrowded under-graduate and graduate curricula. The book can also be used for the first half of a one-year course in statistical mechanics in schools in which no separate course in kinetic theory is offered.* It is appropriate to point out salient features of the present treatment. Although the book starts out at a very elementary level, the later chapters are quite a bit more advanced, the level of difficulty increasing fairly continuously. General distribution functions are introduced in the beginning, but the specific analytic (Maxwellian) form of the equilibrium function is not given until Chap. 5. A unified treatment of viscosity, heat conduction, and self-diffusion is given by the mean-free-path method. The limitations of this method, especially in the case of mutual diffusion, are stressed.

Of the three transport phenomena, diffusion receives the most emphasis. Ordinary mutual diffusion is treated by the momentum-transfer method originated by Maxwell and Stefan and long neglected by authors of textbooks in this field. A new simplified version of this method is presented in Chap. 4, and the detailed treatment in Chap. 8 gives the same formula for the mutual-diffusion coefficient as the Chapman-Enskog first approximation. Free-molecule (Knudsen) diffusion is discussed, and an elementary treatment of thermal diffusion, due to Frankel and Furry, is presented; both topics are of current interest in connection with isotope separation. The connection between the random-walk problem, diffusion, and Brownian motion is discussed. Imperfect-gas behavior, as illustrated in the virial equation of state and in the temperature-depend-

* The author deplores the long-prevailing trend toward absorbing kinetic theory into courses in statistical mechanics, with the inevitable consequences of *anschluss* apparent in the drastically curtailed treatment of transport phenomena.

ence of the viscosity coefficient, is simply interpreted in terms of the van der Waals–Sutherland model and the model of inverse power repulsion between point molecules. The extensive discussion of the dynamics of two-particle encounters and the definitions and evaluations of cross sections in Chap. 8 should be generally useful. A novel feature is the inclusion of a section on chemical kinetics in which a new derivation is given of the bimolecular-reaction-rate formula. The breakdown of classical theory when it is applied to internal molecular degrees of freedom is brought out and, although no quantum theory is used in the book, an attempt is made to indicate the points at which quantum theory gives significantly different results. In order not to interrupt the continuity of the theoretical development, experimental material has been largely relegated to Chap. 10, which is devoted exclusively to basic experimental procedures and includes recent advances in techniques.

The natural dividing line between the elementary and advanced phases of the subject is provided by Boltzmann's equation and the equations of change. An introduction to the advanced transport theory is given in Chap. 11, where we have derived the equations of change, obtained the hydrodynamical equations, and calculated the coefficient of viscosity by the methods of Chapman. Boltzmann's integrodifferential equation is derived and the collision term evaluated; a rigorous derivation of the Maxwell-Boltzmann law is then obtained. The H theorem is proved and its consequences discussed. Chapter 12 contains an up-to-date review of the subject of intermolecular forces and their determination by the methods of kinetic theory. In keeping with the aims of a short, introductory text, a few topics customarily included in books on kinetic theory have been omitted. Thus, although Knudsen flow has been discussed at some length and the slip flow, temperature jump, and accommodation coefficient have been taken up briefly, other interesting properties of gases at low densities have been reluctantly omitted. References have been given in the text and in the Bibliography which will enable the interested reader to consult other sources for treatment of omitted topics and for a fuller account of topics dealt with here in an abbreviated form. In keeping with the nature of the book as a text rather than a treatise, no attempt has been made to give a complete set of references to original papers; however, Chap. 12 includes fairly extensive references to the recent literature.*

The background desired of the student is an intermediate course in mechanics and a standard course in advanced calculus, but neither of these is absolutely essential. The text provides applications of a number

* Very extensive references to the older literature can be found in the sections on kinetic theory included in Partington's treatise on physical chemistry (see the Bibliography).

of mathematical topics that are among the everyday tools of the physicist: solid angles, even and odd functions, the Jacobian determinant, the Lagrange multiplier method, Stirling's formula for the factorial, Fourier series, elliptic integrals, the gamma function, the Dirac delta function, etc. Apart from the elementary addition and subtraction of vectors, vector analysis has not been used. A few of the mathematical topics are reviewed in the chapter appendixes. Although some of the later sections of the book are considerably more mathematical than earlier sections, the level of the mathematics used does not become more advanced, and no additional mathematical preparation is required.* It is recommended that Chaps. 11 and 12, and perhaps the second section of Chap. 9, be omitted from a course for undergraduates and beginning graduate students. More advanced classes may be expected to go rapidly through the earlier and easier parts and thus complete the study of the whole book in one semester.

The author's interest in the field of kinetic theory stems from World War II work at the Columbia University SAM Laboratories and has been maintained partly by research and partly by teaching a biennial course on the subject. The momentum-transfer method, which is extensively used in this book, was rediscovered by Dr. A. J. deBethune and the author during the war without our being aware of the prior work of Maxwell, Stefan, and Langevin. Although very few derivations given here are essentially new or original with the author, the order and arrangement of the material is somewhat novel and is dictated primarily by pedagogical considerations. Thus, for example, the treatment of viscosity is not all included in one chapter; rather, the subject is taken up three times at three different levels of "sophistication." Naturally, more emphasis is given here than in older books to those subjects that are currently of greater interest and importance, such as thermal diffusion, intermolecular forces, and the advanced transport theory.

In the preparation of the manuscript I have consulted other textbooks, monographs, and review articles and papers in the journals. Particularly helpful have been the books by Chapman and Cowling; Herzfeld; Hirschfelder, Curtiss, and Bird; and Kennard. These books are listed in the Bibliography along with other useful references. Although the manuscript was prepared without assistance, I am glad to acknowledge valuable comments received from the Consulting Editor and from Professors R. T. Cox and H. Margenau, who also reviewed the manuscript before publication. I am greatly indebted to Miss Helen Burnette,

---

* It seems hardly necessary to advise the student to read certain sections with pen and paper at hand—in order to check equations, fill in missing steps, and draw simple diagrams that have not been included among the illustrations because they seemed quite simple or trivial.

secretary of the Physics Department at the University of Tennessee, who typed the entire manuscript, including equations, with superlative accuracy.   Finally, I wish to acknowledge the patience, understanding, and encouragement received from my wife, Thelma Present, which have made the writing of this book possible.

R. D. Present

CONTENTS

CHAPTER 1

INTRODUCTION

This chapter takes up in an elementary fashion the basic hypotheses underlying the kinetic theory of gases.

1-1. BASIC HYPOTHESES

The kinetic theory of gases originated in an attempt to explain and correlate the familiar physical properties of gases and gaseous phenomena on the basis of the molecular hypothesis. Among these familiar properties and phenomena may be mentioned the perfect-gas law, the equation of state for imperfect gases, the viscosity of a flowing gas, the conduction of heat and the specific heat, the diffusion of one gas through another, the Brownian motion of small, suspended particles, the density distribution in the atmosphere, etc. The molecular hypothesis is basically the hypothesis that matter is composed of small discrete units known as molecules, that the molecule is the smallest quantity of a substance that retains its chemical properties, that all molecules of a given substance are alike, and that the three states of matter differ essentially in the arrangement and state of motion of the molecules. Further aspects of the molecular hypothesis are discussed in the next section.

In addition to the molecular hypothesis, two further basic hypotheses are used in the development of kinetic theory. One of these hypotheses is that the interaction of gas molecules in collisions with each other and with the walls of the container can be treated in accordance with the conservation laws of classical mechanics, i.e., conservation of momentum and conservation of energy. The validity of this hypothesis, in view of the development of the quantum theory of atomic and molecular structure, will be considered in later sections. The third basic hypothesis is that statistical methods can be used. Because of the tremendous number of molecules involved in any practical sample of a gas, the actual behavior of the gas is expected to be the same as would be predicted from the average behavior of the molecules. In order to calculate this average behavior, we must assume that, after taking into account the dynamical laws and the conditions of the problem, the motions of the molecules

1

are governed by pure chance, all other things being equal.   This "principle of molecular chaos" will be further elucidated later.

In addition to these hypotheses, there are also certain idealizations that are customarily made in elementary treatments for the sake of simplifying the physical or mathematical problem.   To a great extent these idealizations can be eliminated in more rigorous treatments.   For example, the model of a molecule as a rigid elastic sphere, or billiard ball, is especially easy to deal with; it is necessary, however, to replace this crude model by the more realistic picture of a molecule as a particle surrounded by a short-range force field.   Even in this representation, the transport calculations of kinetic theory become intractable unless it is assumed that the force field about a molecule is spherically symmetric.

The kinetic theory of gases can be partly included in a more general statistical treatment of matter in equilibrium which is known as *statistical mechanics*.   This science has a very wide range of application, embracing such diverse topics as the properties of crystals, chemical kinetics in gaseous systems, and the equilibrium in stellar interiors.   Some of the techniques of kinetic theory, e.g., those based on the Boltzmann equation, are more general than the traditional statistical mechanics in that they provide methods for dealing with nonequilibrium steady-state phenomena such as heat conduction in gases.

The main development of the kinetic theory took place in the latter half of the nineteenth century.

1-2. THE MOLECULAR HYPOTHESIS AND THE KINETIC HYPOTHESIS OF HEAT

An amazing record of human intellectual achievement would be obtained by tracing the evolution of atomic-molecular concepts from the ingenious speculations of the ancient Greek philosophers up to the precise mathematical theory of atomic and molecular structure which exists at the present time.   The molecular hypothesis entered physical science in the eighteenth and early nineteenth centuries by three separate channels. It was used to explain Boyle's law by D. Bernoulli (1738); in the form of the kinetic hypothesis of heat it was taken up successively by Bernoulli (1738), Lavoisier and Laplace (1780), and Rumford (1798); and finally, the atomic-molecular hypothesis was used to explain the fundamental laws of chemical combination by Dalton (1808) and Avogadro (1811).   Here we shall briefly summarize the development of the molecular hypothesis.

Gases differ from liquids and solids by completely filling any container in which they are placed, by being extraordinarily compressible, by rapidly diffusing into each other, and by having very low densities. These circumstances suggest that the molecules in a gas are widely separated from one another—i.e., the average distance between molecules is much greater than the molecular size—and that the molecules move about throughout the space occupied by the gas. Since the molecules do not eventually settle to the bottom of the container, the motion must be incessant, and this implies that the molecules preserve their mean speeds and kinetic energies throughout the innumerable collisions that each molecule makes with other molecules and the walls of the container. In mechanics, collisions between two bodies in which the total kinetic energy before and after the collision is the same are termed *elastic* or *perfectly elastic*. Molecular collisions are evidently elastic. The pressure exerted by a gas on the walls of its container is attributed to the bombardment of the walls by the molecules, which rebound elastically after each impact. Measurable fluctuations in the pressure arising from random statistical fluctuations ("unevenness") in the rate of bombardment would not be expected because of the tremendous number of molecules involved.* As the gas is compressed into a smaller volume, the temperature being maintained constant, the density increases and the molecules make more frequent collisions with the walls, thus raising the pressure. In this way Boyle's law is explained.

Heat, according to the kinetic hypothesis of heat, is a "concealed form of motion" associated with the molecules of a substance. Although early surmised, this hypothesis did not receive clear expression or displace the competitive hypothesis of the "caloric fluid" until well into the nineteenth century. This was due partly to lack of experimentation and partly to the late development of the energy concept. The kinetic hypothesis of heat is linked with the general principle of energy conservation (Mayer, 1842, and Joule, 1843), which states that energy cannot be created or destroyed but only transformed. In any ordinary dynamical process, the sum total of the mechanical energy (kinetic plus potential) is found to be less at the end than at the beginning. Thus a ball never rebounds to exactly the height from which it was dropped; i.e., collisions between ordinary (macroscopic) bodies are never perfectly elastic. The loss of mechanical energy is accompanied by the evolution of heat, an observation first emphasized by Rumford. Mayer's brilliant induction, supported by Joule's careful experimentation, states that the quantity of heat evolved must be proportional to the mechanical energy lost. Granted that heat is a form of energy, the kinetic hypothesis goes further and associates this energy with molecular motion. If the discussion of the preceding paragraph is to provide a quantitative explanation of Boyle's law, one must stipulate that the molecular speeds on the average are not altered during the compression. For if they are altered, the collision

* Such fluctuations are, however, detected in the Brownian movement, which provides a convincing confirmation of the bombardment picture.

rate with the wall and the resulting pressure will not be simply proportional to the density of the gas. Evidently this stipulation—that the mean molecular speed or kinetic energy remain constant—must be equivalent to the experimental condition for the validity of Boyle's law that the temperature be maintained constant. Hence the temperature bears a direct relation to the mean kinetic energy of the molecules.

Let us now consider a gas at constant volume and imagine that all molecules have the same speed v. If v is increased, the frequency with which the molecules strike the wall will increase in direct proportion. Each molecule will impart to the wall a quantity of momentum proportional to v. Since the pressure is jointly proportional to the bombardment rate and the momentum imparted in each collision, it will vary as v^2. In an actual gas with a distribution of molecular speeds, the pressure is then expected to be proportional to the mean-square velocity or to the mean kinetic energy of the molecules. Because of the relation just inferred between temperature and molecular kinetic energy, varying the speed v corresponds to varying the temperature. Since the gas is at constant volume, Charles' law tells us that the pressure is proportional to the absolute temperature. Hence the mean kinetic energy of the molecules is proportional to the absolute temperature.

From the preceding discussion, it might seem that heat energy in a gas is exclusively kinetic energy of translation of the molecules. This is not true, except in monatomic gases. As we shall see later, the molecule possesses an internal structure, and energy may in principle be stored in the internal degrees of freedom. During the frequent collisions that occur in a gas, some of the translational kinetic energy will be converted into internal energy of the molecule, e.g., kinetic energy of rotation or kinetic and potential energy of vibration.* In thermal equilibrium, a certain fraction of the heat energy is associated with the translational motion of the molecule as a whole, and the remainder is divided among the internal degrees of freedom. Although the classical kinetic theory makes a definite prediction about the way in which the heat energy is partitioned among all the degrees of freedom (the *equipartition* theorem), the results do not agree with experiment except in the case of monatomic gases. This failure is to be ascribed to the quantization of the internal degrees of freedom, and correctness requires the use of quantum theory. The greatest part of kinetic theory deals with gas properties and gas phenomena which are essentially unaffected by the internal structure of the molecule; hence classical kinetic theory suffices.

---

* The kinetic-theory usage of the term "internal energy" to refer to the energy of molecular rotation and vibration differs from the usage in thermodynamics, where the same term designates the total thermal molecular energy, including translation, rotation, and vibration, as well as the potential energy of the intermolecular forces.

In concluding this discussion of the kinetic hypothesis of heat, we shall mention briefly some applications to the solid and liquid states. These two states of matter are both characterized by close-packing of the molecules. In the solid state, the molecules or their component atoms or ions are fixed in definite geometrical patterns characteristic of the substance (crystal lattices). The structures can be studied by the method of X-ray diffraction and the exact geometrical arrangement determined. The component particles that make up the lattice, whether atoms, ions or molecules, experience both attractive and repulsive forces, the former prevailing at greater distances of the particles from each other and the latter at smaller distances. The attractive forces are, of course, responsible for the binding or cohesion of the solid. The short-range repulsive forces acting only between neighboring particles become important when the "particles" are so close together that their internal (electronic) structures begin to overlap. These forces are responsible for the extremely low compressibility of solids and liquids. The nature of the cohesive forces depends on the type of solid. In the case of ionic lattices, the binding is mainly due to the electrostatic attractions of the unlike ions. At absolute zero, the lattice particles are in positions of stable equilibrium determined by the combined attractive and repulsive force fields. As the temperature is raised, the atoms or ions begin to vibrate about their equilibrium positions. Heat energy in a solid then takes the form of vibrational energy.

As the temperature is raised toward the melting point, atoms may acquire enough energy of thermal agitation to leave their fixed sites and migrate to new positions. At the melting point, these rearrangements occur readily, and the long-range order of the crystal lattice disappears. In the liquid state, atoms can move readily from one set of neighbors to another, and only a short-range order persists.* The phenomenon of evaporation may be explained by considering that a molecule near the surface of the liquid may acquire a thermal energy sufficient to break the bond holding it to the surface. As the temperature is raised, this will happen more frequently, and the rate of evaporation will increase. Since the molecules that evaporate are those possessing the greatest kinetic energy, the mean kinetic energy of the liquid is lowered by evaporation; i.e., the temperature drops. Qualitative explanations of this type, based on the molecular hypothesis and the kinetic representation of heat, are now to be found in most texts on elementary physics; consequently we shall not pursue this topic further.

---

* "Short-range order" means that small groups of atoms have, on the average, a fairly regular arrangement corresponding approximately to that in the solid but that over distances of many atomic diameters the positions of atoms become uncorrelated.

1-3. ATOMS AND THE QUANTUM THEORY

In the preceding section, we referred to the fundamental laws of chemical combination and their explanation according to the atomic-molecular hypothesis. The laws of definite, multiple, and reciprocal proportions by weight* are all consistent with the assumptions (1) that each element is composed of identical atoms, which are indivisible in chemical reactions, (2) that, in forming a given chemical compound, atoms of several elements combine in definite proportions and in a definite arrangement to form a molecule of the compound, and (3) that the compound is made up of identical molecules, the molecule being the smallest amount of the compound that retains its chemical properties. Actually, it has been known for some time that most elements consist of more than one stable species of atom, the different species being referred to as isotopes. Isotopes of the same element are chemically identical but differ in their atomic weight. Provided that the proportion of isotopes in each element is unaltered by chemical reactions, as is practically always the case, the laws of definite, multiple, and reciprocal proportions are still explained. These laws of combination are not alone sufficient to determine the number of atoms in a molecule; they need to be supplemented by Gay-Lussac's law of combining volumes* and Avogadro's hypothesis. The latter hypothesis, which is fundamental in kinetic theory, asserts that under the same conditions of temperature and pressure, equal volumes of all gases contain the same number of molecules.

It is outside the scope of this text to trace the development of the present-day conception of the atom. We may remark, however, that since 1925, when the basic principles of quantum or wave mechanics were discovered, an almost completely satisfactory solution has been found to the main problems of atomic structure and atomic spectra, molecular structure and spectra, chemical valence, magnetism, the solid state, and the structure of metals—to name only part of the extensive domain covered by the new theory. Naturally, some of the conceptions of the classical kinetic theory of gases require re-examination and revision in the light of the new quantum theory. Fortunately, by far the greatest part of the kinetic theory is practically unaffected, and only a small part, e.g., the theory of specific heats, requires drastic alteration. The internal structure of atoms and molecules enters into kinetic theory in two essentially different ways. In those parts of kinetic theory which treat only the translational motion of molecules as a whole, e.g., viscosity and diffusion, the internal structure matters only in so far as it determines the exact nature of the forces acting between two molecules in an encoun-

* See any text on general chemistry.

ter.   The force laws in kinetic theory are semiempirical.   The analytic form of the force law is chosen on the grounds of physical plausibility and mathematical convenience; the force constants are then determined to fit experimental data.   The quantum theory of atomic and molecular structure provides, at least in principle, a method for calculating the interaction at any distance between any pair of molecules.   In practice, such a calculation would be prohibitively complicated, even for simple molecules.   (It has been carried out in detail in the case of two helium atoms and of two hydrogen molecules, and many approximations were necessary.)   As mentioned in the preceding section, the internal structure of the molecule is directly involved in any problem in which account must be taken of the energy stored in internal degrees of freedom.   The molecular rotation and vibration and the electronic motion must all be treated by the methods of quantum theory, and the classical methods are correct only for sufficiently high temperatures.

A few words of explanation may be offered to indicate why the quantum theory leaves virtually intact those major portions of kinetic theory which involve only the translational degrees of freedom of the molecule as a whole.   A characteristic feature of the new quantum theory is that it attributes wave properties to matter.   If a molecule moves parallel to the x axis with a specified velocity or momentum, it is described by an infinite train of plane waves of a definite wave length, and nothing whatsoever is known about the location of the molecule along the x axis.   If the molecule "collides" with another molecule and is deflected by the encounter, no precise mechanical description of the collision process can be given; nor, in fact, would such a description in terms of a classical trajectory be meaningful.   On the other hand, it is possible to calculate precisely the probabilities for deflections of varying amounts and to verify these probabilities by examining many similar collisions.   The theory is thus statistical, and the waves associated with the molecule are, in fact, waves that measure probability.   Because of the wave nature of the molecule, appreciable diffraction effects will occur in an encounter of this sort if the wave length of the molecule is not small compared to the dimensions of the molecule.   The problem must then be treated by the methods of quantum or wave mechanics.   However, if the wave length is small, the wave mechanical equations reduce to Newton's laws of motion, and a classical description is approximately valid.   The wave length of a molecule of momentum p is given by de Broglie's relation $\Lambda = h/p$, where h is Planck's constant.   In the case of nearly all gases at ordinary temperatures, the wave lengths of the molecules are sufficiently small compared to molecular dimensions that quantum corrections can be neglected, particularly in view of uncertainties in the force laws. In the case of the lightest gases H_2 and He, even at ordinary temperatures the quantum corrections are appreciable, and at low temperatures they become very important.* As the temperature is lowered, the mean kinetic energy of the molecules is decreased and the mean de Broglie wave length increases. At temperatures so low that the wave length is much greater than the molecular dimensions, all resemblance to classical behavior is lost.

1-4. STATISTICAL HYPOTHESES

The kinetic theory of gases is a statistical theory; i.e., it is based on the laws of chance. We may inquire first why it is necessary to use statistical methods in addition to dynamical methods. The dynamical description of a particle moving in a straight line is given by Newton's second law of motion, which is a second-order differential equation with two integration constants. These constants are ordinarily taken to be the initial position and speed of the particle. If the values of these two constants are specified and all the forces acting on the particle are known, its entire future dynamical behavior is predicted by the equation of motion. If the particle moves in three dimensions, there are three equations for the x, y, and z components of the motion, respectively, and six integration constants corresponding to the three position coordinates and the three components of the velocity at the beginning of the motion. Regarding a gas as a system of N particles, there would be altogether $3N$ equations of motion and $6N$ integration constants. If the initial position coordinates and velocity components of all the molecules could be determined, together with the force laws for the interactions between two molecules and between a molecule and a wall, it would be possible in principle to calculate the subsequent behavior of the gas down to the finest detail. Such a program is beyond the realm of possibility. Granting the preposterous supposition that the initial conditions could be determined, and assuming for simplicity that the molecules could be treated as billiard balls and the walls as smooth, a stupendous and stupefying amount of calculation would be required to trace out the motions of a minute fraction of the molecules during their first few collisions.

Furthermore, a little consideration shows that a knowledge of the initial conditions and the subsequent behavior of every molecule in the gas would really be of little interest. It is reasonable to suppose that the enormous number of collisions would rapidly efface any idiosyncrasies in the initial conditions and that after a sufficient interval of time the essential characteristics of the state of motion of the molecules would be nearly independent of the initial conditions. Thus, in spite of a highly artificial

---

* As we shall see later, the average value of p in a gas of molecular weight M at absolute temperature T is proportional to $(MT)^{1/2}$.

initial spatial distribution, e.g., along one wall or in one corner, one expects that the molecules will finally be distributed with uniform density throughout the container. Complete knowledge of the history of every molecule in the gas is not what we are seeking; we need to know only so much about the molecular motions as will suffice to explain and predict quantitatively the observable, macroscopic properties of the gas, such as the pressure or viscosity. The equilibrium and steady-state properties of gases under given macroscopic conditions of pressure, temperature, etc., are constant and reproducible and are therefore effectively independent of the exact submicroscopic state of motion of the molecules at any instant. The measurement of these properties involves taking a time average over the instantaneous states of motion. In order to explain the observable properties of gases, we need to introduce assumptions that will enable us to calculate these average values.

It may seem surprising that, in spite of our failure to trace out the trajectory of any of the molecules in the gas, it should be possible to discover the essential properties of the molecular motions needed to calculate average values and hence observable properties of the gas. It is characteristic of statistical methods that they furnish us with information about the probable or average behavior expected of many individuals in cases where it would be impossible to make a significant prediction about one individual. Although it is impossible under ordinary circumstances to predict even roughly the date of death of a normal, healthy person, fairly precise predictions can be made concerning the number of persons in his age group who, again under ordinary circumstances, are expected to be alive after a certain number of years. Such information will be even more pertinent to the person in question if the statistical data are limited to persons not only of the same age but also of the same sex, occupation, geographical location, etc. Furthermore, the reliability of the predictions depends on the size of the collection. Insurance companies deal with a large number of small policy holders; they could not afford the risk involved in transferring the same amount of insurance to a small number of large policy holders. Two significant points are illustrated by this example. In dealing with a system that is too complicated to permit direct predictions of its behavior, we select a representative collection of similar systems and study their probable or average behavior. In the case of a gas under specified conditions of temperature, pressure, or other macroscopic variables, the representative collection will include samples of all the possible submicroscopic states of molecular motion that are compatible with the specified macroscopic conditions. A fundamental postulate must be introduced, however, in connection with the weighting factors or a priori probabilities to be attached to the sample systems. The application of the calculus of probabilities always requires an assumption about a priori probabilities; e.g., in the throwing of a die, one assumes the a priori probability of each face to be one-sixth. Naturally, the fundamental postulate about a priori probabilities in the kinetic theory must be compatible with the laws of mechanics; this can be shown to be the case.

The other point illustrated by the example above is that statistical results become more accurate the larger the collection, and for a small collection the fluctuations or deviations from the most probable behavior become large.* Statistical methods are compatible with "exact" laws in the theory of gases because the number of molecules in any sample of gas is so enormous that the fluctuations introduce a negligible percentage error. Actually, a statistical theory cannot be perfectly exact, nor is this necessarily desirable. A statistical theory is self-corrective in that it provides methods for calculating the expected fluctuations from the average, or most probable, behavior. Certain gaseous phenomena, e.g., the Brownian movement and the scattering of light in the atmosphere, owe their very existence to fluctuations and are fully and quantitatively explained by the statistical theory of gases.

Two essential differences between the use of statistical methods in physics and in the biological and social sciences are to be noted. First, there is the obvious difference that in physics we are dealing with enormously larger collections, so that statistical methods are correspondingly more accurate. A second difference is found in the methods used to obtain the probability distributions. In the biological and social sciences the method is usually empirical;† individual cases are observed and counted, and tables are prepared. In physics the method is purely deductive; a small number of hypotheses are introduced—e.g., that the molecules are of negligible size, that they obey the principles of classical mechanics, that the a priori probabilities can be calculated in a certain way, etc.—and from these hypotheses are deduced the probability functions needed for the calculation of average values.

Two types of average values have been mentioned, and it is important to distinguish between them, at least in principle. We have pointed out that the measurement of a physical property of a gas involves taking a time average over the molecular motions. When the same physical property is calculated, however, it is averaged over representative samples of the gas in different states of molecular motion. Considerable attention has been given to the question of whether the time average and the statistical average can be justifiably equated with each other. A

---

* We mention a very simple example: if a great many coins are tossed, the heads-to-tails ratio will be close to one; if only a few are tossed, this ratio will fluctuate considerably from one.

† Theoretical methods are used in genetics.

discussion of this matter and its relation to the so-called ergodic hypothesis is beyond the scope of this book.*   We shall assume that the statistical averages give us the directly observable properties of gases.   In this text we are concerned with gases that are either in thermodynamic equilibrium or in a steady state involving only slight departures from equilibrium. We make the assumption that, regardless of the initial state of the gas, it will in a very short time attain to one of the states of motion of greatest probability and will remain permanently in some such a state of motion.

The discussion of this subject will be implemented in later chapters, and the assumptions will be presented in more precise form and translated into concrete mathematical language.

* Cf. R. C. Tolman, "The Principles of Statistical Mechanics," Oxford University Press, London, 1938.

CHAPTER 2

DISTRIBUTION FUNCTIONS AND THE PERFECT-GAS LAW

Statistical information about a gas or other physical system is embodied in the so-called distribution function, which is defined and discussed in Sec. 2-1. In Sec. 2-2 the distribution of molecular positions and velocities in a perfect gas at rest in a closed container is considered, and it is shown how the perfect-gas law can be derived without explicit knowledge of the velocity distribution function. The momentum imparted to the wall by molecular impacts is calculated, and the resulting formula for the pressure is seen to be equivalent to the perfect-gas law if the absolute temperature and the mean translational kinetic energy of the molecules are directly proportional. The theory is tested by calculating the specific heat of a monatomic gas; it is then used to obtain the molecular collision rate with the wall and applied to effusive flow through an orifice. Finally, the effusion of a gas mixture is considered.

2-1. DISTRIBUTION FUNCTIONS AND AVERAGE VALUES

In this section we shall formulate some of the elementary ideas involved in the calculation of average values. As a simple example, let us first consider the question of calculating the average number of children per family in a particular community. Let n_i denote the number of families in the community having i children; we may refer to the n_i as distribution numbers. Let $N = \sum_i n_i$ be the total number of families. Then the average number of children per family $\bar{i}$ will be equal to the total number of children divided by N:

$$\bar{i} = N^{-1}(0 \cdot n_0 + 1 \cdot n_1 + 2 \cdot n_2 + \cdots) = \frac{\sum_i i n_i}{\sum_i n_i} \qquad (2\text{-}1)$$

Once the distribution numbers are known, the average value can then be calculated from Eq. (2-1). One may also introduce the "normalized" distribution numbers $f_i = n_i/N$, which specify the *fraction* of families having i children.   Then from Eq. (2-1)

$$\bar{i} = \sum_i i(n_i/N) = \sum_i i f_i \qquad (2\text{-}2)$$

In the foregoing example, the quantity to be averaged was capable of taking on only discrete values; in fact, the possible values of i were positive integers or zero.   The formulation is slightly more difficult in the case that i can take on a continuous range of values.   Suppose that we wish to know the average height of the men in a given community who are 21 years of age or older.   In this case we cannot use the distribution numbers of the previous problem, since the number of men who are exactly of a certain height h—for example, exactly 6.000 . . . ft—is certainly zero.   If, however, we ask for the number of men whose heights lie within a certain *interval*, e.g., between 5.9 ft and 6 ft, a definite and significant answer can be given.   Information about the distribution of heights can then be obtained by dividing the height span into equal-sized intervals Δh and determining the number of men whose heights fall within each interval.   Now, if the height interval Δh were taken to be 1 ft and the men counted in 1-ft intervals, the resulting information about the distribution of heights would be ridiculously inadequate.   Clearly, the smaller the value chosen for Δh, the more detailed would be our knowledge of the distribution.   The results of such a survey could be plotted in a block type of graph, the abscissa giving the height intervals and the ordinate the fraction of men in each height interval.   The graph would then consist of adjacent rectangles, each of width Δh and of height equal to the fraction of men in the interval.   Actually, it is more convenient to use as ordinate, not the fraction of men in the given interval, but the fraction of men in the interval divided by the size of the interval Δh.   In this way, the area of each rectangle gives the fraction of men in the specified interval.   Let F_i be the fraction of men with heights less than h_i, and let $\Delta F_i = F_{i+1} - F_i$ be the fraction with heights between h_i and h_{i+1} where $h_{i+1} = h_i + \Delta h$.   We define the fraction of men *per unit interval* of height by $f_i = \Delta F_i/\Delta h$ and plot f_i versus h_i to obtain the graph described above (see Fig. 2-1).

Now suppose that the interval Δh is reduced and the f_i redetermined.   The ordinate is the same and the total area of all the rectangles is the same as before, being equal to unity; however, the rectangles are now finer and the statistical information more detailed.   We may imagine the intervals to be continually reduced until the rectangles are very thin strips and the step-shaped contour of their tops appears to approach a smooth curve.   This would require, of course, a very large population.   At each stage of the subdivision of intervals, i.e., for each choice of Δh, an average height $\bar{h}_{\Delta h}$ can be calculated in accordance with Eq. (2-2).

$$\bar{h}_{\Delta h} = \sum_i \left[(h_i + h_{i+1})/2\right] \Delta F_i = \sum_i \left[h_i + (\Delta h/2)\right]f_i \, \Delta h \qquad (2\text{-}3)$$

As the interval Δh is made smaller, a more accurate value is obtained for $\bar{h}_{\Delta h}$. Let us now assume that the distribution of heights follows an exact

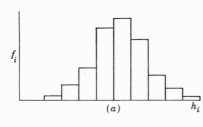

mathematical law as the population increases without limit, i.e., that the sequence of step-shaped curves approaches a smooth curve as Δh is indefinitely reduced. The fraction of men with heights less than h is then a continuous function of h, denoted by $F(h)$. Assuming this function to possess a continuous derivative, the fraction of men per unit interval of height is given in the limit by $f(h) = dF(h)/dh$, and $f(h) \, dh$ then represents the fraction of men with heights between h and $h + dh$. The sequence of average heights $\bar{h}_{\Delta h}$ calculated from Eq. (2-3) approaches a limit as Δh is indefinitely reduced:

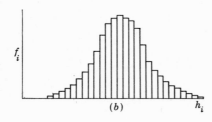

$$\bar{h} = \lim_{\Delta h \to 0} \sum_i \left[h_i + (\Delta h/2)\right]f_i \, \Delta h$$
$$= \int hf(h) \, dh \qquad (2\text{-}4)$$

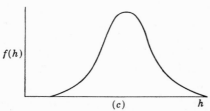

FIG. 2-1. Block graphs (a and b) and a distribution curve (c).

where the integral extends over the complete range of h. The function $f(h)$ is referred to as the normalized *distribution function* for heights, and the curve obtained by plotting $f(h)$ versus h is known as the distribution curve (see Fig. 2-1). The area under the complete curve is equal to unity, and the partial area between $h = h'$ and $h = h''$—i.e., $\int_{h'}^{h''} f(h) \, dh$ —represents the fraction of men with heights between h' and h''. Evidently $f(h) \, dh$ can be interpreted as the probability of a man chosen at random having a height between h and $h + dh$.

2-2. DERIVATION OF THE PERFECT-GAS LAW

Consider a gas in a state of equilibrium in a closed container. Since it is not flowing and there is no mass motion, i.e., no net transport of mass, the gas is said to be at rest, although the individual molecules are in motion. In the absence of mass motion, $\bar{v}_x = \bar{v}_y = \bar{v}_z = 0$, where v_x stands for the x component of the velocity vector, since a molecule is as likely to be moving in the $-x$ direction ($v_x < 0$) as it is to be moving in the $+x$ direction ($v_x > 0$). In a container of ordinary size, the influence of gravity on the molecular motions and distributions can be justifiably ignored. The deviation of molecular paths from straight lines because of gravity is negligibly small; i.e., the average radius of curvature is enormously greater than the average distance a molecule travels between successive collisions (mean free path). The slight increase in density of the gas in going from the top to the bottom of the container will be calculated in a later section; it can be neglected in a container of ordinary size. Hence all directions in space can be treated as equivalent; i.e., there is no preferred direction. Evidently $\overline{v_x^2} = \overline{v_y^2} = \overline{v_z^2} > 0$, where $\overline{v_x^2}$ denotes the average of v_x^2. Furthermore, all positions in the container are equally probable; i.e., there is no preferred location. It is to be recognized that an explicit statistical assumption has been introduced. We assume that in a gas at rest in a container in the absence of an external field of force, the molecules have no preferred location in the container and no preferred direction of motion.

Consider the formulation of this assumption in terms of the distribution functions for position and velocity of the molecules. The distribution function for position is evidently a constant; i.e., the fraction of molecules that are found on the average in the volume element $dx\,dy\,dz$ near the point x, y, z is simply $dx\,dy\,dz$ divided by the entire volume of the box. At any one time, the number of molecules in a particular volume element may deviate widely from the average value, or one may say that the molecular density undergoes fluctuations. The smaller the volume element, the larger the percentage fluctuations will be. Let n denote the molecular number density, i.e., the number of molecules per unit volume of the gas. Evidently the density n and the distribution function for position are directly proportional. Now, if the density is not uniform throughout the gas, e.g., if there is a density gradient, we may try to define the density $n(x,y,z)$ at the point x, y, z by counting the molecules in a small region surrounding x, y, z and dividing by the volume of the region. In defining the mass density of a continuous medium, the region can be chosen indefinitely small; however, if this is done in the case of a gas, the instantaneous density will be zero nearly everywhere in the gas except in a few places where it would be enormously great; furthermore, it would be subject to sudden, enormous fluctuations at any one point. Such a definition would not correspond to any ordinary measurement of density. This difficulty can be avoided in two ways. The region or volume element over which the density is defined can be chosen small enough, compared to the size of the container and the scale of variation in space of the macroscopic properties of the gas, so that the methods of calculus—e.g., integration—can be applied without significant error, and at the same time large enough so that the number of molecules in the element will be very great and therefore subject to only slight fluctuations. Alternatively, the volume element can be chosen arbitrarily small, as above, provided that the number of molecules in the element is averaged over a sufficiently large interval of time, which must, however, be much less than the observable time scale of variation of gas properties. We may combine the advantages of both approaches by defining the molecular density at a point as a time average over an interval of "intermediate" duration of the number of molecules in a region of "intermediate" size surrounding the point divided by the volume of the region. It is indeed possible to choose these "intermediate" magnitudes so that they are neither too big nor too small in an actual gas, as one can readily see.

Turning our attention next to the distribution in velocity of the molecules, we must first distinguish between the velocity $\mathbf{v}$, which is a vector quantity, and the speed v, which is a positive scalar quantity representing the magnitude of the velocity vector. A distribution in velocity comprises a distribution in speed and also in direction of the velocity vector. Consider now the fraction of molecules with velocity vectors in an infinitesimal neighborhood of $\mathbf{v}$. This means that the speeds are to be found between v and $v + dv$ and the directions within the element of solid angle $d\omega$ about $\mathbf{v}$ (the student is referred to Appendix 2-1 for a review of solid angles and spherical coordinates). Let $f^*(\mathbf{v})$ be the distribution function for molecular velocities such that $f^*(\mathbf{v})\, dv\, d\omega$ is the fraction of molecules with velocity vectors in the range of speeds dv and the range of directions $d\omega$ about $\mathbf{v}$. We introduce also the speed distribution function $f(v)$ such that $f(v)\, dv$ gives the fraction of molecules moving in any direction whatsoever with speeds between v and $v + dv$. The relation between the two distribution functions is given by

$$f(v) = \int_0^{4\pi} f^*(\mathbf{v})\, d\omega \qquad (2\text{-}5)$$

where the integration is over all directions, i.e., a solid angle of 4π. If we now introduce the assumption that there is no preferred direction of motion, the chance that the velocity vector is in the solid angle $d\omega$ will be simply $d\omega/4\pi$. The probability that the velocity vector is within an infinitesimal neighborhood of $\mathbf{v}$ is the product* of the probability that the speed is between v and $v + dv$ and the probability that the direction is

---

* The probability for the joint occurrence of independent events is the product of the individual probabilities.

within $d\omega$ of **v**. Hence

$$f^*(\mathbf{v}) \, dv \, d\omega = f(v) \, dv \, (d\omega/4\pi) \qquad (2\text{-}6)$$

From the definition of the distribution function

$$\int_0^\infty f(v) \, dv = 1 \qquad (2\text{-}7)$$

and
$$\int_0^\infty dv \int_0^{4\pi} d\omega \, f^*(\mathbf{v}) = 1$$

A considerable part of the theory of gases can be developed without explicit knowledge of the function $f(v)$, which is called the *Maxwell distribution function* for molecular speeds.

A perfect gas can be defined as a gas in which the molecules, of negligible size, exert no forces on each other except contact forces at the instant of impact. This definition is readily seen to satisfy the thermodynamic stipulation that the internal energy of a perfect gas is independent of its volume and depends only on temperature. If there are attractive forces between the molecules, the internal energy is partly intermolecular potential energy, which increases with increasing separation of the molecules, i.e., with increasing volume of the gas. In deriving the perfect-gas law, the molecules are then assumed to travel in straight lines except at the instant of collision with another molecule or with the wall. A further assumption is that the molecules are small in size compared to the average distance between molecules or the average distance a molecule travels between successive collisions with other molecules (mean free path). This assumption characterizes the gaseous state. The assumption of a very small mass for the molecules ensures that many molecules are involved in any process that is subject to measurement and therefore that statistical considerations can be safely applied. To simplify the treatment of collisions, it is further assumed that the molecules are spherically symmetric. The conditions set out in this paragraph would be met, for example, if the molecule were a very small, perfectly smooth, rigid elastic sphere. Although this "billiard-ball model" is, of course, not to be interpreted as an actual representation of a molecule, it will often prove helpful to represent a molecule in this way as a provisional working hypothesis. In so far as actual gases approximate to perfect gas behavior, the contact-force billiard-ball model is justified as an approximation and it will be used throughout the remainder of this discussion.

2-3. DERIVATION OF THE PERFECT-GAS LAW (CONT.)

The walls of the container are rough on a microscopic scale (order of microns). We shall therefore confine our attention to an element of surface of area dS, which is small enough to be treated as a smooth plane surface for molecular encounters. In an elastic collision between a billiard-ball molecule and the surface dS, the contact forces act at right angles to dS so that the component of molecular velocity parallel to dS is not altered by the collision. Since the collision is elastic, the perpendicular, or normal, component of velocity is reversed by the collision. The molecule is thus specularly reflected from dS; i.e., the angle of reflection is equal to the angle of incidence (see Fig. 2-2a). Let us choose a system of spherical coordinates r, θ, ϕ with origin at the center of dS

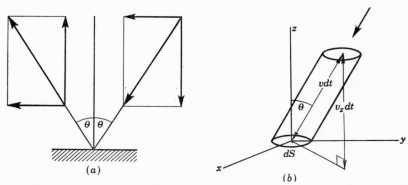

FIG. 2-2. Collisions with the wall: (a) vector velocities or momenta before and after collision; (b) oblique cylinder containing molecules of velocity close to **v** which strike dS during time dt.

and polar (z) axis along the normal to dS. The change in momentum of the molecule is along the z direction. The initial z momentum being mv_z and the final z momentum $-mv_z$, the change in momentum is $-2mv_z$ and the momentum imparted to the wall $2mv_z$ (m is the mass of one molecule).

Consider the group of molecules with velocity vectors in an infinitesimal neighborhood of **v** which strike dS during the time interval dt. These molecules would all be contained at the beginning of dt in an oblique cylinder with base dS and slant length $v\,dt$ whose axis is parallel to **v** (see Fig. 2-2b). The time interval dt is chosen short enough so that the chance for a collision that would deflect a molecule away from the direction of **v** is negligible; i.e., $v\,dt$ is to be much shorter than the average distance between successive collisions. The altitude of the cylinder is $v_z\,dt$ and its volume $v_z\,dt\,dS$. The number of molecules per unit volume with velocity vectors close to **v** within the range of speeds dv and the range of directions $d\omega$ is $nf^*(\mathbf{v})\,dv\,d\omega$. Hence the number of molecules with velocities close to **v** that strike dS during the time dt is

$$nf^*(\mathbf{v})\,dv\,d\omega \cdot v_z\,dt\,dS \qquad (2\text{-}8)$$

and the momentum they impart to the wall is

$$nf(v) \, dv \, (d\omega/4\pi) \cdot 2mv_z \cdot v_z \, dt \, dS \tag{2-9}$$

where the velocity distribution function has been replaced by the speed distribution function in accordance with Eq. (2-6). Denoting by d^3p the pressure exerted on the wall by the molecules in the selected group, it follows from Newton's second law of motion that d^3p is the momentum imparted to the wall per unit area per unit time by these molecules. Alternatively, one may say that the momentum imparted per unit area of the wall is equal to the impulse $d^3p \, dt$. Hence

$$d^3p = nf(v) \, dv \cdot 2mv_z^2 \cdot (d\omega/4\pi) \tag{2-10}$$

In terms of the polar angle θ and the azimuthal angle ϕ of the velocity vector $\mathbf{v}$, one has $v_z = v \cos \theta$ and $d\omega = \sin \theta \, d\theta \, d\phi$. Integrating over all possible directions of $\mathbf{v}$, one finds for the contribution to the pressure of the molecules with speeds between v and $v + dv$

$$
\begin{aligned}
dp &= (2\pi)^{-1}nf(v) \, dv \, mv^2 \int_0^{2\pi} d\phi \int_0^{\pi/2} \cos^2 \theta \sin \theta \, d\theta \\
&= (\tfrac{1}{3})nmv^2f(v) \, dv
\end{aligned} \tag{2-11}
$$

where the integration over θ extends from 0 to $\pi/2$ because molecules approach dS from one side only. The pressure p exerted by all molecules striking the wall is

$$p = (\tfrac{1}{3})nm \int_0^\infty v^2f(v) \, dv = (\tfrac{1}{3})nm\overline{v^2} \tag{2-12}$$

where $\overline{v^2}$ is the mean-square speed of the molecules.

On multiplying Eq. (2-12) by the volume V of the gas, one obtains

$$pV = \frac{2nV}{3} \frac{m\overline{v^2}}{2} = \frac{2}{3} \frac{nV}{L} \frac{Lm\overline{v^2}}{2} \tag{2-13}$$

where L denotes the number of molecules in one mole (gram molecular weight), i.e., Avogadro's number. Let $\nu = nV/L$ represent the number of moles of gas in the container and $U = Lm\overline{v^2}/2$ the kinetic energy of translation of the molecules in one mole. The kinetic energy of translation of the molecule $(mv^2/2)$ is to be distinguished from its kinetic energy of rotation or vibration. As we progress from the billiard-ball model to a more realistic representation of a polyatomic molecule, we shall see, in a later section, that the constituent atoms of the molecule vibrate against each other and that the molecule as a whole rotates. Only in the case of a monatomic gas, where the mass is concentrated at the center of the molecule, can the molecule be treated as a structureless mass point or particle possessing translational energy only. The rotation of the billiard-ball is of no consequence for the present derivation, provided that its surface is perfectly smooth as stipulated. We now insert ν and U into Eq. (2-13) to obtain

$$pV = \frac{2}{3}\,\nu U \qquad\qquad (2\text{-}14)$$

which is to be compared with the experimental perfect-gas law

$$pV = \nu RT \qquad\qquad (2\text{-}15)$$

In Eq. (2-15) T stands for the absolute or Kelvin temperature and R is the gas constant per mole, which is the same for all gases. The theoretical formula (2-14) and the experimental law (2-15) become identical if

$$T = \frac{2U}{3R} \qquad\qquad (2\text{-}16)$$

Thus the absolute temperature and the average translational kinetic energy of the molecules are directly proportional. Equation (2-16) may be interpreted as the *kinetic-theory definition of temperature*. We now introduce Boltzmann's constant $k = R/L$ and obtain for the mean translational kinetic energy of a molecule

$$\frac{m\overline{v^2}}{2} = \frac{3kT}{2} \qquad\qquad (2\text{-}17)$$

It is readily seen that the perfect-gas law can be rewritten as

$$p = nkT \qquad\qquad (2\text{-}18)$$

2-4. MOLECULAR SPEEDS AND THE SPECIFIC HEAT OF A MONATOMIC GAS

Two applications of the theory developed in the preceding section will be given here. From Eq. (2-17) one has

$$(\overline{v^2})^{1/2} = \left(\frac{3kT}{m}\right)^{1/2} = \left(\frac{3RT}{M}\right)^{1/2} \qquad\qquad (2\text{-}19)$$

where M is the molecular weight of the gas. The quantity $(\overline{v^2})^{1/2}$ is referred to as the root-mean-square speed of the molecules, and it is, in general, not equal to the mean speed $\bar{v}$.   In fact

$$(\overline{v^2})^{1/2} = \left[\int_0^\infty v^2 f(v)\,dv\right]^{1/2} \qquad \bar{v} = \int_0^\infty vf(v)\,dv \qquad (2\text{-}20)$$

It will be shown later that $(\overline{v^2})^{1/2}$ and $\bar{v}$ differ by a pure numerical factor close to unity. Still another "representative speed" is the most probable speed. Equation (2-19) shows that the representative speeds are proportional to the square root of the absolute temperature and inversely proportional to the square root of the molecular weight of the gas.

Furthermore, Eq. (2-19) can be used to obtain actual values of $(\overline{v^2})^{1/2}$ from the measurable, macroscopic quantities R, M, and T. At this stage of the development of the subject, the molecular quantities n, L, k, and m are to be regarded as completely unknown parameters of the theory and are not subject to direct measurement. The gas constant R is given to sufficient accuracy as 8.317×10^7 ergs/deg/mole and is approximately equal to 2 calories per degree per mole. As an example of the order of magnitude of molecular speeds, we apply Eq. (2-19) to carbon dioxide at 0°C to obtain a root-mean-square speed of 3.94×10^4 cm/sec.

The specific heat of a monatomic perfect gas can be deduced from the theory of the last section. The specific heat per mole at constant volume is given by $C_v = dU/dT$ where U is the thermal energy per mole of the gas. In the case of a monatomic gas, the thermal energy is purely translational and $U = 3RT/2$. Hence $C_v = 3R/2 \approx 3$ calories per degree per mole. If the gas is heated at constant pressure through a temperature rise dT, the heat added is equal to $dU + p\,dV$ where $p\,dV$ is the work done by the expanding gas. Since at constant pressure $p\,dV = R\,dT$ for one mole of a perfect gas, the specific heat per mole at constant pressure is given by $C_p = C_v + R = 5R/2$ and the ratio of the specific heats is $C_p/C_v = 5/3$. The agreement with room-temperature measurements on all the noble gases is remarkably good. Thus $C_p/C_v = 1.67$ for argon and 1.64 for neon, and the variation with temperature is slight. The specific heats of polyatomic gases are not in agreement with these values $(C_v > 3R/2)$, indicating that the energies associated with rotation and vibration cannot be neglected.

2-5. COLLISIONS WITH THE WALL AND EFFUSION

Let us calculate the rate at which molecules collide with the wall; specifically, we seek the number striking per unit area per unit time. According to Eq. (2-8), the number with velocities close to $\mathbf{v}$ that strike per unit area per unit time is

$$d^3N = nv_z f^*(\mathbf{v})\,dv\,d\omega = nv \cos\theta\, f(v)\,dv \sin\theta\, d\theta\, d\phi/4\pi \qquad (2\text{-}21)$$

upon introducing spherical coordinates as in Sec. 2-3 and using Eq. (2-6). Integrating over all possible directions of $\mathbf{v}$, one has

$$dN = (4\pi)^{-1} nvf(v)\,dv \int_0^{2\pi} d\phi \int_0^{\pi/2} \cos\theta \sin\theta\, d\theta$$
$$= \tfrac{1}{4} nvf(v)\,dv \qquad (2\text{-}22)$$

for the number with speeds between v and $v + dv$ which strike per unit area per unit time. Hence the total number of molecules striking unit area of the wall in unit time is

$$N = \tfrac{1}{4}n \int_0^\infty v f(v) \, dv = \frac{n\bar{v}}{4} \qquad (2\text{-}23)$$

where $\bar{v}$ denotes the mean speed.

Suppose now that a small circular hole of radius a is cut in the wall of the container and that the space surrounding the container is evacuated. Assuming the wall to be very thin, will the number of molecules passing through the orifice in unit time be $\pi a^2(n\bar{v}/4)$? The answer to this question depends on the pressure of the gas in the container and the size of the orifice. It will be seen in the following section that the mean free path λ, i.e., the average distance a molecule travels between successive collisions with other molecules, is inversely proportional to the pressure. For ordinary pressures and holes that are not microscopic in size, the mean free path λ is much smaller than the radius a and, under these conditions, Eq. (2-23) is inapplicable to the flow through the orifice. The reason is that a molecule cannot pass through the orifice without making many collisions with other molecules in the neighborhood of the orifice, the effect of which is to develop a collective-flow behavior, i.e., a mass motion of the gas through the orifice. There is then a preferred direction of motion in the gas, and Eq. (2-6), which was used in the derivation of (2-23), does not hold. A correct treatment of the orifice flow when $\lambda \ll a$ requires the use of the theory of viscous flow.

Consider now the opposite extreme of a very low pressure or a very small hole ($\lambda \gg a$). Under these conditions a molecule will generally pass out of the container without making any collisions in the neighborhood of the orifice; i.e., the molecules leave the container as individuals, quite independently of the motions of other molecules. No mass motion can develop in this case, and the gas in the vicinity of the orifice is practically unaffected by its presence. Equation (2-23) is now applicable and gives the flow of molecules per unit area per unit time through an orifice in a thin wall (thickness $\ll a$) into a vacuum. This type of flow, which is characterized by a pressure so low or an orifice so small that the mean free path is much greater than the dimensions of the orifice, is referred to as *effusive flow*, and the phenomenon is called *effusion*. It is not essential that the gas effuse into a vacuum. If the wall separates two containers maintained at different pressures, both of which are so low that $\lambda \gg a$, then molecules from each container will effuse into the other container. The two effusive flows are independent of each other, since molecular collisions near the orifice are very rare; hence, if both containers are at the same temperature, the net molecular flow per unit area per unit time is

$$F = \frac{\bar{v}}{4}(n_f - n_b) = \frac{\bar{v}}{4kT}(p_f - p_b) \qquad (2\text{-}24)$$

where the subscript f refers to the front or high-pressure side of the wall and the subscript b to the back or low-pressure side. The molecular density n has been replaced by the pressure p in accordance with Eq. (2-18).

In the case of a mixture of two gases, each gas will effuse independently of the other because of the absence of collisions near the orifice. The flow rate of each gas is determined by the difference between its partial pressure in front of and behind the wall. Thus

$$F_1 = \frac{\bar{v}_1}{4kT} (p_{1f} - p_{1b}) \tag{2-25}$$

where p_{1f} and p_{1b} are the partial pressures and $\bar{v}_1$ the mean molecular speed of the first gas. The ratio of the flow rates is

$$\frac{F_1}{F_2} = \frac{\bar{v}_1}{\bar{v}_2} \frac{p_{1f} - p_{1b}}{p_{2f} - p_{2b}} = \left(\frac{M_2}{M_1}\right)^{\frac{1}{2}} \frac{p_{1f} - p_{1b}}{p_{2f} - p_{2b}} \tag{2-26}$$

since the mean speeds are inversely proportional to the square roots of the molecular weights. As an application of this formula, we consider a steady, continuous separation process involving the effusion of a gas mixture of constant initial composition through a membrane containing many small holes. Let the fractional molecular concentration or mole fraction of the first gas in front of the membrane be c_1 and the concentration behind the membrane c_1'. If all the gas behind the membrane has effused through it, then c_1 and c_1' will denote the concentrations before and after effusion. Clearly

$$\frac{p_{1f}}{p_{2f}} = \frac{c_1}{1 - c_1}$$

and
$$\frac{p_{1b}}{p_{2b}} = \frac{c_1'}{1 - c_1'} = \frac{F_1}{F_2} \tag{2-27}$$

For the special case in which $p_b \ll p_f$, one can neglect p_{1b} and p_{2b} in Eq. (2-26), with the result that

$$\frac{c_1'}{1 - c_1'} = \frac{F_1}{F_2} = \left(\frac{M_2}{M_1}\right)^{\frac{1}{2}} \frac{p_{1f}}{p_{2f}} = \left(\frac{M_2}{M_1}\right)^{\frac{1}{2}} \frac{c_1}{1 - c_1} \tag{2-28}$$

Since $c_1' \neq c_1$ (unless the two gases have the same molecular weight), the effusion of the mixture leads to a change in composition in which the concentration of the lighter gas increases. The enrichment in the lighter component is expressed by the so-called *separation factor:*

$$f = \frac{c_1'/(1 - c_1')}{c_1/(1 - c_1)} \geq 1 \tag{2-29}$$

in which c_1 and c_1' refer to the lighter component. In the case of effusion into a vacuum ($p_b \ll p_f$), the separation factor $f = (M_2/M_1)^{\frac{1}{2}}$ according to Eq. (2-28). If p_b/p_f is not negligibly small, it is readily seen that $f < (M_2/M_1)^{1/2}$. The effusive flow and separation formulas are not applicable unless the mean free path is much larger than the dimensions of the holes ($\lambda \gg a$). As a/λ increases toward unity, collisions occur more frequently near the orifice and mass motion sets in; in the case of a gas mixture, the transport rates of the two components become equalized as a result of collisions between unlike molecules and the separation factor tends to unity. These considerations find practical application in the enrichment or separation of mixtures of gases. A particularly important application is to the separation of mixtures of isotopes of the same chemical element.*

PROBLEMS

2-1. Estimate the effect of the earth's gravitational field on molecular free paths by finding the radius of curvature ρ of the parabolic trajectory at its maximum. Show that at ordinary temperatures $\rho \sim 10^6$ cm.

2-2. Show that the total number of molecules effusing per unit time per unit area in a direction lying within the element of solid angle $d\omega$ is $n\bar{v} \cos \theta \, d\omega/4\pi$.

2-3. Derive the formula $N = n\bar{v}/4$ by finding the total number of molecules per unit time striking a small sphere suspended in the gas and then dividing by the surface area.

2-4. Consider a two-dimensional gas whose molecules are constrained to move in a plane. Show that the number of molecules striking unit length of the boundary per unit time is $n\bar{v}/\pi$ where n represents the number of molecules per unit area. Check by the method of Prob. 2-3.

2-5. In a reversible, adiabatic expansion of a gas in a cylinder, the piston moves out slowly with velocity u where $u \ll \bar{v}$. Show that a molecule rebounding from the piston loses $2mvu \cos \theta$ in kinetic energy where v is the speed and θ the angle of incidence. Show that the kinetic energy lost by all the molecules rebounding from the piston is equal to the work done by the expanding gas in accordance with the law of energy conservation.

2-6. Instead of the separation factor f, the separation efficiency Z may be used where Z is defined by

$$Z = \frac{(c_1' - c_1)[1 + (1 - c_1')\epsilon]}{c_1'(1 - c_1')\epsilon} \quad \text{and} \quad \epsilon = \left(\frac{M_2}{M_1}\right)^{1/2} - 1$$

in the case of separation by effusion. If $p_b \neq 0$, show that $Z = 1 - (p_b/p_f)$.

2-7. Two chambers are connected through a membrane with fine holes ($a \ll \lambda$). One chamber is filled with hydrogen and the other with oxygen at twice the pressure of the hydrogen but at the same temperature. What will be observed to happen?

2-8. Two chambers of the same gas at the same pressure but at different temperatures are connected through a membrane with fine holes ($a \ll \lambda$). Assum-

---

* H. de W. Smyth, "Atomic Energy for Military Purposes," Princeton University Press, Princeton, N.J., 1950.

*i*ng that the temperatures are kept constant, what will be observed to happen? Suppose that the chambers are connected not only through the membrane but also by a large pipe $(a \gg \lambda)$. If the temperature difference is maintained, what will happen in this case? What would happen to a mixture of two gases?

2-9. Show that if the distribution function $f(h)$ is unnormalized, then

$$\bar{h} = \frac{\displaystyle\int_0^\infty hf(h)\, dh}{\displaystyle\int_0^\infty f(h)\, dh}$$

2-10. A continuous stream of shot, each of mass 0.5 gm, strikes one pan of a balance at an angle of 30° with the normal at the rate of 40 per sec and with a velocity of 100 cm/sec. Assuming that the shot bounce off elastically and do not rebound, what weight must be put in the other pan for balance?

APPENDIX 2-1

Spherical Coordinates and Solid Angles

The spherical coordinates r, θ, ϕ of a point P denote, respectively, the radius vector from the origin to P, the polar angle or colatitude measured between the $+z$ axis (polar axis) and the radius vector to P, and the azimuth or longitude angle measured between the $+x$ axis and the projection of the radius vector on the xy plane (equatorial plane). If r is fixed and θ and ϕ are varied, P moves on the surface of a sphere of radius r with center at the origin. If r and ϕ are fixed and θ is varied, P moves along a meridian of longitude. If r and θ are fixed and ϕ is varied, P moves along a parallel of latitude which is a circle of radius $r \sin \theta$. The element of arc along the meridian of longitude is $r\, d\theta$ and along the parallel of latitude $r \sin \theta\, d\phi$. Hence the element of area on the surface of the sphere $dS = r^2 \sin \theta\, d\theta\, d\phi$ and the element of volume $d\tau = r^2\, dr \sin \theta\, d\theta\, d\phi$. A latitude circle is described once as ϕ goes from 0 to 2π, and the latitude circles cover the surface of the sphere as θ is varied from 0 to π. The relations between the spherical and cartesian coordinates are: $x = r \sin \theta \cos \phi$, $y = r \sin \theta \sin \phi$, $z = r \cos \theta$ (see Fig. 2-3).

The solid or conical angle is an extension to three dimensions of the radian definition of an angle in a plane. If s is the length of arc on a circle of radius r subtending the plane angle α, then the radian definition is: $\alpha = s/r$. In three dimensions, the circle is replaced by a sphere of radius r and the arc by an area S on the surface of the sphere bounded by an arbitrary curve C. Lines are drawn from the origin at the center of the sphere to points on C. The conical surface with apex at the origin encloses the solid or conical angle ω, and ω is subtended by the area S on the surface of the sphere. The definition of ω in dimensionless steradians is: $\omega = S/r^2$. Since the greatest value of S is $4\pi r^2$, ω takes on values between 0 and 4π. The element of solid angle is defined by $d\omega = dS_0/r^2$ where dS_0 is the subtending element of area on the surface of a sphere of radius r. In terms of spherical coordinates, $d\omega = \sin\theta\,d\theta\,d\phi$. Consider the solid angle $d\omega$ subtended at the point P by the arbitrary element of

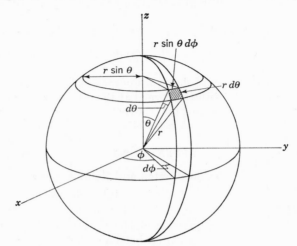

FIG. 2-3. Spherical coordinates.

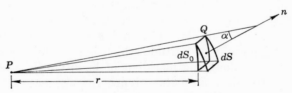

FIG. 2-4. Element of solid angle.

area dS at the point Q (the apex of the conical surface is at P). Draw a sphere of radius $r = \overline{PQ}$ with P as center, and project dS onto the sphere. If dS_0 is the area of the projection and α is the angle between $\overline{PQ}$ and the normal to dS, evidently $dS_0 = dS\cos\alpha$ and $d\omega = dS\cos\alpha/r^2$ (see Fig. 2-4).

CHAPTER 3

MEAN-FREE-PATH METHODS AND
TRANSPORT PHENOMENA

This chapter is devoted to the elementary treatment of the transport phenomena (viscosity, heat conduction, and diffusion) by mean-free-path methods. Without knowledge of the velocity distribution function, a remarkably simple and surprisingly successful theory of transport properties is arrived at in this chapter by means of these methods. The distribution of free paths is obtained, and the mean free path is introduced and related to the intermolecular collision frequency. This quantity is then calculated for rigid, elastic, spherical molecules. As a first application of mean-free-path methods, the molecular transport is treated in a gas of nonuniform density and the diffusion equation is derived with an explicit formula for the coefficients of self-diffusion and single diffusion. A general introduction to viscosity and heat conduction is given in Sec. 3-4, and it is shown that the three phenomena of self-diffusion, viscosity, and heat conduction in gases are closely related. This relationship is brought out by the single, unified treatment of these three transport properties given in Sec. 3-5. The well-known mean-free-path formulas for the coefficients of viscosity and heat conduction are obtained and their pressure- and temperature-dependence discussed. Relations among the three coefficients are obtained, and it is shown how measurements of viscosity can be used to determine the mean free path and also to estimate the order of magnitude of Avogadro's number and the molecular diameter. Some of the limitations of the mean-free-path methods are pointed out. The experimental methods used to measure the transport coefficients will be taken up in Chap. 10.

3-1. DISTRIBUTION OF FREE PATHS AND THE MEAN FREE PATH

One of the most useful concepts of the kinetic theory of gases is that of the mean free path. It has already been indicated that the mean free path is very small at ordinary pressures. This may be seen in a qualitative way by considering the spreading or diffusion of a gas through another

27

gas. In common experience one notes a lapse of several minutes before a fragrant or malodorous gas released in one part of a room can be detected in another part of the room. On the other hand, as we saw in Sec. 2-4, molecules at ordinary temperatures have representative speeds of several hundred meters or yards per second. The apparent paradox is resolved when one realizes that, as a result of collisions with other molecules, the path traced out by any one molecule is a complicated zigzag in which the direction of motion is continually changed by collisions. Although the molecules move very fast between collisions, their motion is so close to being random that they diffuse only very slowly away from the source. Since a molecule that travels a few centimeters away from its source must undergo many interruptions of its motion, the average distance it travels between successive collisions, i.e., the mean free path, must be considerably less than 1 cm at ordinary pressures. In a later section, this example will be treated in more detail.

The concept of the free path is based on the rigid-elastic-sphere model of a molecule. If the molecules are treated as particles surrounded by short-range force fields, a molecular encounter, instead of being an abrupt collision, involves a continuous change in direction of both molecules while they are under the influence of their mutual forces. Such "action-at-a-distance" encounters are not characterized by a sharply defined free path; nevertheless, it is possible to define a generalized mean free path even for this case. The billiard-ball model will be assumed in the discussion that follows, unless it is explicitly stated that another representation is being used. We seek first to determine the distribution in length of the free paths. The free path is most often taken to be the distance traveled by a molecule between two successive collisions. However, the free path may also be measured from the point where a molecule crosses an arbitrary plane to where it makes its first collision beyond the plane. A related problem is that of a beam of particles that traverse a medium in which they may be scattered out of the beam or absorbed; the free path is measured from where the particle enters the medium to the point where it is scattered or absorbed. The distribution law for the free-path lengths is the same in all these cases.

Let $F(\xi)$ be the probability of a free-path length exceeding ξ, i.e., that no collision occurs in the distance ξ. The probability that a collision occurs between ξ and $\xi + d\xi$ is proportional to $d\xi$ and can be written as $\alpha \, d\xi$ where α is independent of ξ because the medium is homogeneous and the chance of a collision is everywhere the same. In general, α will depend on the molecular density, or pressure, the molecular size, and the speed. The probability that no collision occurs between ξ and $\xi + d\xi$ is $1 - \alpha \, d\xi$. The probability that no collision takes place in the distance $\xi + d\xi$ is equal to the product of the independent probabilities that no collision occurs in ξ and none in $d\xi$. Thus

$$F(\xi)(1 - \alpha\, d\xi) = F(\xi + d\xi) = F(\xi) + (dF/d\xi)\, d\xi$$

and $\qquad\qquad\qquad dF/d\xi = -\alpha F \qquad \alpha > 0$ $\qquad\qquad$ (3-1)

Integrating Eq. (3-1) and imposing the obvious condition that $F(0) = 1$, one obtains

$$F(\xi) = e^{-\alpha\xi} \qquad\qquad (3\text{-}2)$$

The probability for the occurrence of a free path terminating between ξ and $\xi + d\xi$ is given by

$$f(\xi)\, d\xi = F(\xi) - F(\xi + d\xi) = -(dF/d\xi)\, d\xi$$
$$= \alpha F(\xi)\, d\xi = \alpha e^{-\alpha\xi}\, d\xi \quad (3\text{-}3)$$

Clearly $f(\xi)$ represents the distribution function for free-path lengths, and the mean free path is given by

$$\lambda = \bar{\xi} = \int_0^\infty \xi f(\xi)\, d\xi = \alpha \int_0^\infty \xi e^{-\alpha\xi}\, d\xi = \alpha^{-1} \qquad (3\text{-}4)$$

The mean free path is the reciprocal of the attenuation constant α. In the case of "action-at-a-distance" encounters of a beam of particles traversing a homogeneous medium, the constant α has a precise meaning, can be measured in many cases, and in some cases can be calculated. The generalized mean free path λ is defined as α^{-1}. Equations (3-2), (3-3), and (3-4) hold equally well for the several different definitions of free path mentioned earlier in this section. Furthermore, the mean free path has the same value whether the free paths are measured from one collision to the next or from the point where a molecule crosses a selected plane to the site of its first collision beyond the plane. This is true because the chance of a collision is independent of the dynamical history of the molecule; a molecule crossing the plane has exactly the same expectation with respect to its free path whether its last collision was made close to the plane or at an arbitrary distance behind it. The probability that a molecule will travel a distance ξ from the site of its last collision without making a further collision is $e^{-\xi/\lambda}$; the probability that a molecule will travel a distance ξ from an arbitrary point without colliding is also $e^{-\xi/\lambda}$ with the same value of λ. No account has been taken in the foregoing of the distribution in velocities. The mean free path of a rigid-sphere molecule of speed v is an increasing function of v, as we shall see in the brief discussion at the end of the next section. This mean free path must then be averaged over the distribution of molecular speeds to obtain an average mean free path for all molecules regardless of speed. The average mean free path will be denoted by λ in the following discussion.

Let us now introduce the average number of collisions per unit time $\vartheta(\xi)\, d\xi$ in which the free-path length is between ξ and $\xi + d\xi$. Then the average total distance traversed by a molecule in unit time is obtained by adding up the free paths multiplied by the frequency of their occurrence. Thus the mean speed is given by

$$\bar{v} = \int_0^\infty \xi \vartheta(\xi) \, d\xi = \bar{\xi} \int_0^\infty \vartheta(\xi) \, d\xi = \lambda \Theta \qquad (3\text{-}5)$$

where Θ is the average number of collisions made by one molecule in unit time, taking all free paths into account. An alternative way of obtaining Eq. (3-5) is to note that in a long time t a molecule travels a distance $\bar{v}t$ and makes Θt collisions with an average distance λ between successive collisions. Hence $\bar{v}t = \lambda \Theta t$ and $\bar{v} = \lambda \Theta$ as in Eq. (3-5). No distinction is made between $\bar{v}$ as a time average for one molecule and as a statistical average over the velocity distribution. The collision frequency per molecule Θ can also be interpreted as the probability per unit time that a molecule collides.

3-2. CALCULATION OF THE COLLISION FREQUENCY

Throughout this section, molecules are treated as smooth, rigid, elastic spheres of diameter d. When a collision takes place, the centers of the two molecules are a distance d apart. A sphere of radius d described about the center of a molecule is called its "sphere of influence," since no other molecule can have its center within the sphere. For simplicity, we first assume that all molecules except one are at rest and that the moving molecule has a speed v. We further assume that the stationary molecules are held fixed so that the moving molecule retains its speed v after a collision. The sphere of influence of the moving molecule traces out a cylinder of length v and of cross-sectional area πd^2 in unit time. Any molecule whose center is in this cylinder will be struck by the moving molecule. The number of centers of stationary molecules in the cylinder is $\pi d^2 v n$ where $\pi d^2 v$ is the volume of the cylinder and n the molecular density. Hence the number struck per unit time, i.e., the collision frequency, is $\pi d^2 v n$. The cylinder is not straight but has kinks or bends in it at places where collisions have occurred. The presence of the kinks does not materially affect the volume of the cylinder, the correction being negligible for mean free paths that are much larger than the molecular diameter.

An alternative way of obtaining the result is to hold one molecule fixed and set all the other molecules in motion in the same direction with the same speed v. Since the collision frequency obviously depends only on relative motion, the same result should be obtained. The fixed molecule presents an effective target area to the other molecules of πd^2, where πd^2 is the area of cross section of the sphere of influence. The moving molecules approach in a beam of density n, and those that are deflected by the fixed molecule in unit time have their centers within a right circular cylinder of length v with the cross section of the sphere of influence about the fixed molecule as base. The number of collisions per unit time between the fixed molecule and the other molecules is then $\pi d^2 v n$ as before.

When account is taken of the motion of all the molecules, the collision frequency becomes $\pi d^2 \bar{v}_r n$ where $\bar{v}_r$ represents a suitably averaged value for the relative velocity of a pair of colliding molecules. We carry out the calculation of $\bar{v}_r$, making the arti-ficial assumption that all molecules are moving with the same speed v. Let θ be the angle between the velocity vectors of two colliding molecules. The relative velocity v_r is the vector difference of the two velocity vectors and is given by the third side of the triangle formed by the velocity vectors laid out from a common point. Since the triangle is isosceles, it is read-ily seen that $v_r = 2v \sin (\theta/2)$. In order to perform the average over directions, it is necessary to know the probability of occurrence of an angle

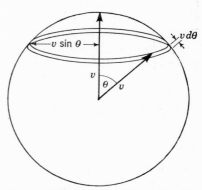

FIG. 3-1. Velocity diagram used to obtain $P(\theta)$.

between θ and $\theta + d\theta$, which we shall denote by $P(\theta)\, d\theta$. Let us lay off both velocity vectors from a common point at the origin of a system of spherical coordinates, taking one of the vectors along the polar (z) axis in the $+z$ direction (see Fig. 3-1). The polar angle of the other vector is θ, and both vectors terminate on a sphere of radius v. If the angle between the two vectors is between θ and $\theta + d\theta$, the terminus of the second vector is situated on a thin band between the latitude circles defined by the angles θ and $\theta + d\theta$. The probability of an angle between θ and $\theta + d\theta$ is then the ratio of the area of the thin band to the total area of the sphere, i.e.,

$$P(\theta)\, d\theta = \frac{(2\pi v \sin \theta)(v\, d\theta)}{4\pi v^2} = \frac{\sin \theta\, d\theta}{2} \tag{3-6}$$

where the circumference of the latitude circle $2\pi v \sin \theta$ is the length of the band and $v\, d\theta$ is its width. The mean value of $\sin (\theta/2)$ is given by

$$\begin{aligned}
\overline{\sin (\theta/2)} &= \int_0^\pi \sin (\theta/2)\, P(\theta)\, d\theta \\
&= \tfrac{1}{2} \int_0^\pi \sin (\theta/2) \sin \theta\, d\theta \\
&= \tfrac{1}{2} \int_0^\pi \sin (\theta/2)\, 2 \sin (\theta/2) \cos (\theta/2)\, d\theta \\
&= 2 \int_0^{\pi/2} \sin^2 \theta' \cos \theta'\, d\theta' \\
&= \tfrac{2}{3} \tag{3-7}
\end{aligned}$$

where $\theta' = \theta/2$. Hence $\bar{v}_r = 4v/3$, and the collision frequency becomes $(\frac{4}{3})\pi d^2 vn$. The increase by a factor of $\frac{4}{3}$ over the previous expression $\pi d^2 vn$ is explained by the three-dimensional treatment of the motions in the second case, which allows for collisions between a molecule and another molecule approaching it from the side.

Actually, the formula for the collision frequency just obtained takes no account of the distribution in molecular speeds. One might guess that the correct expression would be $(\frac{4}{3})\pi d^2 \bar{v} n$, where v has been replaced by its average value $\bar{v}$. However, the numerical factor of $\frac{4}{3}$ follows from a calculation in which the two colliding molecules are assumed to have the same speed. In the general case this is not true; hence the correct formula cannot be obtained by merely replacing v by $\bar{v}$. By explicit use of the Maxwell distribution function for molecular velocities, the collision frequency per molecule is found to be (see Eq. (5-27))

$$\Theta = \sqrt{2}\,\pi d^2 \bar{v} n \tag{3-8}$$

The difference between the two numerical factors is only 6 per cent. This difference is quite unimportant in view of the fundamental crudeness of the billiard-ball model and the uncertainty in the molecular diameter d. Substituting Eq. (3-8) into Eq. (3-5), we find that

$$\lambda = \frac{\bar{v}}{\Theta} = \frac{1}{\sqrt{2}\,n\pi d^2} = \frac{kT}{\sqrt{2}\,p\pi d^2} \tag{3-9}$$

This formula, based on the billiard-ball model, shows that the mean free path is inversely proportional to the density and to the cross section of the sphere of influence (target area) of the molecule. If the temperature is held constant, λ varies inversely with the pressure. The dependence of Θ and of λ on the density n and the target area πd^2 is in accord with intuitive expectation.

The mean free path as a function of speed has already been mentioned. If $\lambda(v)$ denotes the average distance traveled by a rigid-sphere molecule of a particular speed v between successive collisions with molecules of all velocities, it is found that $\lambda(v)$ is a function of v which increases monotonically from $\lambda(0) = 0$ to $\lambda(\infty) = \sqrt{2}\,\lambda$. The limiting values are easily understood: if the molecule is at rest between collisions, its free path is obviously zero; if $v \rightarrow \infty$, the other molecules may be considered at rest, the collision frequency $\Theta = nv\pi d^2$, and $\lambda(v) = v/\Theta = (n\pi d^2)^{-1} = \sqrt{2}\,\lambda$. Details of the calculation of $\lambda(v)$ may be found elsewhere.*

---

* Cf. J. H. Jeans, "Kinetic Theory of Gases," Cambridge University Press, London, 1946, p. 138.

3-3. COLLISIONS WITH THE WALL AND SELF-DIFFUSION

As an introduction to the use of mean-free-path methods and as an exercise preliminary to the study of diffusion, we shall recalculate the rate at which molecules collide with the wall. This problem has already been treated in Sec. 2-5. We choose a system of spherical coordinates with origin at the center of the element of area dS of the wall and with the polar axis normal to dS. Consider an element of volume $d\tau$ of the gas located at r, θ, and ϕ (see Fig. 3-2). The average number of molecules colliding in $d\tau$ per unit time is equal to the average number of molecules in $d\tau$ times the probability per unit time that a molecule collides, i.e.,

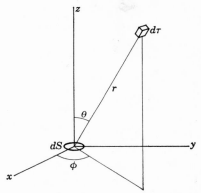

$$n\, d\tau\, \Theta = (\bar{v}/\lambda)n\, d\tau$$

The same result is obtained by noting that λ^{-1} is the average number of collisions per unit distance and that $\bar{v}n\, d\tau$ is the total distance traveled by all the molecules in $d\tau$ per unit time.

FIG. 3-2. Coordinate system showing element of area dS of the wall and element of volume $d\tau$ of the gas.

Since the colliding molecules leave $d\tau$ in random directions, the fraction of these molecules moving in the direction of the element dS is $d\omega/4\pi$, where $d\omega$ is the solid angle subtended by dS at the center of $d\tau$. This fraction is equal to $dS\,|\cos\theta|/4\pi r^2$. Not all these molecules reach dS. The number of molecules in unit time that collide in $d\tau$, leave $d\tau$ in the direction of dS, and reach dS without further collisions is

$$\frac{\bar{v}n\, d\tau}{\lambda}\frac{dS\,|\cos\theta|}{4\pi r^2}\, e^{-r/\lambda} \tag{3-10}$$

where $e^{-r/\lambda}$ gives the probability that a molecule travels a distance r from the site of its last collision without a further collision. The total number of molecules striking unit area of the wall per unit time is obtained by integrating over the volume of the gas.

$$\begin{aligned}
N &= \frac{\bar{v}n}{4\pi\lambda}\iiint d\tau\,\frac{|\cos\theta|}{r^2}\,e^{-r/\lambda}\\
&= \frac{\bar{v}n}{4\pi\lambda}\int_0^{2\pi}d\phi\int_0^{\pi/2}d\theta\,\sin\theta\,\cos\theta\int_0^{\infty}dr\,e^{-r/\lambda} \tag{3-11}\\
&= n\bar{v}/4 \tag{3-12}
\end{aligned}$$

Since the integration over θ extends only from 0 to $\pi/2$, $|\cos\theta|$ is replaced by $\cos\theta$. The integral over r is extended to infinity, since the dimensions of the container are much greater than the mean free path. Equation (3-12) is the same as (2-23). It is to be noted that molecules leaving an element $d\tau$ not headed for dS but deflected into dS by a collision have been taken into account. Each molecule reaching dS is assigned to that element of the gas $d\tau$ in which it made its last collision before striking the wall.

Now suppose that the gas is not in equilibrium but that a small variation in density exists. Assuming the density gradient, i.e., the space variation of density, to be along the z direction, we can make a Taylor expansion about the origin (an arbitrary point in the gas)

$$n(z) = n(0) + z\left(\frac{dn}{dz}\right)_0 + \frac{z^2}{2}\left(\frac{d^2n}{dz^2}\right)_0 + \cdots \tag{3-13}$$

where the derivatives are evaluated at the origin. The criterion that the variation in density be small is that within a distance z of the order of a mean free path λ, the contribution to $n(z)$ of higher-order derivatives than d^2n/dz^2 must be negligible. Let us take an element of area in the xy plane at the origin and calculate the net flow of molecules per unit area per unit time. In view of the nonuniform density, a nonzero result is expected for the net transport of molecules in the direction of the gradient. We can use Eq. (3-11) for the number of molecules crossing unit area per unit time from above provided that $n = n(z)$ is taken inside the integral. In the case of the molecules crossing from below, the range of θ is from $\pi/2$ to π, and $\cos\theta = -|\cos\theta|$. An expression of the same form as Eq. (3-11) with the θ integration extending from $\pi/2$ to π and with n taken inside the integral gives the upward flow of molecules with a negative sign. The net downward transport of molecules per unit area per unit time is obtained by subtracting the two integrals to give

$$\frac{\bar{v}}{4\pi\lambda}\int_0^{2\pi} d\phi \int_0^\pi d\theta \sin\theta \cos\theta \int_0^\infty dr\, e^{-r/\lambda}n(z)$$

$$= \frac{\bar{v}}{2\lambda}\int_0^\pi d\theta \sin\theta \cos\theta \int_0^\infty dr\, e^{-r/\lambda}n(r\cos\theta)$$

$$= \frac{\bar{v}}{2\lambda}\int_{-1}^1 d\mu\, \mu \int_0^\infty dr\, e^{-r/\lambda}n(r\mu) \tag{3-14}$$

where $\mu = \cos\theta$. We introduce the expansion (3-13) into Eq. (3-14) to obtain

$$\frac{\bar{v}}{2\lambda}\left[n(0)\int_{-1}^1 d\mu\, \mu \int_0^\infty dr\, e^{-r/\lambda}\right.$$

$$+ (dn/dz)_0 \int_{-1}^1 d\mu\, \mu^2 \int_0^\infty dr\, re^{-r/\lambda}$$

$$\left. + \tfrac{1}{2}(d^2n/dz^2)_0 \int_{-1}^1 d\mu\, \mu^3 \int_0^\infty dr\, r^2e^{-r/\lambda}\right] \tag{3-15}$$

The first and third terms vanish on integrating over μ. The vanishing of the first term expresses the obvious fact that in a uniform gas there can be no net transport. The exponential factor in the radial integral makes the integrand small for values of r and z which are greater than λ. Hence, by hypothesis, the contribution to (3-15) from higher-order terms in the Taylor expansion of $n(z)$ can be neglected. The radial integral in the second term of (3-15) is equal to λ^2; hence (3-15) becomes

$$\frac{\bar{v}}{2\lambda}\frac{2}{3}\lambda^2\left(\frac{dn}{dz}\right)_0 \tag{3-16}$$

According to (3-16), if the density increases in the $+z$ direction, i.e., $dn/dz > 0$, there will be a net transport of molecules downward, i.e., in the $-z$ direction.

In the special case just treated of a one-dimensional variation in density, the density gradient is defined to be a vector of magnitude $|dn/dz|$ pointing in the direction of increasing density. The net transport is then proportional to the density gradient and opposite in direction. Let G denote the net transport of molecules per unit area per unit time at the origin. Interpreting G as a vector that is positive in the $+z$ direction, we obtain finally

$$G = -(\bar{v}\lambda/3)\,dn/dz \tag{3-17}$$

where the subscript referring to the origin has been dropped. It is left as an exercise for the reader to show that the net transport across unit area of the xy plane is still given by Eq. (3-17) when the density $n(x,y,z)$ varies slowly in the x and y as well as z directions.

Equation (3-17) is an example of a *diffusion equation*. Any process in which the net transport of a substance is directly proportional to the gradient of the density or concentration of that substance and opposite in direction is referred to as a *diffusion process*. The constant of proportionality is called the *diffusion coefficient*. In the common case of mutual diffusion in a gas mixture, the inequalities in concentration are smoothed out by the interdiffusion of the two components. In the derivation of the preceding paragraphs only one kind of molecule is involved. However, it must be emphasized that this derivation does not apply to the flow of a pure gas under the influence of a pressure gradient. At ordinary pressures, a gradient in the total pressure causes a mass motion of the gas (viscous flow), which has not been taken into account in the preceding derivation.

Equation (3-17) has three possible applications. It can be applied to the hypothetical case of a dilute gas of moving molecules diffusing through a gas of fixed molecules (λ represents the mean free path for collisions between a moving molecule and the fixed molecules). This is sometimes called "single diffusion."* It can be applied to a mutual diffusion of dissimilar gases if and only if the fractional concentration of one molecular species is negligibly small (this will be discussed in Sec. 4-1). A further application is to the diffusion of a gas through a gas of the same kind at *uniform total* pressure for arbitrary concentrations. This so-called *self-diffusion* can be realized approximately through the use of isotopic tracer molecules. Self-diffusion can be regarded as a special case of mutual diffusion in which the two components have nearly the same molecular weights and molecular diameters (or effective cross sections) so that $\bar{v}$ and λ are nearly the same for both. Equation (3-17) can be rewritten for the case of self-diffusion as

$$G_1 = -D_{11} \, dn_1/dz \qquad G_2 = -D_{11} \, dn_2/dz \qquad (3\text{-}18)$$

where G_1 is the net transport of tracer molecules per unit area per unit time, n_1 the density of tracer molecules, and $D_{11} = \bar{v}\lambda/3$ the self-diffusion coefficient. In view of Eq. (3-9), D_{11} varies inversely with the total density or pressure.

3-4. VISCOSITY AND HEAT CONDUCTION

Fluids in motion, e.g., gases at ordinary pressures as well as liquids, give evidence of an internal friction called *viscosity*. Consider a fluid that is confined between two infinite parallel planes, the lower one (coinciding with the xy plane) being at rest and the upper one (at $z = h$) being in motion along the y direction with velocity u_0 (see Fig. 3-3). Imagine the fluid subdivided into many thin layers parallel to the planes, and assume that the top layer adheres to the moving plane and the bottom layer to the fixed plane. As a consequence of internal friction between adjacent layers, the layer below the top layer will experience a forward drag and will in turn exert a forward drag upon the layer beneath it. In this way a velocity gradient is created in the fluid, and in the steady state each layer at height z will have a velocity $u(z)$ with $u(0) = 0$ and $u(h) = u_0$. It is to be noted that the velocity is in the y direction, but its gradient is in the z direction. The frictional forces on the two surfaces of a layer (forward drag on the upper surface and backward drag on the lower) are parallel to the surfaces and, since they tend to shear the layers, are referred to as shearing forces. The shearing stress is defined as the shearing force per unit area of the surface over which the force is acting (e.g., in the case of a shearing couple applied to the covers of a book, the area in question is that of a page of the book). Since a shearing

---

* This case is realized in the diffusion of slow neutrons through matter; cf. H. Soodak and E. Campbell, "Elementary Pile Theory," John Wiley & Sons, Inc., New York, 1950.

stress, in contrast to a hydrostatic pressure, is parallel to the surface over which it acts, it is necessary to specify two directions for a shearing stress, i.e., the directions of the force and of the normal to the surface over which it acts. In the case we are considering, the shearing stress will be denoted* by P_{zy}.

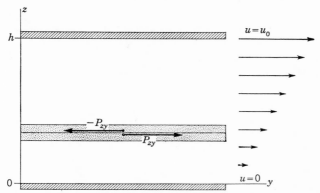

Fig. 3-3. Shearing stresses and velocity profile for a viscous fluid confined between a stationary and a moving plate.

Now, P_{zy} and the velocity gradient du/dz are found to be directly proportional in viscous fluids. In the example given, one expects P_{zy} to increase with increasing velocity u_0 of the upper plane and to decrease with increasing separation h of the two planes. If the lower plane is also in motion with velocity u_0', the shearing stress will depend on the relative velocity $u_0 - u_0'$. The simplest relationship that can hold is for P_{zy} to be directly proportional to $\Delta u = u_0 - u_0'$ and inversely proportional to $\Delta z = h$. Denoting the constant of proportionality by η, one obtains: $P_{zy} = \eta(\Delta u/\Delta z)$. This equation can be written in a more general form to include the case of a nonuniform gradient:

$$P_{zy} = \eta(du/dz) \tag{3-19}$$

The constant η is referred to as the *coefficient of viscosity* of the fluid. In the above example, a force must be applied to the upper plane to maintain its uniform motion and to the lower plane to keep it at rest; these forces are proportional to the viscosity η. Equation (3-19) is applicable to any one-dimensional viscous-flow problem, i.e., one in which the flow is along a straight line. A very useful application of Eq. (3-19) is to the flow through a long straight pipe under the influence of a pressure gradient. This application is discussed in Appendix 3-1.

---

* According to convention, the first subscript gives the direction of the normal and the second that of the force.

We have not yet considered the important question of how to explain the existence of internal friction in a fluid. In the case of gases, the kinetic theory not only provides a simple qualitative explanation of the viscosity of a gas but in addition furnishes a quantitative theory of viscosity in which Eq. (3-19) is derived and a theoretical formula for η developed. Returning to the example of a gas confined between two parallel planes in relative motion, let us consider an imaginary plane at $z = z_0$ which is being crossed by molecules from above and below. The motion of the molecules in the x and z directions is random ($\bar{v}_x = \bar{v}_z = 0$), but in the y direction their average component of velocity is equal to the velocity of mass motion [$\bar{v}_y = u(z)$]. Molecules cross the plane in both directions with equal frequency. Each molecule that crosses from above carries with it momentum and energy which are transferred from the layer above the plane to the layer below. Molecules that cross from below transfer momentum and energy from the lower to the upper layer. Because of the velocity gradient, the molecules above the plane have a greater average y component of momentum $mu(z)$ than the molecules below the plane. Hence there is a net transfer of y momentum across the plane from above to below. The increase in the y momentum of the lower layer per unit time is equal to the force exerted on it and the decrease in y momentum of the upper layer per unit time is equal to the reaction force. The effect is then the same as if the upper layer exerted a frictional drag in the y direction on the lower layer. The net transfer of y momentum per unit time per unit area of the plane is equal to the shearing stress P_{zy}. Viscosity in a gas originates, therefore, in the molecular transport of the momentum of flow in the direction of the velocity gradient (but opposite in sense). An example often given to illustrate the kinetic-theory explanation of viscous flow is that of two trains moving with uniform speeds on adjacent tracks. As the faster train overtakes and passes the slower one, packages are thrown across from each train to the other. The effect is to accelerate the slower train and decelerate the faster one.

Turning next to heat conduction in a gas, we note that heat flow takes place in any medium in which a temperature difference exists. In a simple case like the heat flow through a wall, the transport of heat per unit area per unit time is found to be directly proportional to the temperature difference divided by the thickness, i.e., to the temperature gradient across the wall. The heat-flow vector q is defined as the quantity of heat flowing per unit time through a unit area at right angles to the direction of flow. Experiment shows that the direction of heat flow at any point of a heat-conducting medium is along the direction of the temperature gradient at that point. Assuming a one-dimensional heat flow with the temperature gradient along the z axis, the law of heat conduction becomes

$$q = -K(dT/dz) \qquad (3\text{-}20)$$

where K is the *coefficient of heat conduction* or *thermal conductivity* of the medium.   The negative sign in Eq. (3-20) takes account of the fact that the heat-flow vector is opposite in sense to the temperature gradient $(K > 0)$; i.e., if the temperature increases in the $+z$ direction, the heat flow is in the $-z$ direction.

The mechanism of heat conduction in a gas is readily understood in terms of kinetic theory.   If the gas is confined between two parallel planes maintained at different temperatures, the molecules colliding with the hotter plane acquire thermal energy that is then communicated to other molecules in collisions and eventually reaches the cooler plane. When a steady state of temperatures has been reached, the heat flow and the temperature gradient are uniform throughout the gas.   Considering two adjacent layers of the gas parallel to the confining planes, molecules pass from each layer into the other, with the result that there is a net transport of thermal energy from the hotter layer to the cooler.   In the case of a monatomic gas, the thermal energy is exclusively kinetic energy of translation of the molecules.   The thermal energy of a polyatomic gas includes rotational and vibrational energies also.

3-5. UNIFIED TREATMENT OF THE TRANSPORT PHENOMENA

From the preceding discussion of the gaseous phenomena of self-diffusion, viscosity, and heat conduction, it is apparent that the three are closely related.   In all three cases there is a gradient of some physical property of the gas and also a molecular transport, and the transport is directly proportional to the gradient and in the opposite sense.   In self-diffusion, the transport of tracer molecules is proportional to the density (or concentration) gradient of the tracer molecules.   In viscosity the shearing stress, which represents the transport of the momentum of flow in the direction of the velocity gradient, is proportional to the velocity gradient in the flowing gas.   In heat conduction, the transport of thermal energy is proportional to the temperature gradient.   Viscosity, heat conduction, and diffusion are referred to as the *transport phenomena.*   They are amenable to parallel mathematical treatments by the methods of kinetic theory.   We take up next an elementary treatment of transport phenomena using mean-free-path methods.   It is assumed throughout that the mean free path is *small* compared to the dimensions of the apparatus containing the gas.

Let $A(z)$ denote a molecular property of the gas (referred to a single molecule), which varies uniformly in the z direction.   We consider the net transport of A across an imaginary plane in the gas located at $z = z_0$.

The average number of molecules crossing the plane per unit area per unit time in either direction is proportional to $n\bar{v}$. When a molecule crosses the plane, it transports a value of A which is mainly characteristic of the place where it made its last collision before crossing but which is influenced to some extent by the location of prior collisions. Let $A(z_0 + \Delta z)$ represent the mean value of A transported in the negative z direction (downward) by the molecules crossing the plane from above. In first approximation, Δz would represent the average distance from the plane at which a molecule makes its last collision before crossing; in higher approximation, Δz would depend also on the probable location of previous collisions. Regardless of the order of approximation, Δz is expected to be proportional to the mean free path and of the same order of magnitude, i.e., $\Delta z = a\lambda$ where a is a numerical factor of the order of unity. The net amount of the property A transported upward per unit area per unit time is proportional to $n\bar{v}[A(z_0 - \Delta z) - A(z_0 + \Delta z)]$. Assuming that Δz is small compared to the distance over which dA/dz varies appreciably, we can replace the bracket by $-2\,\Delta z\,dA/dz$ even if A does not vary uniformly.* Thus the net transport is proportional to $-2an\bar{v}\lambda\,dA/dz$. Denoting the net transport of A per unit area per unit time by Γ_A and introducing a new constant of proportionality b_A, we obtain the general transport equation

$$\Gamma_A = -b_A(n\bar{v}\lambda)(dA/dz) \qquad (3\text{-}21)$$

The transport rate is seen to be proportional to the average speed and to the product of the mean free path and the density. Since λ varies inversely with n according to Eq. (3-9), the transport rate is independent of the density and of the pressure of the gas (if the property A is also). As the pressure is raised, more molecules contribute to the transport, but the transport is effective over a shorter distance and the two effects exactly compensate.

Let us apply Eq. (3-21) to self-diffusion: then tracer molecules of density n_1 diffuse through a gas of uniform total density n under the influence of a concentration gradient $d(n_1/n)/dz$. The property of a molecule that is transported in this case is its identity, i.e., the probability that it is a tracer molecule. Thus $A = n_1/n$ and $\Gamma_A = G_1$, where G_1 is the net transport of tracer molecules per unit area per unit time. The transport equation for self-diffusion is

$$G_1 = -b_A n\bar{v}\lambda \frac{d}{dz}\frac{n_1}{n} = -b_A\bar{v}\lambda \frac{dn_1}{dz} \qquad (3\text{-}22)$$

If we choose $b_A = \frac{1}{3}$, Eq. (3-22) becomes identical with Eq. (3-18). In general one might expect some correlation between the property A that is transported and its effective transport distance. The effect of this

* We assume that $dA/dz \gg \lambda d^2A/dz^2 \gg \lambda^2 d^3A/dz^3\ldots$

correlation would be to make the numerical factors a and b_A different for the three transport processes. The subscript A on b_A in Eq. (3-21) indicates this possibility. In the elementary mean-free-path theory, one neglects this refinement and sets $b_A = \frac{1}{3}$ for all three transport phenomena.

Turning next to viscosity, we identify the molecular property A with the average momentum of a molecule in the direction of flow. As in Sec. 3-4, the gas is confined between two parallel planes perpendicular to the z axis which are in relative motion along the y direction. The flow velocity $u(z)$ then has a gradient in the z direction. Since the average velocity component of the molecules in the flow direction $\bar{v}_y$ is the same as $u(z)$, we have $A = mu(z)$ where m is the mass of one molecule. In this case Γ_A denotes the net molecular transport of y momentum per unit time per unit area of the plane at $z = z_0$, i.e., just the shearing stress P_{zy} over the plane. Substituting in Eq. (3-21) and setting $b_A = \frac{1}{3}$, one obtains

$$P_{zy} = -(mn\bar{v}\lambda/3)\,du/dz \tag{3-23}$$

This is to be compared with Eq. (3-19). The difference in sign reflects a different convention with respect to the definition of P_{zy}. Comparison of the two equations gives the elementary kinetic-theory formula for the viscosity coefficient of a gas (first obtained by Maxwell in 1860)

$$\eta = \tfrac{1}{3}mn\bar{v}\lambda = \tfrac{1}{3}\rho\bar{v}\lambda \tag{3-24}$$

where ρ is the mass density of the gas. Since λ varies inversely with n, η is independent of density or pressure. The reason for this has been previously pointed out. Although this result is apparently contrary to intuitive expectation, it is very accurately confirmed by experiment. Only at very low and very high pressures does the viscosity depart from a constant value. The general treatment of this section is based on the assumption that the mean free path λ is small compared to the dimensions of the apparatus but not so small as to be comparable with molecular dimensions. Departures of η from constancy occur for pressures so low or so high as to invalidate this assumption. The temperature dependence of η can also be obtained from Eqs. (3-24) and (3-9). On the basis of the billiard-ball model, $n\lambda$ is independent of temperature, and since $\bar{v} \propto T^{1/2}$, η should vary as $T^{1/2}$. This temperature dependence does not agree very well with experiment for most gases.* The viscosity is found to increase with rising temperature but somewhat more rapidly than $T^{1/2}$, and the temperature dependence is different for different gases. Although the discrepancy is small, it is significant and reflects the fundamental crudeness of the billiard-ball approximation. The existence of attractive forces between the molecules tends to bring about more

* See Fig. 12-2 and Table A of the General Appendix.

frequent collisions, so that the mean free path is actually shorter than for nonattracting rigid-sphere molecules. As the temperature is raised and the molecular speeds increase, the deflecting effect of the attractive forces is decreased and the mean free path is lengthened. This causes the viscosity to increase more rapidly with rising temperatures than $T^{1/2}$. A more accurate treatment will be given in Sec. 6-3.

The final application of the transport equation is to the phenomenon of heat conduction. In this case A represents the mean thermal energy per molecule and Γ_A the net transport of thermal energy per unit area per unit time, i.e., just the heat-flow vector q. The thermal energy of a monatomic gas is translational, and $A = m\overline{v^2}/2 = 3kT/2$ according to Eq. (2-17). Hence Eq. (3-21) gives

$$q = -(n\bar{v}\lambda k/2)\, dT/dz \qquad (3\text{-}25)$$

with $b_A = \frac{1}{3}$. The thermal conductivity of a monatomic gas is then

$$K = n\bar{v}\lambda k/2 \qquad (3\text{-}26)$$

The extension to polyatomic gases can be made without explicit calculation of the average internal (rotational and vibrational) energy, if one introduces the measured specific heat of the gas. When the temperature changes by an amount dT, the change in energy per gram of the gas is $c_v\, dT$ where c_v is the specific heat at constant volume referred to one gram. Hence $dA = mc_v\, dT$ where m is the mass of one molecule. Inserting $dA/dz = mc_v\, dT/dz$ in Eq. (3-21), one obtains, with $b_A = \frac{1}{3}$,

$$q = -(mn\bar{v}\lambda c_v/3)\, dT/dz \qquad (3\text{-}27)$$

and the thermal conductivity is given by

$$K = \tfrac{1}{3}mn\bar{v}\lambda c_v = \tfrac{1}{3}\rho\bar{v}\lambda c_v \qquad (3\text{-}28)$$

Equations (3-26) and (3-28) show that K should be independent of density, and this prediction is in accord with experience.

3-6. APPLICATIONS OF THE TRANSPORT FORMULAS

At this stage of the development of the subject, the formulas for the self-diffusion coefficient D_{11}, the viscosity coefficient η, and the thermal conductivity K cannot be directly compared with experiment. All three formulas contain the mean speed $\bar{v}$, which can be exactly calculated from the gas constant R, the absolute temperature T, and the molecular weight M. The mass density ρ, which appears in the formulas for η and K, is a known property of the gas, as is c_v. However, the mean free path λ, which enters all the formulas, depends on the molecular density n and the molecular diameter d. In order to find n, we must first know the value of Avogadro's number L. Accurate values of L are obtained by methods outside the scope of this discussion.   The molecular diameter d is to be regarded as an unknown quantity whose magnitude we shall attempt to estimate.

The transport formulas do predict simple relations among the three coefficients which can be checked directly.   Using $b_A = \frac{1}{3}$ for all three transport phenomena, one obtains

$$\eta = \rho D_{11} \quad \text{and} \quad K = c_v \eta \qquad (3\text{-}29)$$

Measurements of D_{11} with isotopic tracer molecules combined with viscosity measurements at the same temperature yield values of $\rho D_{11}/\eta$ between 1.3 and 1.5.   The measured values of $K/c_v \eta$ range from 1.3 to 2.5.   The departures of these ratios from unity indicate that the values of b_A are somewhat different for the three transport phenomena, and the range of variation indicates a dependence of b_A on the nature of the gas which is quite appreciable in the case of heat conduction.   One expects b_A to be greater for the transport of translational energy than for either the transport of internal (rotational and vibrational) energy or the transport of momentum in viscous flow.   Molecules with large components of velocity in the direction of transport will transport larger-than-average translational energies.   This correlation between the transport velocity and the quantity transported tends to make b_A larger than $\frac{1}{3}$.   On the other hand, there appears to be little correlation between the internal energy and the transport velocity.   In the case of viscous flow, the molecules with large components of velocity in the direction of transport will not have larger-than-average velocity components in the flow direction and will not transport larger-than-average amounts of flow momentum; i.e., the velocity components at right angles are uncorrelated.   Hence one expects $K/c_v \eta$ to be greatest for monatomic gases and to decrease toward unity as the number of internal degrees of freedom of the molecule increases.   Indeed, $K/c_v \eta$ is found to be close to 2.5 for all the rare gases and to decrease with increasing complexity (and internal energy) of the molecule.

We have seen that the transport phenomena in gases are simply explained by mean-free-path methods and that these methods furnish simple formulas for the coefficients of heat conduction, viscosity, and self-diffusion.   We have seen that these formulas lead to simple relations among the three coefficients and that the variation of the coefficients with pressure and temperature is also predicted.   The agreement of this simple theory with experiment is indeed remarkable.   With some confidence in the essential correctness of the kinetic theory picture of a gas, we may now proceed to use the derived formulas to obtain an order of magnitude estimate of the fundamental molecular quantities L (Avogadro's number) and d (the molecular diameter).   From Eqs. (3-24) and (3-9),

$$\eta = \frac{mn\bar{v}}{3} \frac{1}{\sqrt{2}\,n\pi d^2} = \frac{1}{3\pi\,\sqrt{2}} \frac{M\bar{v}}{Ld^2} \qquad (3\text{-}30)$$

where M is the molecular weight. To sufficient accuracy we may write

$$Ld^2 \approx M(\overline{v^2})^{\frac{1}{2}}/13\eta \qquad (3\text{-}31)$$

where $\overline{v^2} = 3RT/M$. Equation (3-31) expresses Ld^2 in terms of directly measurable, macroscopic properties of the gas. In order to determine L and d separately, a second and independent relation between them is required. Let us assume that the molecules are close-packed in the solid state, but instead of using the formula for the volume occupied by close-packed spheres, we assign each molecule to a cube of side d as a rough approximation. Then the molar volume in the solid state is of the order of magnitude of Ld^3. Introducing the mass density ρ_s in the solid state, we obtain

$$Ld^3 \approx M/\rho_s \qquad (3\text{-}32)$$

for the second relation. Hence

$$d = \frac{Ld^3}{Ld^2} \approx \frac{M}{\rho_s} \frac{13\eta}{M(\overline{v^2})^{\frac{1}{2}}} \approx \frac{13\eta}{\rho_s} \left(\frac{M}{3RT}\right)^{\frac{1}{2}} \qquad (3\text{-}33)$$

where T is the absolute temperature at which η is measured. Carbon dioxide gas has a viscosity of 13.8×10^{-5} dyne-sec/cm^2 at 0°C, and the solid has a density of 1.53 gm/cm^3 at -79°C. From Eq. (3-33) we find an approximate diameter $d \approx 3.0 \times 10^{-8}$ cm for the CO$_2$ molecule. Avogadro's number L, obtained from (3-31) or (3-32), is then $\sim 10 \times 10^{23}$. The currently accepted value of L is 6.025×10^{23} molecules per mole. A very similar calculation, made by Loschmidt in 1865, provided the first order of magnitude estimates of Avogadro's number and the sizes of atoms and molecules.

We note that the transport formulas can also be used to determine the mean free path λ, when the transport coefficients have been measured. Thus λ may be found from measurements of η by means of Eq. (3-24). For most gases at standard conditions, the mean free path is in the neighborhood of 10^{-5}–10^{-6} cm. This order of magnitude is a very reasonable one. It is sufficiently large compared to molecular dimensions and the range of intermolecular forces (10^{-7}–10^{-8} cm) to justify the assumption that at ordinary pressures the molecules move as free particles, i.e., in straight lines, over paths that are large compared to their diameters. At the same time, it is sufficiently small to make understandable the slow rate of diffusion, as discussed in Sec. 3-1.

The limitations of the mean-free-path method have been to some extent indicated. A precise determination of b_A would require taking into account the dependence of the mean free path on velocity and, more important, the effect on the transport rate of more than one collision preceding the crossing of the plane (the so-called "persistence of velocities" correction).* The concept of the mean free path loses its direct significance if the molecule is treated as a particle surrounded by a field of force. Other methods, more rigorous than the ones used in this chapter, have been developed in order to treat the transport phenomena more accurately. The mean-free-path method can be modified and elaborated to take into account the dependence of mean free path on velocity, the influence of prior collisions on the transport, and, to some extent, the effect of intermolecular forces. These amendments of the method are not very satisfactory, however, and the most rigorous and accurate results are obtained by methods that do not involve the use of the mean free path. In the next chapter the subject of mutual diffusion will be treated by the "momentum-transfer" method.

PROBLEMS

3-1. An apparatus for measuring viscosity consists of two coaxial cylinders, both 25 cm in length, the outer one rotating at the rate of 1.10 rev/min and the inner one attached to a wire suspension whose twist measures the torque on the inner cylinder. The radius of the outer cylinder is 6 cm and the gap between the cylinders, containing the gas, is 0.2 cm wide. If the torque is measured as 4.40 dyne-cm, what is the viscosity of the gas? (Make the approximation that the gap is of negligible width compared to the circumference of the cylinders.)

3-2. Find the root-mean-square free path in terms of the mean free path. What is the most probable free path?

3-3. If Δz in Sec. 3-5 is defined as the average distance from the transport plane at which a molecule makes its last collision before crossing, show that $\Delta z = 2\lambda/3$ by averaging $r \cos \theta$ over the distribution given by Eq. (3-10).

3-4. Using the result of Problem 3-3, show that $b_A = \frac{1}{3}$ for any of the transport phenomena described by Eq. (3-21).

3-5. Show that the expression (3-16) for the net transport of molecules in the z direction is valid even if $n = n(x,y,z)$ is not a function of z alone; i.e., show that the terms in $\partial n/\partial x$, $\partial n/\partial y$, $\partial^2 n/\partial x\, \partial z$, $\partial^2 n/\partial x^2$, etc., in the Taylor expansion give vanishing contributions to the transport in the z direction.

3-6. The estimate of L and d arrived at in Sec. 3-6 can be improved in several ways: (a) by using the more accurate viscosity formula for elastic sphere molecules: $\eta = 0.499\, nm\bar{v}\lambda$ (see p. 222); (b) by inserting the correct mean speed from Eq. (5-16): $\bar{v} = (8RT/\pi M)^{1/2}$; (c) by replacing Eq. (3-32) by an accurate formula for close-packed spheres; (d) by applying the formulas to molecules of spherical symmetry, e.g., rare-gas atoms. The fraction of the available volume that is taken up by rigid spheres in either face-centered cubic or hexagonal close-packing is $\pi \sqrt{2}/6$. Solid argon is a face-centered cubic crystal of density 1.65 gm/cm³

* See Jeans, *op. cit.*, pp. 147 and 162.

at 20°K. The viscosity of argon gas at 0°C is 2.10×10^{-4} dyne-sec/cm². Find the molecular diameter d of argon and Avogadro's number L.

3-7. The ratio $K/\eta c_v$ for a polyatomic gas can be estimated by considering the transports of translational energy and of internal energy separately. Let K^{tr} and K^{int} represent the translational and internal contributions to K, and let c_v^{tr} and c_v^{int} denote the corresponding parts of c_v. We expect $K^{tr}/\eta c_v^{tr}$ to be close to the ratio observed for all monatomic gases and therefore set $K^{tr}/\eta c_v^{tr} = \frac{5}{2}$. The argument presented after Eq. (3-29) leads us to assume that $K^{int}/\eta c_v^{int} = 1$. Hence we obtain $K/\eta c_v = (5C_v^{tr}/2C_v) + (C_v^{int}/C_v)$ where the specific heats per gram have been replaced by the molar heat capacities on the right-hand side $(C_v^{tr} = 3R/2)$. Let γ denote the experimental specific-heat ratio C_p/C_v of the polyatomic gas.

    a. Show that $C_v^{tr}/C_v = 3(\gamma - 1)/2$ and that $K/\eta c_v = (9\gamma - 5)/4$ (Eucken, 1913).

    b. Compare Eucken's formula with data in the "Handbook of Chemistry and Physics."

3-8. The *free time* is defined as the time taken to execute a free path. Find the distribution law for the free times.

APPENDIX 3-1

The Poiseuille Flow Formula

Let us consider the flow of a gas through a long straight tube of circular cross section. Under ordinary circumstances, the mean free path λ of the gas is negligibly small compared to the radius a of the tube. Provided that the velocity of transport is not so great that the flow becomes turbulent, the steady-state motion of the gas will be similar to the laminar flow of a liquid and will be governed by the viscosity. The transport velocity u of the fluid is a function of the radial distance r from the axis of the tube (x axis). In the case of a gas, u represents the mean velocity component of the molecules in the flow direction, i.e., parallel to the axis of the tube. The fluid flows effectively in coaxial cylindrical shells of thickness dr, the velocity $u(r)$ increasing from zero at the wall to a maximum on the axis. A layer of liquid in contact with the wall is expected to adhere to it, and a layer of gas adjacent to the wall might be expected to have a negligible velocity because of surface irregularities. Hence we take $u(a) = 0$. The tube is assumed to be long enough so that end effects can be neglected.

Consider a short cylinder of fluid of radius r and length dx. In steady flow, the pressure difference dp between its ends produces a force that is balanced by the viscous drag over its curved surface. According to Eq. (3-19), the viscous shearing stress is $\eta \, du/dr$ where $du/dr < 0$. The viscous drag on the curved surface is then $2\pi r \, dx \, \eta \, du/dr$ and the condition for steady flow is given by

$$2\pi r \, dx \, \eta \, du/dr + \pi r^2 \, dp = 0$$

whence
$$du/dr \doteq -(r/2\eta) \, dp/dx \tag{3-34}$$

This integrates to
$$u = -(r^2/4\eta) \, dp/dx + C \tag{3-35}$$

The boundary condition at the wall $u(a) = 0$ determines the integration constant C. Hence
$$u = \frac{a^2 - r^2}{4\eta} \frac{dp}{dx} \tag{3-36}$$

giving the well-known parabolic "velocity profile." The molecular flow in the cylindrical shell between r and $r + dr$ is $nu \times 2\pi r \, dr$. The total molecular flow through the tube (molecules per unit time) is

$$F = n \int_0^a u 2\pi r \, dr = \frac{2\pi n}{4\eta} \frac{dp}{dx} \int_0^a (a^2 - r^2) r \, dr$$
$$= \frac{\pi a^4 n}{8\eta} \frac{dp}{dx} = \frac{\pi a^4}{8\eta kT} p \frac{dp}{dx} \tag{3-37}$$

In the above equations, dp/dx, u, and F are all assumed to be positive. Conservation of molecules makes F independent of x in the steady state. Hence

$$F \int_0^l dx = \frac{\pi a^4}{8\eta kT} \int_{p_B}^{p_F} p \, dp = \frac{\pi a^4}{8\eta kT} \frac{p_F^2 - p_B^2}{2} = \frac{\pi a^4 \bar{p} \, \Delta p}{8\eta kT}$$

where l is the length of the tube, $\Delta p = p_F - p_B$ the pressure drop from one end at pressure p_F to the other at pressure p_B, and $\bar{p} = (p_F + p_B)/2$. The Poiseuille formula for the number of gas molecules flowing per unit time through the tube is

$$F = \frac{\pi a^4 \bar{p} \, \Delta p}{8\eta kT l} \tag{3-38}$$

and the mass flow is

$$F' = \frac{\pi a^4 \bar{p} \, \Delta p}{8\eta R' T l} \tag{3-39}$$

in terms of the gas constant R' for one gram. The flow is seen to vary as the fourth power of the radius and to depend on the mean of the end pressures $\bar{p}$ as well as on the pressure difference Δp. The preceding formulas are strictly valid only if $\lambda \ll a$; this is a necessary condition for the applicability of the viscosity equations and only in this limit can one properly set the transport velocity at the wall equal to zero. In Sec. 4-3 we shall calculate the flow through a long tube for the other limiting case in which $\lambda \gg a$ and briefly discuss what is known about the transition region.

PROBLEM

A3-1. Assuming that the fluid slips past the wall with the velocity $u(a) = u_0$, show that Eq. (3-37) for the molecular flow per unit time is replaced by

$$F = n\pi a^2 [u_0 + (a^2/8\eta) \, dp/dx] \tag{3-37'}$$

CHAPTER 4

DIFFUSION

This chapter deals with the more important kinds of gaseous diffusion. The common process of interdiffusion of two different gases, referred to as *mutual diffusion*, is discussed in Sec. 4-1, where it is shown that mean-free-path methods are inappropriate and lead to incorrect results for the diffusion coefficient. In Sec. 4-2 an elementary treatment of mutual diffusion, based on the momentum-transfer method, is presented; this approach, which was originally developed by Maxwell and Stefan, gives an essentially correct result for the diffusion coefficient. Section 4-3 deals with a different kind of gaseous diffusion, the *free-molecule diffusion*, discovered by Knudsen, in which a gas flows through a tube at pressures so low that the mean free path is much larger than the tube diameter. Knudsen's formula for the flow through a long circular capillary is derived, and some consideration is given to the transition from the Poiseuille to the Knudsen flow regimes. In Sec. 4-4 we derive the general differential equation governing all types of diffusion and investigate a particular solution of this equation, representing an instantaneous plane source, which leads to a useful formula for the mean-square displacement of a diffusing particle. This section will end with a discussion of the random walk in one dimension and its relation to diffusion.

4-1. MUTUAL DIFFUSION

In Sec. 3-1 we referred to the spreading or diffusion of a gas through another gas. Actually, the two gases referred to were interdiffusing in such a way as to smooth out inequalities in the concentration. This process is referred to as mutual diffusion. The qualitative explanation of mutual diffusion is a simple and obvious one: as a result of the random thermal motion, molecules go from regions of higher concentration toward regions of lower concentration and also in the opposite sense. Since there are more molecules in the regions of higher concentration, more molecules are transported toward regions of lower concentration than in the reverse direction. Let n_1 and n_2 represent the molecular densities of the two gases and G_1 and G_2 the diffusion rates in molecules per square centimeter per second. The standard form of the law for mutual diffusion is obtained when the component gases interdiffuse under conditions of uniform total molecular density with no net flow of molecules. If the concentration gradient is in the z direction, one finds that

$$G_1 = -D_{12}\, dn_1/dz$$
$$G_2 = -D_{21}\, dn_2/dz \tag{4-1}$$

where D_{12} and D_{21} are positive constants of proportionality. The sign convention is the same as that used in Eq. (3-17). Under conditions of uniform total pressure and temperature, the total density $n_1 + n_2$ is uniform, and if there is no net flow of molecules the diffusive transports are equal and opposite. Then

$$dn_2/dz = -dn_1/dz$$
$$G_2 = -G_1 \tag{4-2}$$

Substituting Eqs. (4-2) into Eqs. (4-1), one finds that $D_{21} = D_{12}$, so that a single coefficient suffices to describe the diffusion process. D_{12} is referred to as the *coefficient for mutual diffusion*. Ordinarily, if the diffusion takes place at uniform total pressure and uniform temperature, the net flow of molecules will be automatically zero. However, if molecules are being introduced into one part of the diffusing system and removed from another part (so-called *sources* and *sinks*), there will be a net flow taking place at uniform total pressure and Eqs. (4-1) cannot be used directly. Mutual diffusion frequently takes place under circumstances in which the total density is not uniform. The pressure gradient produces a drift motion of the gas, and the diffusion is superimposed on this. Assume the concentration gradient and the gradient in total pressure to be both along the z direction, and let u represent the velocity of drift motion so that $(n_1 + n_2)u$ is the net flow of molecules per square centimeter per second. The transport rate of each component in molecules per square centimeter per second is*

$$G_i = n_i u - (n_1 + n_2)D_{12}\frac{d}{dz}\left(\frac{n_i}{n_1 + n_2}\right) \qquad i = 1,2 \tag{4-3}$$

where the transport by diffusion has been added to the transport by drift. Equations (4-3) reduce to Eqs. (4-1) when the pressure is uniform and there is no drift. It is to be noted that if the component gases have different molecular weights, the mass transport is different from zero when the molecular transport vanishes.

Since the mutual diffusion of two gases is of the nature of a transport process, it should be amenable to the mean-free-path method of treatment. In contrast to the very successful applications in the preceding chapter, the mean-free-path method gives a very poor approximation for the coefficient of mutual diffusion. This can be seen without a detailed

* The small Chapman-Enskog "pressure-diffusion" term is omitted.

calculation, and we can also avoid the problem of determining the mean free path of each type of molecule in a mixture of two gases. Consider the extreme case in which the density or concentration of the first gas is negligible compared to that of the second $[c_1 = n_1/(n_1 + n_2) \to 0]$. Since isolated molecules of gas 1 are diffusing through gas 2, the mean free path $(\lambda_1)_{c_1 \to 0}$ refers to collisions between unlike molecules. Thus $(\lambda_1)_{c_1 \to 0} = \bar{v}_1/\Theta_{12}$ where $\bar{v}_1$ is the mean thermal speed of the type-1 molecules and Θ_{12} is the collision frequency per type-1 molecule for unlike collisions. Since $dn_2/dz \to 0$, the diffusive transport of gas 2 is negligible, and we have the case of a dilute gas diffusing through a stationary gas. This problem has already been treated in Sec. 3-3, and it follows from the results of that section that

$$(D_{12})_{c_1 \to 0} = \tfrac{1}{3}\bar{v}_1(\lambda_1)_{c_1 \to 0} = \tfrac{1}{3}\bar{v}_1{}^2\Theta_{12}{}^{-1} \tag{4-4}$$

In the other extreme case in which the concentration of gas 2 is negligible (for the same total density), a similar equation is obtained:

$$(D_{12})_{c_2 \to 0} = \tfrac{1}{3}\bar{v}_2(\lambda_2)_{c_2 \to 0} = \tfrac{1}{3}\bar{v}_2{}^2\Theta_{21}{}^{-1} \tag{4-5}$$

However, $$\Theta_{12} = n\bar{v}_r\pi((d_1 + d_2)/2)^2 = \Theta_{21} \tag{4-6}$$

where n is the density of the stationary gas, $\bar{v}_r$ is the average relative velocity of a pair of unlike molecules, and d_1 and d_2 are molecular diameters. Hence

$$\frac{(D_{12})_{c_1 \to 0}}{(D_{12})_{c_2 \to 0}} = \left(\frac{\bar{v}_1}{\bar{v}_2}\right)^2 = \frac{M_2}{M_1} \tag{4-7}$$

where M_1 and M_2 are molecular weights. Equation (4-7) predicts a large variation of D_{12} with concentration when the molecular weight of one gas is much greater than that of the other. In the case of a mixture of H_2 and CO_2, the extreme variation in D_{12} found experimentally is only a few per cent, whereas Eq. (4-7) predicts a variation by a factor of 22. Thus the elementary mean-free-path theory predicts large variations of D_{12} with the proportions of the mixture which are never observed. Actually, D_{12} is nearly independent of composition. Obviously, this difficulty does not exist in the case of self-diffusion.

The lack of success of the mean-free-path treatment of mutual diffusion is customarily attributed to the special nature of the transport in diffusion. In the cases of viscosity and heat conduction, the molecular property A that is transported is a dynamical quantity, i.e., momentum in one case and energy in the other. But in diffusion, A represents the concentration of a particular component or, interpreted as a molecular property, the probability that a molecule is of a particular type. In the mean-free-path treatment of the viscosity of a mixture of two gases, the dependence of the viscosity coefficient on composition is in fair agreement with experiment.* In this case it is not very important whether a given molecule collides with a like or an unlike molecule before crossing the transport plane. In the case of mutual diffusion, the last collision before crossing the transport plane has a very different effect, depending on whether it is with a like or an unlike molecule. In a collision with a like molecule, if either of the two molecules crosses the plane, the transport is unaffected by the collision. Neither molecule may cross the plane or both may; these two possibilities leave the transport approximately unaffected. Hence one expects that a collision with a like molecule will have little, if any, effect on the diffusive transport. A simple and fairly rigorous argument, to be presented in the next section, shows that the process of mutual diffusion is unaffected by collisions between like molecules and that D_{12} is independent of the effective target areas or cross sections for like-molecule collisions. On the other hand, if a molecule collides with an unlike molecule, the diffusive transport will depend sensitively on the result of the collision. A molecule of type 1 headed toward the transport plane may collide head-on with a molecule of type 2, with the result that the second molecule crosses the plane instead of the first. Thus, like- and unlike-molecule collisions have very different effects on the transport of probability but not on the transport of momentum or energy.

The mean-free-path treatment of mutual diffusion makes D_{12} depend on the mean free path of each kind of molecule in the mixture. These mean free paths are appropriate to the mixture and depend on the proportions of the component gases as well as the cross sections for both like-molecule and unlike-molecule collisions. Thus, the transport of type-1 molecules is calculated, as in Sec. 3-3, by considering the molecules of type 1 leaving a volume element of the gas after a collision with a molecule of either type, proceeding toward an element of area of the transport plane, and arriving there if not intercepted by a collision with a molecule of either type. The resulting dependence of D_{12} on the cross sections for like-molecule collisions is incorrect in principle, and the dependence on concentration is grossly at variance with experiment. If the cross sections for like-molecule collisions are set equal to zero in the mean-free-path formula for D_{12}, the resulting formula is independent of the proportions of the mixture and is very nearly correct. However, there is nothing in the mean-free-path theory which would justify the complete omission of the effects of like-molecule collisions. In the next section we shall study the problem of mutual diffusion from an entirely different point of view—one in which the mean free path is not used.†

* See E. H. Kennard, "Kinetic Theory of Gases," McGraw-Hill Book Company, Inc., New York, 1938, p. 161.
† For a more detailed criticism of mean-free-path methods in diffusion, see the paper by S. Chapman, *Phil. Mag.*, vol. 5, p. 630, 1928.

4-2. ELEMENTARY TREATMENT OF MUTUAL DIFFUSION BY THE MOMENTUM-TRANSFER METHOD

The existence of a concentration gradient in mutual diffusion implies a gradient in the partial pressure of each gas, since $p_i = n_i kT$ and the total pressure $p = p_1 + p_2$ is uniform. Consider a thin "slice" of gas of unit area and thickness $|dz|$ in the case of a one-dimensional diffusion along the z direction. The gas of type 1 contained in the slice is subject to a net force dp_1 in the z direction, and this corresponds to a change in the total z component of momentum of the molecules of type 1. Since there is no motion of the gas as a whole, viscous shearing stresses are not set up; i.e., there will be no variation in the transport velocity of either type of molecule at right angles to the concentration gradient and no transport of z momentum in the x or y directions. The z momentum communicated to the walls can be neglected at ordinary pressures, since collisions of a molecule with the walls are very infrequent compared to collisions with other molecules of the gas when the mean free path is much smaller than the dimensions of the apparatus. The total z component of momentum of the molecules of type 1 in the thin slice is unaltered by collisions between type-1 molecules according to the law of conservation of momentum. We conclude that the net force dp_1 is entirely associated with the exchange of z momentum between gas 1 and gas 2. As a result of unlike-molecule collisions, there will be a net transfer of z momentum from one gas to the other, and the net force dp_1 is equal to the transfer taking place per unit time in the thin slice. Correspondingly, dp_2, which is equal to $-dp_1$, represents the reaction force on the second gas. If we denote by M_{12} the average amount of z momentum transferred from gas 1 to gas 2 per unit volume per unit time, it follows that*

$$dp_1 = kT\, dn_1 = -M_{12}\, dz \qquad (4\text{-}8)$$

The momentum-transfer method† of treating mutual diffusion is based on Eq. (4-8) and involves an explicit calculation of M_{12}. When the calculated value of M_{12} is inserted in Eq. (4-8), the resulting equation takes on the standard form (4-1) for mutual diffusion with an explicit expression appearing for the diffusion coefficient D_{12}. Only collisions between unlike molecules are taken into account in M_{12}, and the formula for D_{12} depends only on the cross section for unlike collisions.

---

* A positive value of M_{12} indicates that gas 1 loses momentum in the $+z$ direction through unlike collisions; in this case $dp_1/dz < 0$.

† This method is to be accredited to J. C. Maxwell, *Phil. Trans. Royal Soc.*, vol. 157, p. 49, 1867; "Collected Works," vol. 2, p. 26 (see bibliography of the present book) and to J. Stefan, *Wien. Ber.*, vol. 65, p. 323, 1872. The Maxwell-Stefan method has been neglected by authors of textbooks in this field. A different elementary presentation is given by W. H. Furry, *Amer. Jour. Phys.*, vol. 16, p. 63, 1948.

We shall now give an elementary approximate treatment of mutual diffusion according to the momentum-transfer method. We shall calculate the average number of unlike collisions taking place in unit volume per unit time and the average momentum transferred per collision between unlike molecules. The product of these two averages will represent M_{12} approximately but not exactly, since the average of a product is not in general equal to the product of the average values of the factors. However, this approximation leads to an unimportant error in a numerical coefficient, as will be seen from a more rigorous treatment in a later chapter. Following the discussion in Sec. 3-2, we consider a molecule of type 1 moving among molecules of type 2 with density n_2. Denoting the molecular diameters by d_1 and d_2, we see that the cross section of the sphere of influence for unlike collisions is πd_{12}^2 where $d_{12} = (d_1 + d_2)/2$ is the average molecular diameter. The number of collisions per unit time between the molecule of type 1 moving with speed v and the molecules of type 2, if assumed at rest, would be $\pi d_{12}^2 v n_2$. Actually, v must be replaced by a suitably averaged value for the relative velocity of a pair of unlike molecules, taking into account the distribution of molecular velocities. Denoting this average value by $\bar{v}_r$, we obtain for the unlike-molecule collision frequency per unit volume of the gas

$$n_1 n_2 \bar{v}_r \pi d_{12}^2 \qquad (4\text{-}9)$$

where the collision frequency per molecule of type 1 has been multiplied by the number of type-1 molecules per unit volume. We expect $\bar{v}_r$ to be a simple symmetric function of $\bar{v}_1$ and $\bar{v}_2$ which reduces to $\sqrt{2}\,\bar{v}$ when the molecules are alike (cf. Eq. (3-8)). Clearly, $\bar{v}_r = (\bar{v}_1^2 + \bar{v}_2^2)^{1/2}$ satisfies this condition and can be justified by a detailed calculation with the Maxwell distribution function (see Eq. (5-27)). We rewrite (4-9) as

$$n_1 n_2 \pi d_{12}^2 (\bar{v}_1^2 + \bar{v}_2^2)^{1/2} \qquad (4\text{-}10)$$

This represents the average number of collisions per unit volume per unit time between unlike molecules.

We consider next the average momentum transferred in a collision between two unlike molecules. Let us denote by u_1 the *diffusive transport velocity* of gas 1. If the diffusion takes place in the z direction, then u_1 is identical with the mean z component of velocity $\bar{v}_{1z}$ of the molecules of type 1. Since there is no net flow of molecules in the standard case of mutual diffusion, we have

$$n_1 u_1 + n_2 u_2 = 0 \qquad (4\text{-}11)$$

The average momentum of molecule 1 before collision is $m_1 u_1$ in the z direction. The center of mass of the two molecules has a mean velocity in the z direction of

$$\bar{u}_c = \frac{m_1 u_1 + m_2 u_2}{m_1 + m_2} \tag{4-12}$$

The problem of a collision between two billiard balls will be studied in detail in Sec. 8-2, where it will be shown that in a center-of-mass frame of reference—i.e., a system of coordinates moving along with the center of mass of the two bodies—all directions of reflection or rebound will occur with equal likelihood. This means that if the molecules are regarded as billiard balls, the average velocity and momentum of a molecule after collision, referred to the center-of-mass system, is zero. The average velocity of a molecule after collision is then equal to the velocity of the center of mass. Therefore the average momentum of molecule 1 in the z direction after collision is simply $m_1 \bar{u}_c$. The average z momentum lost by a molecule of type 1 in an unlike collision is

$$m_1(u_1 - \bar{u}_c) = m^*(u_1 - u_2) \tag{4-13}$$

where $m^* = m_1 m_2/(m_1 + m_2)$ is the "reduced mass." Clearly, the effect of the unlike collisions is to transfer z momentum from the lighter to the heavier gas.

Combining Eqs. (4-10) and (4-13), we obtain an approximate expression for the momentum transferred per unit volume per unit time from gas 1 to gas 2:

$$M_{12} \approx m^*(u_1 - u_2)n_1 n_2 \pi d_{12}^2 (\bar{v}_1^2 + \bar{v}_2^2)^{1/2} \tag{4-14}$$

The most important result exhibited by this formula is the way in which M_{12} depends on the partial densities n_1 and n_2 and the transport velocities u_1 and u_2. To emphasize this dependence, we rewrite (4-14) as

$$M_{12} = n_1 n_2 (u_1 - u_2) f_{12} \tag{4-15}$$

where f_{12} does not depend on u_1, u_2, n_1, or n_2. A result of the same form as Eq. (4-15) is obtained from a more rigorous treatment, to be presented in a later section, in which the billiard-ball model is not assumed and the distribution of molecular velocities is taken into account. The diffusive transport of type-1 molecules per unit area per unit time is clearly given by

$$G_1 = n_1 u_1 = -n_2 u_2 = -G_2 \tag{4-16}$$

using Eq. (4-11). Substituting Eq. (4-16) into Eq. (4-15), one has

$$M_{12} = nG_1 f_{12} \tag{4-17}$$

where $n = n_1 + n_2$ is the total density of molecules. This result is now inserted in Eq. (4-8), giving

$$kT(dn_1/dz) = -M_{12} = -nG_1 f_{12} \tag{4-18}$$

and rewriting (4-18) in the standard form (4-1) for mutual diffusion, one obtains finally

$$G_1 = -\frac{kT}{nf_{12}}\frac{dn_1}{dz} = -D_{12}\frac{dn_1}{dz} \tag{4-19}$$

and the general formula for the mutual-diffusion coefficient

$$D_{12} = kT/nf_{12} \tag{4-20}$$

According to Eq. (4-20), the mutual diffusion coefficient is independent of the proportions of the mixture, a result which is in approximate accord with observation.   More refined developments of the theory predict a slight variation of D_{12} with composition in agreement with experiment. Using the approximate value of f_{12} given by Eq. (4-14), an explicit expression for D_{12} is obtained:

$$D_{12} \approx \frac{kT}{nm^*\pi d_{12}^2(\bar{v}_1^2 + \bar{v}_2^2)^{1/2}} \tag{4-21}$$

or, replacing $(\bar{v}_1^2 + \bar{v}_2^2)^{1/2}$ by $(\overline{v_1^2} + \overline{v_2^2})^{1/2}$,

$$D_{12} \approx \left(\frac{kT}{3m^*}\right)^{1/2}\frac{1}{n\pi d_{12}^2} \tag{4-22}$$

A more accurate treatment gives formula (4-22) with a slightly different numerical factor:

$$D_{12} = \frac{3}{8}\left(\frac{\pi kT}{2m^*}\right)^{1/2}\frac{1}{n\pi d_{12}^2} \tag{4-23}$$

where $d_{12} = (d_1 + d_2)/2$ and d_1 and d_2 are the diameters of the molecules treated as rigid elastic spheres.   Equation (4-23) can be used to determine the molecular diameters from the mutual-diffusion coefficients of a triad of gases.   Measurements of D_{12}, D_{23}, D_{31} give three equations from which to deduce the values of d_1, d_2, d_3.   The values so obtained are consistent with the molecular diameters determined by other methods.   In Sec. 8-3 we shall present a more accurate treatment of mutual diffusion, by the momentum-transfer method, which will not be restricted to the billiard-ball approximation.

4-3. FREE-MOLECULE DIFFUSION AND THE FLOW IN TUBES AT LOW PRESSURES

In Appendix 3-1, the viscous flow of a fluid through a long tube of circular cross section was taken up and the Poiseuille formula derived. This formula is applicable to the laminar flow of gases at ordinary pressures, which are high enough so that the mean free path is very small compared to the diameter of the tube.   If this condition is not fulfilled, the basic equation for viscous flow cannot be applied.   No satisfactory theory of the flow exists in the intermediate pressure region for which the mean free path and the tube diameter are of comparable size. However, when the pressure is so low that the mean free path greatly exceeds the tube diameter, the flow becomes amenable to simple theoretical treatment. The flow in this limit is commonly referred to as *free-molecule diffusion*, or *Knudsen flow*, after its discoverer. It is of practical importance in connection with high-vacuum work.

We undertake now to treat the free-molecule flow in a long circular tube of radius a. The two ends are maintained at different pressures, and the temperature is uniform throughout. If the pressure is so low that $\lambda \gg a$, a molecule of the gas must collide many times with the wall of the tube before it encounters another molecule. For this reason, the flow of the gas is determined almost entirely by the collisions with the wall and is practically unaffected by intermolecular collisions. In the limiting case of free-molecule flow, the latter are neglected. Since the flow is determined by the collisions with the wall, the effect of such a collision on the path of a molecule must be investigated. A specular, or mirrorlike, reflection of the molecule would require a surface that is smooth on the submicroscopic scale of molecular dimensions. The most nearly ideal reflecting surface in nature is a cleavage plane of a perfect single crystal. Even here, however, the reflection need not be specular. Although it is outside the scope of this book to enter into a detailed discussion of the collisions between neutral molecules and solid surfaces,[*] a few remarks may help to indicate the nature of the problem and to make plausible the experimental results. The wave properties of matter mentioned in Sec. 1-3 must be taken into account. The criterion of smoothness for a surface reflecting waves is that the irregularities must be small compared to the wave length, in this case the de Broglie wave length Λ of the molecules ($\sim 10^{-9}$ cm at room temperature). If the surface is a crystal cleavage plane, the irregularities will be mainly due to the thermal vibrations of the lattice atoms (amplitude $A \sim 10^{-9}$ cm at room temperature). A necessary condition for specular reflection is that $\Lambda \gg A \cos \theta$ where θ is the angle of incidence. Thus, even in the most favorable case, specular reflection may not occur. Furthermore, if the impinging molecules adhere to the crystal surface for an appreciable length of time, the reflection will not be specular even though the previous condition is satisfied. In actual practice, the wall surfaces are highly irregular on the submicroscopic scale, and one would expect the direction of reflection from the wall to bear little if any relation to the direction of incidence (*diffuse reflection*). This would be the case if a gas molecule, upon reaching the surface, were temporarily trapped in a

---

[*] Cf. Massey and Burhop, "Electronic and Ionic Impact Phenomena," Oxford University Press, London, 1952.

small pocket or if it were adsorbed and later evaporated. Experiments by Knudsen* and others on the reflection of molecular beams from glass and polished metal surfaces indicate close to 100 per cent diffuse reflection.

If the actual irregular wall surface is replaced by a smooth mathematical surface and we inquire about the number of molecules diffusely reflected from an element of area of this surface per unit time, we may proceed as if the reflected molecules originated in an equilibrium gas layer on the other side of the surface, e.g., a gas layer consisting of the gas trapped in surface pockets. The number of molecules reflected from unit area of the wall per unit time in a particular direction is then equal to the number crossing unit area of the mathematical surface in that direction. This is obtained from Eq. (2-21) by integrating over speeds:

$$n \cos \theta' \frac{d\omega}{4\pi} \int vf(v) \, dv = n\bar{v} \cos \theta' \frac{d\omega}{4\pi} \qquad (4\text{-}24)$$

where θ' is the angle between the direction of motion of the molecules and the normal to the surface and $d\omega$ is the element of solid angle specifying a small range of directions about the given direction.

The free-molecule flow is calculated by determining the net molecular transport through a cross section of the tube. Denoting by dS an element of area of the cross section, we first calculate the net transport through dS and then integrate over the entire cross section. The molecules that pass through dS are traveling in straight-line paths from one point in the wall to another, since the effects of intermolecular collisions and gravity are neglected. Consider the set of molecules which leave a surface element dS' of the wall and pass directly through the element of cross section dS. Using Eq. (4-24), the number of molecules that proceed from dS' through dS per unit time is found to be

$$d^2N = n\bar{v} \, dS' \cos \theta' \, d\omega/4\pi \qquad (4\text{-}25)$$

where $d\omega$ is the element of solid angle subtended by dS at the center of dS'. Let the line joining the centers of dS and dS' be of length r and make angles of θ and θ' with the normals to dS and dS', respectively. Referring to Fig. 4-1, we see that r, θ, and ϕ represent the spherical coordinates of the center of dS' referred to an origin at the center of dS. Let $d\omega'$ be the element of solid angle subtended by dS' at the center of dS. Then

$$d\omega = dS \, |\cos \theta|/r^2$$
$$d\omega' = dS' \cos \theta'/r^2 = \sin \theta \, d\theta \, d\phi \qquad (4\text{-}26)$$

and $\quad d^2N = \dfrac{n\bar{v} \, dS' \cos \theta' \, dS \, |\cos \theta|}{4\pi \quad r^2} = \dfrac{n\bar{v} \, dS}{4\pi} |\cos \theta| \sin \theta \, d\theta \, d\phi \quad (4\text{-}27)$

The quantity n appearing in Eqs. (4-24) through (4-27) represents the

* M. Knudsen, "The Kinetic Theory of Gases," Methuen & Co., Ltd., London; John Wiley & Sons, Inc., New York, 1950.

number density of molecules in the neighborhood of the surface element dS'. We choose the z axis parallel to the axis of the tube and locate the xy plane in the cross section containing dS. Let s denote the projection of r on the xy plane. Then $z = r \cos \theta = s \cot \theta$ is the distance from the xy plane to the cross section through the center of dS' (see Fig. 4-1).

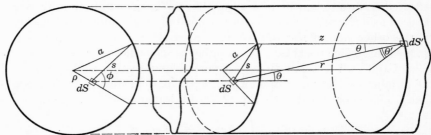

FIG. 4-1. Coordinate system used in calculating free-molecule diffusion in a long tube.

The density n is an unknown function of z and will be written $n(z)$. We assume a slow variation of density along the tube and expand $n(z)$ in a Taylor series about $z = 0$:

$$n(z) = n(0) + z \left(\frac{dn}{dz} \right)_0 + \frac{z^2}{2} \left(\frac{d^2n}{dz^2} \right)_0 + \cdots \tag{4-28}$$

The total number of molecules traversing dS per unit time in the $-z$ direction is

$$dN_- = \frac{\bar{v}\, dS}{4\pi} \int_0^{2\pi} d\phi \int_0^{\pi/2} n(z) \cos \theta \sin \theta \, d\theta \tag{4-29}$$

and in the $+z$ direction is

$$dN_+ = \frac{\bar{v}\, dS}{4\pi} \int_0^{2\pi} d\phi \int_{\pi/2}^{\pi} n(z)(-\cos \theta) \sin \theta \, d\theta \tag{4-30}$$

where the limits of the θ integration correspond to a tube of infinite length. Combining Eqs. (4-29) and (4-30), we obtain for the net flow through dS

$$dN = dN_+ - dN_- = -\frac{\bar{v}\, dS}{4\pi} \int_0^{2\pi} d\phi \int_0^{\pi} n(z) \cos \theta \sin \theta \, d\theta \tag{4-31}$$

We insert (4-28) into (4-31) and neglect higher derivative terms beyond the second. Then, since $z = s \cot \theta$,

$$dN = -\frac{\bar{v}\, dS}{4\pi} \int_0^{2\pi} d\phi \left[n(0) \int_0^{\pi} \cos \theta \sin \theta \, d\theta \right.$$

$$+ \left(\frac{dn}{dz} \right)_0 s \int_0^{\pi} \cot \theta \cos \theta \sin \theta \, d\theta$$

$$\left. + \frac{1}{2} \left(\frac{d^2n}{dz^2} \right)_0 s^2 \int_0^{\pi} \cot^2 \theta \cos \theta \sin \theta \, d\theta \right] \tag{4-32}$$

The first θ integral in Eq. (4-32) clearly vanishes. The third θ integral, when expressed in terms of $\mu = \cos \theta$, is

$$\int_{-1}^{1} \frac{\mu^3 \, d\mu}{1 - \mu^2} \equiv \lim_{\epsilon \to 0} \int_{-1+\epsilon}^{1-\epsilon} \frac{\mu^3 \, d\mu}{1 - \mu^2} = 0 \qquad (4\text{-}33)$$

The integral in (4-33) vanishes because the integrand is an odd function of μ and the limits are symmetric about zero (an odd function is one that changes into its negative when the variable is replaced by its negative). The second θ integral in Eq. (4-32) is equal to $\pi/2$. Hence

$$
\begin{aligned}
dN &= -\frac{\bar{v} \, dS}{8} \left(\frac{dn}{dz}\right)_0 \int_0^{2\pi} s \, d\phi \\
&= -\frac{\bar{v} \, dS}{8} \left(\frac{dn}{dz}\right)_0 \int_0^{2\pi} [(a^2 - \rho^2 \sin^2 \phi)^{1/2} - \rho \cos \phi] \, d\phi \qquad (4\text{-}34) \\
&= -\frac{\bar{v}a \, dS}{2} \left(\frac{dn}{dz}\right)_0 \int_0^{\pi/2} (1 - \rho'^2 \sin^2 \phi)^{1/2} \, d\phi \qquad (4\text{-}35)
\end{aligned}
$$

where ρ denotes the distance from the element dS to the axis of the tube and $\rho' = \rho/a$ is the same distance in units of a. The expression for s, which is the distance from dS to the projection of dS' on the xy plane, is obtained from Fig. 4-1 by simple trigonometry. The integral appearing in (4-35) is in the standard form of the complete elliptic integral of the second kind and is customarily denoted by $E(\rho')$. The net molecular flow per unit area of the cross section is given by

$$G(\rho') = \frac{dN}{dS} = -\frac{\bar{v}a}{2} E(\rho') \frac{dn}{dz} \qquad (4\text{-}36)$$

where the subscript will be dropped from dn/dz in the remaining equations. The flow is not uniform over the cross section but varies with distance from the axis. The total net flow through the tube is obtained by integrating (4-35). Inserting $dS = 2\pi\rho \, d\rho = 2\pi a^2 \rho' \, d\rho'$, we obtain

$$
\begin{aligned}
N &= -\pi a^3 \bar{v} \frac{dn}{dz} \int_0^1 d\rho' \rho' \int_0^{\pi/2} (1 - \rho'^2 \sin^2 \phi)^{1/2} \, d\phi \\
&= -\pi a^3 \bar{v} \frac{dn}{dz} \int_0^{\pi/2} d\phi \int_0^1 d\rho' \rho'(1 - \rho'^2 \sin^2 \phi)^{1/2} \\
&= -\frac{\pi a^3 \bar{v}}{3} \frac{dn}{dz} \int_0^{\pi/2} d\phi \frac{1 - \cos^3 \phi}{\sin^2 \phi} \qquad (4\text{-}37)
\end{aligned}
$$

The integral in (4-37) can be expressed as

$$
\begin{aligned}
\int_0^{\pi/2} \frac{\cos^3 \phi - 1}{\cos^2 \phi - 1} \, d\phi &= \int_0^{\pi/2} \left(\cos \phi + \frac{1}{1 + \cos \phi}\right) d\phi \\
&= \left(\sin \phi + \tan \frac{\phi}{2}\right)_0^{\pi/2} = 2
\end{aligned}
$$

and the final result is

$$N = -\pi a^2 \frac{2\bar{v}a}{3} \frac{dn}{dz} \qquad (4\text{-}38)$$

Equation (4-38) gives the net transport of molecules per unit time through the tube. Since the transport is proportional to the density gradient and opposite in direction, the flow is of the nature of a diffusion. The mean molecular flow per unit area averaged over the cross section is given by

$$\bar{G} = -(2\bar{v}a/3) \, dn/dz \qquad (4\text{-}39)$$

from which we infer an averaged diffusion coefficient of $2\bar{v}a/3$. This may be compared with the self-diffusion coefficient $\bar{v}\lambda/3$. In both types of diffusion a molecule executes a free path terminated by a collision, after which the molecule moves off in a random direction. The free-molecule diffusion coefficient has the diameter of the tube appearing in place of the mean free path. One would expect the average free path between successive wall collisions in free molecule flow to be of the order of magnitude of the tube diameter (see Prob. 4-9).

Before Eq. (4-38) can be compared with experiment, the value of $\bar{v}$ must be determined from the distribution of molecular speeds. We have assumed the molecules leaving the wall to proceed from an equilibrium gas layer, e.g., the gas trapped in surface pockets, and the corresponding distribution of velocities would be the equilibrium, or Maxwellian, distribution. It will be shown in Chap. 5 that the mean speed calculated with the Maxwell distribution function is given by

$$\bar{v} = \left(\frac{8kT}{\pi m}\right)^{1/2} = \left(\frac{8RT}{\pi M}\right)^{1/2} \qquad (4\text{-}40)$$

Inserting Eq. (4-40) in the transport equation (4-38), one obtains

$$N = -\frac{2\pi a^3}{3}\left(\frac{8RT}{\pi M}\right)^{1/2}\frac{dn}{dz} \qquad (4\text{-}41)$$

In a steady flow, N must be constant along the tube; therefore the density gradient dn/dz is uniform and can be replaced by $\Delta n/l$ where Δn is the difference in density between the ends and l is the length of the tube. Since $\Delta n = \Delta p/kT$, we obtain for the flow rate in moles

$$F(\text{moles}) = \frac{2\pi a^3}{3}\left(\frac{8RT}{\pi M}\right)^{1/2}\frac{\Delta p}{lRT} \qquad (4\text{-}42)$$

and for the flow rate in grams

$$F(\text{gms}) = \frac{4}{3}\left(\frac{2\pi}{R'T}\right)^{1/2}\frac{a^3\,\Delta p}{l} \qquad (4\text{-}43)$$

where $R' = R/M$ is the gas constant per gram. Knudsen and others[*] have investigated the flow of various gases through fine glass capillaries at pressures so low that the mean free path λ exceeded the diameter by a factor of 100 or more. Their results have confirmed Eq. (4-43) to within an experimental error of the order of 1 per cent. The assumption of a diffuse reflection of the molecules from the wall is thus verified.

The free-molecule flow through a tube differs from the viscous (Poiseuille) flow (cf. Appendix 3-1) in several respects. The former varies as the cube of the radius, whereas the latter varies as the fourth power. The viscous flow is jointly proportional to the pressure difference between the ends of the tube and the average of the end pressures, whereas the free-molecule flow is simply proportional to the pressure drop alone (this difference corresponds to the fact that the pressure gradient is uniform in the free-molecule case but not in the Poiseuille regime). The relation between the flow rate F and the pressure drop Δp in free-molecule flow is analogous to the Ohm's-law relation between the current and the potential drop across a resistor. The flow-resistance $\Delta p/F$ is independent of pressure and is directly proportional to the length of the tube and inversely proportional to the cube of the radius. When an apparatus to be evacuated is connected to a high-speed pump, the connecting tube must have a diameter large enough to permit a flow rate equal to the rate at which the pump operates. We also observe that the free-molecule flow depends on the nature of the gas only through the molecular weight M and that the molecular-flow rate is inversely proportional to $M^{1/2}$ as in effusion. In fact, effusion through a circular orifice can be considered as a special case of Knudsen flow in which the length of the tube is small compared to its diameter. If a free-molecule flow of a binary gas mixture takes place, the component gases will diffuse along the tube independently of each other, and Eq. (4-42) can be applied to each gas separately if Δp is interpreted as the partial pressure drop. The ratio of the flow rates is the same as in Eq. (2-26); thus the discussion following Eq. (2-26) is equally applicable to this case.

Slip Flow and Flow at Intermediate Pressures. We shall now discuss briefly the transition from Poiseuille to Knudsen flow. No quantitative kinetic-theory treatment of the flow in the transition region where λ and a are comparable exists at the present time. If λ is smaller than a but not negligibly small, it is customary to use the Poiseuille formula with an additive correction term, representing the effect of "slip" at the surface of the tube, which augments the flow. The theory of this correction

[*] M. Knudsen, *Ann. d. Physik*, vol. 28, p. 75, 1909; W. Gaede, *Ann. d. Physik*, vol. 41, p. 289, 1913; P. Clausing, *Ann. d. Physik*, vol. 7, p. 569, 1930; W. Klose, *Ann. d. Physik*, vol. 11, p. 73, 1931; H. Adzumi, *Bull. Chem. Soc. Japan*, vol. 12, pp. 199, 285, 291, 295, and 304, 1937; S. Visner, *Phys. Rev.*, vol. 82, p. 297, 1951.

term is unrigorous, and it will be discussed here only briefly. It is assumed that the flow velocity of the gas adjacent to the wall is not zero but has a finite value u_0. Then, according to the result of Prob. A3-1 in Appendix 3-1 (Eq. (3-37')), the flow of molecules per unit time is given by

$$F = n\pi a^2[u_0 + (a^2/8\eta) \, dp/dx] \qquad (4\text{-}44)$$

An estimate of u_0 is obtained from mean-free-path considerations. Let the gas flow past a plane wall, the flow being in the x direction and the normal to the wall in the z direction. The flow velocity u is then a function of z and the viscous shearing stress is $\eta \, du/dz$. In a steady flow, the x momentum transferred per unit time to unit area of the wall by molecular impact is equal to the shearing stress in the gas next to the wall. According to the elementary mean-free-path theory, the x momentum that a molecule carries to the wall is determined by the site of its last collision before reaching the wall. The average distance of this site from the wall is $2\lambda/3$ (cf. Prob. 3-3), and the average x momentum of a molecule at this site is $m[u_0 + (2\lambda/3) \, du/dz]$. Assuming diffuse reflection of the molecules from the wall, i.e., no preferred direction of reflection or reemission, the mean x momentum carried off after impact with the wall is zero. Since the number of collisions per unit area per unit time is $n\bar{v}/4$, the momentum transfer to the wall per square centimeter per second is

$$\frac{n\bar{v}}{4} \, m \left(u_0 + \frac{2\lambda}{3} \frac{du}{dz} \right) \qquad (4\text{-}45)$$

We equate this to the shearing stress in the gas and substitute for η its elementary value given by Eq. (3-24):

$$\frac{nm\bar{v}u_0}{4} + \frac{nm\bar{v}\lambda}{6} \frac{du}{dz} = \eta \frac{du}{dz} = \frac{nm\bar{v}\lambda}{3} \frac{du}{dz} \qquad (4\text{-}46)$$

whence $\qquad\qquad\qquad u_0 = (2\lambda/3) \, du/dz \qquad\qquad\qquad (4\text{-}47)$

Applying this result to the flow through a long tube, one obtains for the "slip velocity"

$$u_0 = -\frac{2\lambda}{3} \left(\frac{du}{dr} \right)_{r=a} = \frac{2\lambda}{3} \frac{a}{2\eta} \frac{dp}{dx} \qquad (4\text{-}48)$$

using Eq. (3-34). On substituting for u_0 in Eq. (4-44), one obtains the modified Poiseuille formula

$$F = \frac{\pi a^4}{8\eta kT} \, p \, \frac{dp}{dx} \left[1 + \frac{8\lambda}{3a} \right] \qquad (4\text{-}49)$$

in place of Eq. (3-37). The effect of "slip" is to introduce the factor in brackets; the correction term increases with λ/a and augments the flow. If the elementary value of η is inserted in Eq. (4-49), the correction term for the additional flow becomes

$$\Delta F = \frac{\pi a^3}{m \bar{v}} \frac{dp}{dx} = \frac{\pi}{8} \frac{\pi a^3}{\bar{v}} \frac{8kT}{\pi m} \frac{dn}{dx} = \frac{\pi}{8} \pi a^3 \bar{v} \frac{dn}{dx} \qquad (4\text{-}50)$$

with the aid of Eq. (4-40). Comparing Eq. (4-50) with Eq. (4-38), we see that the "slip flow" ΔF has the same form as the free-molecule flow but is smaller by a factor of $3\pi/16$.

Integrating the modified Poiseuille flow equation, one obtains

$$\int_0^l F \, dx = F \int_0^l dx = \frac{\pi a^4}{8\eta kT} \int_{p_B}^{p_F} p \, dp + \frac{\pi a^3}{m \bar{v}} \int_{p_B}^{p_F} dp \qquad (4\text{-}51)$$

whence
$$F = \frac{\pi a^4 \bar{p} \, \Delta p}{8 \eta k T l} + \frac{\pi a^3 \, \Delta p}{m \bar{v} l} \qquad (4\text{-}52)$$

where $\bar{p} = (p_F + p_B)/2$ and $\Delta p = p_F - p_B$. If the *specific* flow $F/\Delta p$ is plotted against $\bar{p}$, a straight line should be obtained and the ordinate intercept should measure the slip flow according to Eq. (4-52). Since the slip-flow expression differs from the free-molecule flow by a factor of $3\pi/16$ and the latter is known to be correct for $\lambda \gg a$, Eq. (4-52) cannot be accurate at low pressures. One might surmise that the difference in numerical factors is a consequence of the approximate nature of the slip correction and that the slip term should actually be identical with the free-molecule formula. If this were the case, the specific flow curve ($F/\Delta p$ versus $\bar{p}$) would be linear at all pressures. The experiments of Knudsen and others* have established the existence of a minimum for the specific flow in long tubes at pressures for which $a/\lambda \approx 0.2$. The viscous-flow theory with the slip correction is not valid for $\lambda \sim a$, and Eqs. (4-49) and (4-52) cannot be extrapolated into this low-pressure region. Although no quantitative theory of the flow in the transition region ($\lambda \sim a$) has been given, a qualitative explanation of the specific-flow minimum follows from a recently developed theory† of the self-diffusion in capillary tubes at low pressures. This explanation correctly predicts the occurrence of the minimum in the case of long tubes and its absence in the case of very short tubes ($l \sim a$) and porous media.

4-4. THE GENERAL-DIFFUSION EQUATION AND THE RANDOM-WALK PROBLEM

In the several types of diffusion that have been studied, it was found that the net transport of a molecular species across a unit surface in the gas was proportional to the space rate of change of the partial density at right angles to the surface. Although the discussion was limited for

---

* M. Knudsen, *loc. cit.* and other references given on page 61.
† W. G. Pollard and R. D. Present, *Phys. Rev.*, vol. 73, p. 762, 1948.

convenience to a one-dimensional transport, the result holds for an arbitrary surface in a gas whose density varies slowly in an arbitrary direction. Thus the net transport across unit area of the xy plane is proportional to $\partial n/\partial z$ and is independent of $\partial n/\partial x$ and $\partial n/\partial y$ when $n = n(x,y,z)$ (see Prob. 3-5 for the self-diffusion case). Consider the transport across an element dS in the general case. Let l_x, l_y, and l_z be the direction cosines of the positive normal to dS; then the transport per unit area of dS is

$$G_{\perp} = -D\left[l_x \frac{\partial n}{\partial x} + l_y \frac{\partial n}{\partial y} + l_z \frac{\partial n}{\partial z}\right] \qquad (4\text{-}53)$$

where D is the diffusion coefficient, $\partial n/\partial x$ is the partial derivative evaluated at dS, and the expression in brackets is the directional derivative of n in the direction of the normal to dS. It is customary to express Eq. (4-53) in vector notation. The vector **grad** n, whose components along the x, y, and z axes are $\partial n/\partial x$, $\partial n/\partial y$, and $\partial n/\partial z$, has the well-known properties that (1) its direction is that of the greatest space rate of change of n and (2) its component along an arbitrary direction is the directional derivative of n along that direction.* The greatest net transport, which is in the direction of **grad** n, will be denoted by the vector **G**. Then Eq. (4-53) can be rewritten in terms of the magnitudes $|\mathbf{G}|$ and $|\mathbf{grad}\ n|$ as

$$G_{\perp} = |\mathbf{G}| \cos \alpha = D|\mathbf{grad}\ n| \cos \alpha \qquad (4\text{-}54)$$

where α is the angle between **grad** n and the normal to dS. Since the orientation of dS is arbitrary and **G** is in the same direction as **grad** n but opposite in sense, we obtain the vector equation for diffusion

$$\mathbf{G} = -D\ \mathbf{grad}\ n \qquad (4\text{-}55)$$

The component of **G** in a given direction gives the diffusive transport per unit area through a surface perpendicular to the given direction.

Let us next consider a nonsteady diffusive flow, i.e., one that is changing with time. For simplicity, consider a one-dimensional diffusion in the x direction, i.e., $n = n(x,t)$ and $G = G(x,t)$. Confining our attention to the region bounded by the fixed planes $x = x_0$ and $x = x_0 + dx_0$, the inward transport per unit area of the former plane is $G(x_0)$ and the outward transport per unit area of the latter plane

$$G(x_0 + dx_0) = G(x_0) + (\partial G/\partial x)_0\ dx_0$$

Then the net inflow of molecules into the region per unit area per unit time is

$$G(x) - G(x + dx) = -\left(\frac{\partial G}{\partial x}\right)dx = -\frac{\partial}{\partial x}\left(-D\frac{\partial n}{\partial x}\right)dx \qquad (4\text{-}56)$$

---

* Cf., e.g., G. Joos, "Theoretical Physics," 2nd ed., Hafner Publishing Company, New York, 1950, p. 21.

dropping subscripts. Assuming no sources or sinks of molecules in the region, it follows from the conservation of molecules that (4-56) must be equal to the rate of increase of molecules per unit area of the region, and this is given by $\partial(n\,dx)/\partial t$. Hence

$$\frac{\partial n}{\partial t}\,dx = \frac{\partial}{\partial x}\left(D\,\frac{\partial n}{\partial x}\right)dx \qquad (4\text{-}57)$$

and if D is independent of x we obtain the partial differential equation for a one-dimensional diffusion process

$$\frac{\partial n}{\partial t} = D\,\frac{\partial^2 n}{\partial x^2} \qquad (4\text{-}58)$$

which reduces in the steady state to

$$\partial^2 n/\partial x^2 = 0 \qquad (4\text{-}59)$$

The three-dimensional form of Eq. (4-58) is similarly found to be*

$$\frac{\partial n}{\partial t} = D\left(\frac{\partial^2 n}{\partial x^2} + \frac{\partial^2 n}{\partial y^2} + \frac{\partial^2 n}{\partial z^2}\right) \qquad (4\text{-}60)$$

A particular solution of Eq. (4-58) of unusual physical interest is

$$n(x,t) = ct^{-\frac{1}{2}}e^{-(x^2/4Dt)} \qquad t \geq 0 \qquad (4\text{-}61)$$

It is left as an exercise for the reader to verify this solution by direct substitution of (4-61) into Eq. (4-58). A graph of this function versus x for $t > 0$ gives the well-known Gauss error curve with its peak at $x = 0$. Increasing the parameter t has the dual effect of broadening the curve and decreasing the height of the peak. As $t \to \infty$, $n(x,t) \to 0$ for any finite value of x. As $t \to 0$, $n(x,t) \to 0$ if $x \neq 0$ (as one sees from a standard evaluation of the indeterminate form); but at $x = 0$, $n(x,t) \to \infty$ as $t \to 0$. The behavior of $n(x,t)$ in this limit is that of the function

$$\delta(x - x_0) = \lim_{\xi \to 0} \frac{1}{\xi\pi^{\frac{1}{2}}} e^{-(x-x_0)^2/\xi^2} \qquad (4\text{-}62)$$

On integrating Eq. (4-62) one finds

$$\int_{-\infty}^{\infty} \delta(x - x_0)\,dx = 1 \qquad (4\text{-}63)$$

This ill-behaved function, known as the *Dirac delta function*, is zero everywhere except at x_0 where it is infinite, and its integral is equal to unity.

* Equation (4-60) is most easily derived by vector field methods. The well-known equation of continuity, expressing conservation of molecules, takes the form $\nabla \cdot \mathbf{G} + \partial n/\partial t = 0$. Substituting $\mathbf{G} = -D\,\nabla n$, we obtain $\partial n/\partial t = D\,\nabla^2 n$.

The physical interpretation of (4-61) is that it represents an instantaneous source of molecules on the yz plane. At $t = 0$, a certain number of molecules N per unit area are created at $x = 0$; they subsequently diffuse to the right and left of the plane. In order to determine the constant c in (4-61), we integrate $n(x,t)$ from $x = -\infty$ to $+\infty$ and set the result equal to N. Thus

$$\int_{-\infty}^{\infty} n(x,t)\ dx = 2ct^{-\frac{1}{2}} \int_{0}^{\infty} e^{-ax^2}\ dx = \frac{2c}{t^{\frac{1}{2}}} \frac{1}{2} \left(\frac{\pi}{a}\right)^{\frac{1}{2}} = c(4\pi D)^{\frac{1}{2}} = N \quad (4\text{-}64)$$

where $a = (4Dt)^{-1}$. Then

$$n(x,t) = \frac{N}{2(\pi Dt)^{\frac{1}{2}}}\ e^{-x^2/4Dt} \quad (4\text{-}65)$$

represents the density of molecules after a time t at a distance x from the source. The solution (4-61) can also be interpreted as a distribution function. Let

$$f(x,t)\ dx = \frac{dx}{(4\pi Dt)^{\frac{1}{2}}}\ e^{-x^2/4Dt} \quad (4\text{-}66)$$

Then $f(x,t)\ dx$ represents the probability that a molecule found at $x = 0$ at time $t = 0$ will be found between x and $x + dx$ at time t. Let us evaluate the mean-square displacement $\overline{x^2}$ during the time t for a diffusing molecule.

$$\begin{aligned}
\overline{x^2} &= \int_{-\infty}^{\infty} x^2 f(x,t)\ dx = (\pi Dt)^{-\frac{1}{2}} \int_{0}^{\infty} x^2 e^{-ax^2}\ dx \\
&= (\pi Dt)^{-\frac{1}{2}} \cdot -\frac{\partial}{\partial a} \int_{0}^{\infty} e^{-ax^2}\ dx = -(\pi Dt)^{-\frac{1}{2}} \frac{d}{da}\left(\frac{\pi^{\frac{1}{2}}}{2a^{\frac{1}{2}}}\right) \\
&= \frac{1}{4a(Dta)^{\frac{1}{2}}} = 2Dt \quad (4\text{-}67)
\end{aligned}$$

Thus the root-mean-square displacement during a time t in a one-dimensional diffusion is equal to $(2Dt)^{\frac{1}{2}}$. Since the mutual-diffusion coefficients of the common gases at standard conditions are between 0.1 and 1 cm^2/sec, the root-mean-square displacement is given approximately by

$$x_{r.m.s.} \sim t^{\frac{1}{2}} \qquad cm \quad (4\text{-}68)$$

if t is in seconds. Thus it takes about an hour for a gas to "spread" a distance of 60 cm through another gas. However, traces of the first gas will have diffused much farther than this. In common experience, gases are found to mix more rapidly than this estimate indicates because of currents; even very slight currents produce a more rapid spreading than diffusion.

The Random Walk and Its Relation to Diffusion.   We shall now approach the diffusion problem from an entirely different point of view, and we shall find that we are led to an equation of the same form as Eq. (4-66). The new point of view is that of the *random walk*. Consider the following simple example in one dimension. A man standing halfway up a long flight of stairs tosses a coin. If heads turn up, he moves up one step; if tails, he moves down one step. He then tosses the coin again and moves up or down another step. The random walk consists of a sequence of such steps; after each step the coin is tossed to determine whether the next step will be up or down. The probability of occurrence of a particular sequence of n steps is $(\frac{1}{2})^n$, since the n events are independent. After taking n steps, the man finds himself m steps away from his starting place (where $m > 0$ for an upward displacement). Let $P_{n,m}$ denote the probability that a sequence of n steps leads to a displacement of m steps. Let p denote the number of upward steps and q the number of steps down; then $p + q = n$ and $p - q = m$. If n is even, m can only be even; if n is odd, m is odd. The total number of different sequences of n steps all of which lead to a displacement of m steps is equal to the number of different ways in which n objects can be separated into two groups containing p and q, respectively, i.e., $n!/p!q!$. Since all these sequences have the same probability $(\frac{1}{2})^n$, we obtain

$$P_{n,m} = \frac{n!}{p!q!}\left(\frac{1}{2}\right)^n \tag{4-69}$$

The case of interest is that in which n, p, and q are very large numbers; then the awkward factorials can be approximated by Stirling's formula and a simpler expression than (4-69) obtained. According to Stirling's approximation (cf. Appendix 4-1),

$$n! \simeq (2\pi n)^{1/2}(n/e)^n \tag{4-70}$$

Hence Eq. (4-69) can be rewritten with the aid of (4-70) as

$$\begin{aligned} P_{n,m} &\simeq \frac{(2\pi n)^{1/2}(n/e)^n}{(2\pi p)^{1/2}(p/e)^p(2\pi q)^{1/2}(q/e)^q 2^n} \\ &\simeq \frac{n^{n+1/2}}{p^{p+1/2}q^{q+1/2}}\frac{1}{2^n(2\pi)^{1/2}} \end{aligned} \tag{4-71}$$

Since $p = (n + m)/2$ and $q = (n - m)/2$, this reduces to

$$\begin{aligned} P_{n,m} &\simeq \frac{1}{\pi^{1/2}}\frac{(n/2)^{n+1/2}}{(n/2)^{p+1/2}[1 + (m/n)]^{p+1/2}(n/2)^{q+1/2}[1 - (m/n)]^{q+1/2}} \\ &\simeq \left(\frac{2}{\pi n}\right)^{1/2}\frac{1}{[1 + (m/n)]^{p+1/2}[1 - (m/n)]^{q+1/2}} \end{aligned} \tag{4-72}$$

Taking natural logarithms,* one obtains

$$\log\left[\left(\frac{\pi n}{2}\right)^{\frac{1}{2}} P_{n,m}\right] \simeq -\left(p+\frac{1}{2}\right)\log\left(1+\frac{m}{n}\right) - \left(q+\frac{1}{2}\right)\log\left(1-\frac{m}{n}\right)$$

$$\simeq -\left(p+\frac{1}{2}\right)\left[\frac{m}{n}-\frac{1}{2}\left(\frac{m}{n}\right)^2 \cdots\right]$$

$$-\left(q+\frac{1}{2}\right)\left[-\frac{m}{n}-\frac{1}{2}\left(\frac{m}{n}\right)^2 \cdots\right] \qquad (4\text{-}73)$$

$$\simeq (q-p)\frac{m}{n} + (p+q+1)\frac{m^2}{2n^2} \cdots$$

$$\simeq -\frac{m^2}{n} + (n+1)\frac{m^2}{2n^2} \cdots$$

$$\simeq -\frac{m^2}{2n} \cdots$$

where the logarithms have been expanded in powers of m/n and only the lowest-power term has been written down. If n is large, $P_{n,m}$ is negligibly small unless $|m| \ll n$. For, if the coin is tossed many times, the fraction of heads p/n and the fraction of tails q/n will deviate little from one-half; accordingly $|m|/n = |p-q|/n$ will be small on the average.† Neglecting the higher-power terms in m/n, one obtains the approximate formula

$$P_{n,m} \simeq \left(\frac{2}{\pi n}\right)^{\frac{1}{2}} e^{-m^2/2n} \qquad |m| \ll n \qquad (4\text{-}74)$$

for the probability of a one-dimensional random walk. Let the random walk be along the x direction starting from $x = 0$ and the steps of the same length l. Then $x = ml$ represents the displacement, $X = nl$ the total path length, and

$$P_{n,m} \simeq \left(\frac{2l}{\pi X}\right)^{\frac{1}{2}} e^{-x^2/2lX} \qquad |x| \ll X \qquad (4\text{-}75)$$

Let $P(x,X)\,dx$ be the probability of a displacement between x and $x + dx$ when the total path length is X. In the small range dx, $P_{n,m}$ will not vary appreciably. Thus $P(x,X)\,dx$ is equal to the product of $P_{n,m}$ with the number of values of m occurring in the range dx for fixed n. This gives

$$P(x,X)\,dx = P_{n,m}\frac{dx}{l}\frac{1}{2} \qquad (4\text{-}76)$$

where the factor $\frac{1}{2}$ enters because for fixed n the values of m are either

---

* All logs used in this book are to be understood as natural logarithms.

† One finds readily that $\overline{m^2} = n$. Thus $(\overline{m^2})^{\frac{1}{2}}/n = (1/n)^{\frac{1}{2}}$, and this approaches zero as n approaches infinity.

all odd or all even.   Hence

$$P(x,X) \, dx \; = \; \frac{dx}{(2\pi lX)^{\frac{1}{2}}} \, e^{-x^2/2lX} \tag{4-77}$$

This formula is related to diffusion in the following way.   Imagine a one-dimensional gas whose molecules, moving in the x direction, encounter fixed molecules at regular intervals of length l and after each encounter have equal chances of proceeding undeflected or having their motions reversed (i.e., the angle of scattering is either 0 or π with intermediate values excluded).   This artificial diffusion process obeys the diffusion equation (4-58) with an appropriate value of D, and the solution (4-66) of the differential equation is equivalent physically to the solution (4-77) of the random-walk problem.   The distribution functions $f(x,t)$ and $P(x,X)$ are mathematically equivalent; the effective diffusion coefficient is given by

$$D = \frac{1}{2} \frac{X}{t} \, l = \frac{\bar{v}l}{2} \tag{4-78}$$

where $\bar{v}$ is the average speed of the diffusing molecules.   The logical next step would be to extend the random-walk problem to three dimensions and to generalize the treatment to provide for a distribution in step lengths (free paths).*   In a three-dimensional random flight it is assumed that at the end of each free path the molecule starts its new free path at random; i.e., there is no preferred direction of motion of a molecule after collision.   Now, it will be shown in Chap. 8, Sec. 8-2, that when two rigid elastic spheres collide, the scattering is isotropic in the center-of-mass frame of reference but not in the fixed (laboratory) system,† in which the angular distribution after collision favors the direction of motion before collision.   This effect, which is referred to as the *persistence of velocities*, invalidates the random-flight description.   Nevertheless, the random-flight description can be regarded as an approximation that provides insight into the nature of the diffusion process.   Equation (4-78) shows that the diffusion coefficient is proportional to the product of the average speed $\bar{v}$ and an appropriate mean step size $\bar{l}$.   In self-diffusion, $\bar{l}$ is the mean free path of the gas, and in free-molecule diffusion through a long capillary it is equal to the tube diameter.

PROBLEMS

4-1. A test tube contains a little ether that evaporates and diffuses through the air above it.   Assume that air currents above the test tube keep the concen-

---

* See S. Chandrasekhar, *Rev. Mod. Phys.*, vol. 15, p. 1, 1943.

† In the special case in which one collision partner is at rest and is much heavier than the other, the two frames of reference coincide.

tration of ether at the top of the tube effectively at zero without disturbing the diffusion in the tube. Let x = height above the liquid surface, h = height from the liquid surface to the top of the tube, n = total molecular density of the air-ether mixture, $n_1(x)$ = molecular density of ether, and $n_1(0)$ the saturation density of ether at the liquid surface. Show that

$$n_1(x) = n\left\{1 - \left[1 - \frac{n_1(0)}{n}\right]^{1-x/h}\right\}$$

4-2. Show that the ratio of the number of collisions between molecules in the gas to collisions with the wall in a capillary tube is a/λ.

4-3. Verify that (4-61) is a solution of Eq. (4-58).

4-4. If one gas diffuses through a second gas that is stationary—i.e., there is no net transport of the second gas—the process is sometimes referred to as "single diffusion." If D_1 is the coefficient of single diffusion, then $-D_1\, dn_1/dz$ represents the net transport rate per square centimeter per second of gas 1. Show that $D_1 = (n/n_2)D_{12}$ where $n = n_1 + n_2$ is the total density and D_{12} is the mutual-diffusion coefficient.

4-5. Show that the root-mean-square displacement of a diffusing molecule is approximately the geometric mean of its mean free path and the total distance it traverses.

4-6. Show that in the free-molecule diffusion through a long tube, the molecular flow per unit area per unit time is $-(va/2)\, dn/dz$ at the wall and $-(\pi \bar{v} a/4)\, dn/dz$ on the axis.

4-7. In the calculation of the free-molecule flow through a long tube, obtain the result, Eq. (4-38), by inverting the order of integration

$$\iint dS \int d\phi\ s \rightarrow \int d\phi \iint dS\ s$$

thus performing the integration over the cross section first for a fixed azimuth.

4-8. In the treatment of slip in Sec. 4-3, all molecules were assumed to be diffusely reflected from the wall. If the fraction f are diffusely reflected and $1 - f$ specularly reflected, show that the slip velocity u_0 and the slip flow ΔF are increased by the factor $(2 - f)/f$.

4-9. Show by direct calculation that the average distance traveled by a molecule between two successive wall collisions, in free-molecule flow through a long tube, is equal to the tube diameter.

APPENDIX 4-1

Stirling's Formula

Stirling's approximation for $n!$ when $n \gg 1$ can be obtained as follows. It is readily seen, e.g., by mathematical induction, that

$$n! = \int_0^\infty e^{-t}t^n\, dt \tag{4-79}$$

Introducing a new variable $x = t/n$, one obtains

$$n! = n^{n+1} \int_0^\infty e^{-nx} x^n \, dx$$

$$= n^{n+1} e^{-n} \int_0^\infty e^{n - nx + \log x^n} \, dx \qquad (4\text{-}80)$$

$$= \frac{n^{n+1}}{e^n} \left[\int_0^2 e^{n(1 - x + \log x)} \, dx + \int_2^\infty e^{-n(x - 1 - \log x)} \, dx \right]$$

As n is made large, the second integral becomes negligible. We let $x = 1 + \varepsilon$ in the first integral and expand $\log(1 + \varepsilon)$ in the series: $\varepsilon - \varepsilon^2/2 + \varepsilon^3/3 \cdots$. Then

$$n! \simeq n^{n+1} e^{-n} \int_{-1}^1 e^{n(-\varepsilon^2/2 + \varepsilon^3/3 \cdots)} \, d\varepsilon \qquad (4\text{-}81)$$

The principal contribution to the value of the integral when n is large comes from the neighborhood of $\varepsilon = 0$; thus $\varepsilon^3/3$ and higher-order terms can be neglected. Furthermore, the range of integration can be extended to $\pm \infty$ without appreciable error. Then

$$n! \simeq n^{n+1} e^{-n} \int_{-\infty}^\infty e^{-n\varepsilon^2/2} \, d\varepsilon$$

$$\simeq \frac{n^{n+1}}{e^n} \left(\frac{2}{n} \right)^{1/2} \int_{-\infty}^\infty e^{-\xi^2} \, d\xi \qquad (4\text{-}82)$$

Since the last integral is equal to $\pi^{1/2}$, we obtain Stirling's asymptotic formula

$$n! \simeq (2\pi n)^{1/2} (n/e)^n \qquad (4\text{-}83)$$

for large n. It is shown elsewhere* that the relative error of this approximation is about $(12n)^{-1}$.

---

* Cf., e.g., J. V. Uspensky, "Introduction to Mathematical Probability," McGraw-Hill Book Company, Inc., New York, 1937. The reader who is familiar with the method of steepest descents is referred to the proof in H. and B. Jeffreys, "Methods of Mathematical Physics," Cambridge University Press, London, 1956, p. 507.

CHAPTER 5

THE MAXWELL-BOLTZMANN DISTRIBUTION LAW

The Maxwell velocity distribution function and the more general Maxwell-Boltzmann law are introduced in this chapter. A simple, unrigorous derivation based on the barometric formula is given in Appendix 5-1 and an abbreviated presentation of the statistical-mechanical proof in Appendix 5-2. The rigorous kinetic-theory derivation, based on Boltzmann's equation, will be taken up in Chap. 11. In the present chapter, the Maxwell law is used to find the mean, mean-square, and most probable speeds and also to calculate the mean value of the relative velocity of two unlike molecules in a gas mixture (thus justifying the collision frequency and mean-free-path formulas of Secs. 3-2 and 4-2). In Sec. 5-3 we take up the rotation and the vibration of a diatomic molecule and calculate the mean energy that is associated with the internal degrees of freedom. The equipartition theorem is proved and applied to the specific heat of a diatomic gas with the well-known and historically important result that classical kinetic theory fails to account for the energy associated with internal degrees of freedom. The effects of "quantization" are briefly discussed.

5-1. THE MAXWELL-BOLTZMANN LAW AND THE VELOCITY DISTRIBUTION FUNCTION

Nearly all the theory in the preceding chapters was developed without explicit use of the exact distribution law for molecular velocities.* In a few cases certain results based on the Maxwell law were quoted without proof, e.g., the collision frequency stated in Eqs. (3-8) and (4-10) and the formula for $\bar{v}$ (Eq. (4-40)). The equilibrium velocity distribution function was originally deduced by Maxwell from a simple argument that was recognized to be unsatisfactory; more rigorous proofs were subsequently developed. The law itself is verified through its consequences; i.e., formulas such as (4-43), which are deduced from the Maxwell law, are found to agree with experiment. The refinement of molecular-beam techniques within recent years has made it possible to measure accurately and directly the distribu-

---

*It is thus apparent that certain results of kinetic theory depend only on the fact that the theory is statistical and not on the nature of the statistics.

tion of molecular speeds, and the results are in excellent agreement with the Maxwell law (see Sec. 10-1). The point of view adopted in this chapter is that the Maxwell law, like the inverse-square laws of gravitation (Newton) and of electrostatics (Coulomb), is based directly on experiment and requires no theoretical proof. Nevertheless, it is important to recognize that the law can be deduced from very general assumptions by the methods of kinetic theory and also from the general principles of statistical mechanics. These derivations provide an insight into the nature of the equilibrium state, indicate the circumstances under which Maxwell's law can be expected to hold, and provide methods for calculating corrections to the law when, as in nonuniform states, it ceases to be valid. For this reason a brief review is given here of four methods of deriving the Maxwell distribution function, and the reader is referred to Appendixes 5-1 and 5-2 and Chap. 11 for further details.

In his original deduction of the law, Maxwell* assumed that each component of the velocity is distributed independently of the values of the other components. This assumption, together with the assumption of an isotropic distribution, leads simply and directly to the correct form of the law. Since the velocity components are related by the dynamical equations governing molecular encounters, the basic assumption is not evident and its ultimate justification requires a proof as elaborate as that needed to derive the law itself. A related objection is that the derivation lacks physical content; no use is made of kinematical or dynamical relationships. Now it seems evident that the equilibrium distribution is brought about and maintained by molecular collisions. Hence a proof that contains no reference to dynamics is hardly likely to be adequate, as Maxwell himself recognized. Actually this "derivation" is a mathematical exercise showing that the basic assumption, if one accepts it, is sufficient to determine the form of the distribution function.

A second derivation, due to Boltzmann,† treats the dynamical behavior of the molecules in an external field of force but omits the effects of molecular collisions. Consider a vertical column of air, assumed to be at uniform temperature, in the earth's gravitational field. The pressure and density variation with altitude are obtained from the hydrostatic equation together with the perfect-gas law, i.e., without the use of kinetic theory. The velocity distribution that is compatible with this density variation and has the same average speed for molecules at all heights (uniform temperature) is found to be the Maxwellian one. Although

---

* J. C. Maxwell, "Collected Works," vol. 1, p. 380; F. W. Sears, "Thermodynamics, Kinetic Theory, and Statistical Mechanics," Addison-Wesley Publishing Company, Reading, Mass., 1953.

† L. Boltzmann, *Wien. Ber.*, vol. 74, p. 503, 1876; K. F. Herzfeld, "*Kinetische Theorie der Wärme,*" *Müller-Pouillets Lehrbuch der Physik*, Braunschweig, 1925.

collisions with the earth's surface are taken into account, the collisions in the gas are not. This derivation, although unrigorous, is presented in Appendix 5-1 because of its simplicity and interesting physical content.

A third proof, a rigorous one mainly due to Boltzmann, takes detailed account of the dynamics of molecular encounters. The velocity distribution function is found to satisfy an integrodifferential equation (Boltzmann equation). The solution of this equation for the state of equilibrium in a uniform gas is just the Maxwell function. The lengthy and somewhat complicated derivation will be taken up in Chap. 11.

A fourth method of proof, also rigorous, is based on statistical mechanics; its most general formulation is due to Gibbs. The equilibrium state of the gas is defined to be the one of greatest probability. Methods are developed for calculating the probability of a particular state of the gas, and the expression for the probability is maximized subject to the two conditions of conservation of total number of molecules and conservation of total energy. This leads to the Maxwell-Boltzmann distribution law. The derivation is somewhat abstract, and no explicit account is taken of molecular collisions. The laws of dynamics enter through the condition of energy conservation and also through the method of assigning a priori probabilities. An abbreviated presentation of this method of proof will be found in Appendix 5-2.

The Maxwell-Boltzmann distribution function gives the probability that a molecule has position coordinates between x and $x + dx$, y and $y + dy$, and z and $z + dz$ and momentum components between p_x and $p_x + dp_x$, p_y and $p_y + dp_y$, and p_z and $p_z + dp_z$. This function is given by Eq. (5-77) of Appendix 5-2 as

$$\Phi(x,y, \ldots ,p_z) \, dx \, dy \cdots dp_z$$

$$= \frac{e^{-\beta\varepsilon(x,y,\ldots,p_z)} \, dx \, dy \cdots dp_z}{\int dx \int dy \cdots \int dp_z \, e^{-\beta\varepsilon(x,y,\ldots,p_z)}} \quad (5\text{-}1)$$

where β is a constant and $\varepsilon(x,y, \ldots ,p_z)$ is the total energy of a molecule whose position and momentum lie in the specified range. The sextuple integral in the denominator "normalizes" the distribution function to represent a probability. If the molecules are in a conservative field of force, the exponential can be expressed as

$$e^{-\beta\varepsilon(x,y,\ldots,p_z)} = e^{-\beta(p_x{}^2+p_y{}^2+p_z{}^2)/2m}e^{-\beta V(x,y,z)} \quad (5\text{-}2)$$

where $V(x,y,z)$ is the potential energy of a molecule at the point x, y, z. It is evident from Eqs. (5-52) and (5-56) of Appendix 5-1 that the value of the constant β is $(kT)^{-1}$. This will be shown in a different way below.

According to Eq. (5-2), the distribution function Φ factors into two independent distribution functions for momentum and position. In order to obtain the momentum (or velocity) distribution we integrate the right-hand side of Eq. (5-1) with respect to x, y, and z. It is customary to use velocity components v_x, v_y, and v_z instead of p_x, p_y, and p_z. Then the velocity distribution function is*

$$F(v_x,v_y,v_z)\, dv_x\, dv_y\, dv_z = \frac{e^{-(\beta m/2)(v_x{}^2+v_y{}^2+v_z{}^2)}\, dv_x\, dv_y\, dv_z}{\int dv_x \int dv_y \int dv_z\, e^{-(\beta m/2)(v_x{}^2+v_y{}^2+v_z{}^2)}} \qquad (5\text{-}3)$$

Although no molecule can have a kinetic energy in excess of the total energy of the gas, little error is made by extending the integrals in the denominator from $-\infty$ to $+\infty$. In the foregoing discussion it has been tacitly assumed that the molecules were particles or mass points with no internal structure. Although this assumption is justified in the case of a monatomic gas, it is necessary for the polyatomic case to include in ε the energies associated with the internal degrees of freedom, i.e., with rotation and vibration. This will be done in Sec. 5-3. The inclusion of the internal degrees of freedom has no effect on the distribution of velocities in the translational motion. This is because the translational and internal motions are independent. The internal motions contribute extra terms to ε which do not depend on the velocity of translation; the exponential of the Maxwell-Boltzmann law factors into two independent exponentials for the translational and internal coordinates. Thus the distribution functions for the translational and internal motions are independent.

We now proceed with the evaluation of the integrals in (5-3) and the determination of the constant β. Inserting

$$\int_{-\infty}^{\infty} dv_x\, e^{-\beta m v_x{}^2/2} = \left(\frac{2}{\beta m}\right)^{\!1/2} \int_{-\infty}^{\infty} d\xi\, e^{-\xi^2} = \left(\frac{2\pi}{\beta m}\right)^{\!1/2} \qquad (5\text{-}4)$$

in Eq. (5-3), we obtain

$$F(v_x,v_y,v_z)\, dv_x\, dv_y\, dv_z = \left(\frac{\beta m}{2\pi}\right)^{\!3/2} e^{-(\beta m/2)(v_x{}^2+v_y{}^2+v_z{}^2)}\, dv_x\, dv_y\, dv_z \qquad (5\text{-}5)$$

Since the velocity distribution is isotropic, it follows that

$$\frac{\overline{mv_x{}^2}}{2} = \frac{\overline{mv_y{}^2}}{2} = \frac{\overline{mv_z{}^2}}{2} = \frac{1}{3}\frac{\overline{mv^2}}{2} = \frac{kT}{2} \qquad (5\text{-}6)$$

using Eq. (2-17). The distribution function for the velocity component v_x is

$$\Psi(v_x)\, dv_x = \left(\frac{\beta m}{2\pi}\right)^{\!1/2} e^{-\beta m v_x{}^2/2}\, dv_x \qquad (5\text{-}7)$$

---

* In accordance with common usage, the distribution function multiplied by the appropriate set of differentials will also be referred to, loosely, as the distribution function.

Hence
$$\frac{m\overline{v_x^2}}{2} = \frac{m}{2}\left(\frac{\beta m}{2\pi}\right)^{\frac{1}{2}} \int_{-\infty}^{\infty} dv_x \; v_x^2 e^{-\beta m v_x^2/2} \tag{5-8}$$

$$= \frac{m}{2}\left(\frac{\beta m}{2\pi}\right)^{\frac{1}{2}}\left(\frac{2}{\beta m}\right)^{\frac{3}{2}} \int_{-\infty}^{\infty} d\xi \; \xi^2 e^{-\xi^2}$$

$$= \frac{m}{2}\left(\frac{\beta m}{2\pi}\right)^{\frac{1}{2}}\left(\frac{2}{\beta m}\right)^{\frac{3}{2}}\frac{\pi^{\frac{1}{2}}}{2} = \frac{1}{2\beta} \tag{5-9}$$

The integral in (5-8) can be evaluated by the method used to obtain Eq. (4-67). Combining (5-6) with (5-9) gives

$$\beta = \frac{1}{kT} \tag{5-10}$$

whence $\quad F(v_x, v_y, v_z)\; dv_x\, dv_y\, dv_z = \left(\frac{m}{2\pi kT}\right)^{\frac{3}{2}} e^{-(m/2kT)(v_x^2 + v_y^2 + v_z^2)}\; dv_x\, dv_y\, dv_z$

$$\tag{5-11}$$

Equation (5-11) is the Maxwell law for the normalized velocity distribution. As has already been indicated in Eq. (5-7), each component of the velocity is distributed independently of the other components. Thus

$$F(v_x, v_y, v_z) = \Psi(v_x)\Psi(v_y)\Psi(v_z) \tag{5-12}$$

and
$$\Psi(v_x) = \left(\frac{m}{2\pi kT}\right)^{\frac{1}{2}} e^{-mv_x^2/2kT}$$

The graph of $\Psi(v_x)$ versus v_x is the Gauss error curve with maximum at $v_x = 0$. The breadth and height of the curve are determined by the absolute temperature T; as T is increased, the distribution curve becomes broader (and flatter because of normalization).

5-2. THE MAXWELL DISTRIBUTION FUNCTION (CONT.). APPLICATION TO THE COLLISION FREQUENCY

We shall next obtain the distribution law for the molecular speeds. It is convenient for this purpose to visualize a velocity space in which the velocity vectors are laid off from the origin. We transform from cartesian coordinates v_x, v_y, v_z to spherical coordinates v, θ, ϕ where v is the magnitude of the velocity vector, i.e., the speed. From the Jacobian determinant of the transformation,* it follows that

$$dv_x\, dv_y\, dv_z = v^2\, dv\, \sin\theta\, d\theta\, d\phi = v^2\, dv\, d\omega \tag{5-13}$$

The speed distribution function $f(v)\, dv$ is obtained by integrating the

* See any book on advanced calculus.

velocity distribution over all directions (cf. Eq. (2-5)):

$$f(v)\ dv = \int_0^{4\pi} d\omega\ F(v_x,v_y,v_z)v^2\ dv$$

$$= \left(\frac{m}{2\pi kT}\right)^{3/2} e^{-mv^2/2kT}\ 4\pi v^2\ dv \tag{5-14}$$

The angle integration gives 4π because F is independent of angle.   We note that the velocity distribution function F differs from the function

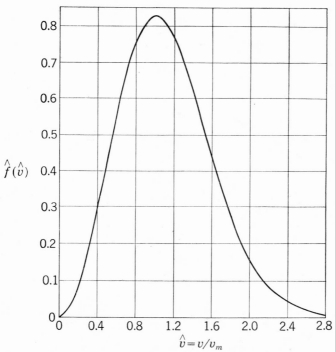

FIG. 5-1. The Maxwell speed distribution $f(v)\ dv = \hat{f}(\hat{v})\ d\hat{v} = 4\pi^{-1/2}\hat{v}^2 e^{-\hat{v}^2}\ d\hat{v}$ in terms of the dimensionless variable $\hat{v} = v/v_m = (m/2kT)^{1/2}v$.

$f^*(\mathbf{v})$ of Sec. 2-2 by the factor v^2.   The volume element $4\pi v^2\ dv$, which appears in (5-14), represents a spherical shell in the velocity space of inner radius v and outer radius $v + dv$; this shell contains all velocity points corresponding to the range of speeds v to $v + dv$.   Equation (5-14) gives the fraction of molecules, moving in any direction whatsoever, which have speeds between v and $v + dv$.   This distribution law was first published by Maxwell in the year 1860.

A graph of $f(v)$ versus v is shown in Fig. 5-1.   Although the most probable value of a velocity component is zero, this is not true of the speed. The exponential factor in (5-14) favors small speeds; this factor is proportional to the density of points in the velocity space and is greatest at the origin. However, the volume of the spherical shell corresponding to a fixed interval dv decreases with the square of v as v decreases. Since the exponential approaches unity while the volume of the shell approaches zero for small v, it is unlikely that a molecule will have a small speed. The rapid falling-off of the exponential makes it also unlikely that a molecule will have a large speed. The most probable speed, corresponding to the maximum of the distribution curve, is obtained by setting $df/dv = 0$. This gives

$$v_m = (2kT/m)^{1/2} \tag{5-15}$$

The mean speed $\bar{v}$ can be calculated with the aid of (5-14). It is readily found that

$$\bar{v} = \int_0^\infty vf(v)\,dv = 4\pi\left(\frac{m}{2\pi kT}\right)^{3/2}\int_0^\infty e^{-mv^2/2kT}v^3\,dv = \left(\frac{8kT}{\pi m}\right)^{1/2} \tag{5-16}$$

From Eqs. (2-19), (5-15), and (5-16) one obtains

$$(\overline{v^2})^{1/2} > \bar{v} > v_m \tag{5-17}$$

These inequalities are made plausible by the asymmetry of the distribution curve.

As an interesting and useful application of the distribution law, we shall calculate the mean value of the relative velocity of two unlike molecules in a binary gas mixture. Denoting the magnitude of the relative velocity by v_r and its mean value by $\bar{v}_r$, we obtain, by averaging over the distribution functions of both molecules,

$$\bar{v}_r = \iiint dv_{1x}\,dv_{1y}\,dv_{1z}\iiint dv_{2x}\,dv_{2y}\,dv_{2z}\,F_1(\mathbf{v}_1)F_2(\mathbf{v}_2)v_r$$
$$= \left(\frac{m_1}{2\pi kT}\right)^{3/2}\left(\frac{m_2}{2\pi kT}\right)^{3/2}\int_{-\infty}^\infty dv_{1x}\cdots\int_{-\infty}^\infty dv_{2z}\,v_r e^{-(m_1v_1^2+m_2v_2^2)/2kT} \tag{5-18}$$

where $v_r = [(v_{1x} - v_{2x})^2 + (v_{1y} - v_{2y})^2 + (v_{1z} - v_{2z})^2]^{1/2}$. It is convenient to transform from $\mathbf{v}_1$ and $\mathbf{v}_2$ to the center-of-mass velocity $\mathbf{v}_c$ and the relative velocity $\mathbf{v}_r$. In vector notation

$$\mathbf{v}_r = \mathbf{v}_1 - \mathbf{v}_2 \qquad \mathbf{v}_c = \frac{m_1\mathbf{v}_1 + m_2\mathbf{v}_2}{m_1 + m_2} \tag{5-19}$$

and in terms of components

$$v_{rx} = v_{1x} - v_{2x} \qquad v_{cx} = \frac{m_1v_{1x} + m_2v_{2x}}{m_1 + m_2} \tag{5-20}$$

with similar expressions for y and z components. Solving Eqs. (5-20), one obtains

$$v_{1x} = v_{cx} + \left(\frac{m_2}{m_1 + m_2}\right) v_{rx}$$

$$v_{2x} = v_{cx} - \left(\frac{m_1}{m_1 + m_2}\right) v_{rx}$$

(5-21)

The Jacobian determinant of the transformation from v_{1x}, v_{2x} to v_{rx}, v_{cx} is

$$\begin{vmatrix} \partial v_{1x}/\partial v_{rx} & \partial v_{1x}/\partial v_{cx} \\ \partial v_{2x}/\partial v_{rx} & \partial v_{2x}/\partial v_{cx} \end{vmatrix} = \begin{vmatrix} m_2/(m_1 + m_2) & 1 \\ -m_1/(m_1 + m_2) & 1 \end{vmatrix} = 1$$

It is readily seen that

$$m_1 v_{1x}{}^2 + m_2 v_{2x}{}^2 = (m_1 + m_2)v_{cx}{}^2 + m^* v_{rx}{}^2$$

whence $\frac{1}{2}m_1 v_1{}^2 + \frac{1}{2}m_2 v_2{}^2 = \frac{1}{2}(m_1 + m_2)v_c{}^2 + \frac{1}{2}m^* v_r{}^2$ (5-22)

where $m^* = m_1 m_2/(m_1 + m_2)$ is the reduced mass. Equation (5-22) expresses the well-known theorem that the kinetic energy of the particles is equal to the kinetic energy of the total mass, moving with the velocity of the center of mass, plus the kinetic energy of relative motion. We transform from cartesian to spherical coordinates in the two new velocity spaces:

$$dv_{cx}\, dv_{cy}\, dv_{cz} = v_c{}^2\, dv_c \sin \theta_c\, d\theta_c\, d\phi_c$$

$$dv_{rx}\, dv_{ry}\, dv_{rz} = v_r{}^2\, dv_r \sin \theta_r\, d\theta_r\, d\phi_r$$

(5-23)

and observe that, when (5-22) is inserted in the exponent, the integrand of Eq. (5-18) is independent of the angles θ_c, ϕ_c, θ_r, and ϕ_r. Integration over the angles gives

$$\bar{v}_r = (2\pi kT)^{-3}(m_1 m_2)^{3/2}(4\pi)^2 I_2\left(\frac{m_1 + m_2}{2kT}\right) I_3\left(\frac{m^*}{2kT}\right)$$

(5-24)

where* $I_2\left(\dfrac{m_1 + m_2}{2kT}\right) = \displaystyle\int_0^\infty e^{-(m_1+m_2)v_c{}^2/2kT} v_c{}^2\, dv_c$

$$= \left(\frac{\pi}{2}\right)^{1/2}\left(\frac{kT}{m_1 + m_2}\right)^{3/2}$$

(5-25)

and

$$I_3\left(\frac{m^*}{2kT}\right) = \int_0^\infty e^{-m^* v_r{}^2/2kT} v_r{}^3\, dv_r = 2\left(\frac{kT}{m^*}\right)^2$$

(5-26)

Equation (5-24) reduces to the simple form

$$\bar{v}_r = \left(\frac{8kT}{\pi m^*}\right)^{1/2} = \left(\frac{8kT}{\pi m_1} + \frac{8kT}{\pi m_2}\right)^{1/2} = (\bar{v}_1{}^2 + \bar{v}_2{}^2)^{1/2}$$

(5-27)

This result was anticipated in Eq. (4-10). If the molecules are all alike, it follows that $\bar{v}_r = \sqrt{2}\, \bar{v}$. This result justifies the collision frequency and mean-free-path formulas (3-8) and (3-9).

* The integral formulas in the general appendix will prove useful.

5-3. INTERNAL DEGREES OF FREEDOM OF A DIATOMIC MOLECULE

Part of the energy of a polyatomic molecule is stored in the internal degrees of freedom of rotation and vibration.   If the distribution functions for the internal coordinates and the momentum or velocity components are known, it is possible to calculate the mean energy stored in the internal degrees of freedom and thence the internal contribution to the specific heat.   We shall treat in detail the simplest case of the diatomic molecule.   A system of N particles, free from constraints, possesses $3N$ degrees of freedom.   The electrons of the molecule are not counted, and their contribution to the mean energy and specific heat is ignored.   This assumption has already received a posteriori justification in Sec. 2-4, where the specific heats of monatomic gases, calculated without any reference to the electrons and their motions, were found to agree very well with experiment.   Ultimate justification of the assumption comes from the quantum theory.   The internal degrees of freedom are therefore associated with motions of the nuclei.

A diatomic molecule free from constraints possesses six degrees of freedom; i.e., six coordinates are needed to specify completely the positions of the two nuclei.   Three coordinates are conveniently chosen to specify the position of the center of mass of the molecule; since the three velocity components that correspond to these coordinates specify the translational motion of the molecule as a whole, these three degrees of freedom are called *translational*.   The line joining the nuclei of the diatomic molecule is referred to as the axis of the molecule.   Two coordinates alone suffice to fix the orientation of the axis, e.g., the spherical coordinates θ and ϕ.   These degrees of freedom are called *rotational* because the molecule rotates as the axis changes its orientation.   The rotation can be referred to any two mutually perpendicular axes in a plane perpendicular to the molecular axis and passing through the center of mass.   Since the nuclei are treated as point masses and the electrons are ignored, no meaning is attached to a rotation about the molecular axis.   If the nuclei were constrained to remain a fixed distance apart, there would then be but five degrees of freedom: three translational and two rotational.   Such a model is referred to as "the rigid-rotator," or "dumbbell," model.   In the absence of such a constraint, the nuclei will in general vibrate in and out together under the influence of the attractive forces that bind the two atoms together and the repulsive forces that prevent them from coalescing.   The vibrational coordinate is the distance between the two nuclei.   There is then one degree of freedom of vibration.   This accounts for the six degrees of freedom of the unconstrained molecule.

We shall first take up the rotational degrees of freedom.   In treating the pure rotation without translation and vibration, we fix the center of mass at the origin and consider only rigid rotations with the nuclei a fixed distance d apart. Let d_1 and d_2 denote the distances from the center of mass to each nucleus. Then

$$d_1 = \frac{m_2 d}{(m_1 + m_2)} \qquad d_2 = \frac{m_1 d}{(m_1 + m_2)} \tag{5-28}$$

Nucleus 1 moves on a sphere of radius d_1; its spherical coordinates are d_1, θ, and ϕ where θ and ϕ specify the orientation of the molecular axis. The spherical coordinates of nucleus 2 are d_2, $\pi - \theta$, and $\phi + \pi$. The velocity of each nucleus can be resolved into two rectangular components tangent to the circles of longitude and latitude. Denoting the elements of arc by $ds_\theta = r\, d\theta$ and $ds_\phi = r \sin \theta\, d\phi$ and using the dot notation for a time derivative, one obtains for the velocity components

$$v_{1\theta} = \frac{ds_{1\theta}}{dt} = d_1 \dot{\theta}$$

$$v_{1\phi} = \frac{ds_{1\phi}}{dt} = d_1 \sin \theta\, \dot{\phi}$$

$$v_{2\theta} = \frac{ds_{2\theta}}{dt} = -d_2 \dot{\theta} \tag{5-29}$$

$$v_{2\phi} = \frac{ds_{2\phi}}{dt} = d_2 \sin (\pi - \theta)\, \dot{\phi} = d_2 \sin \theta\, \dot{\phi}$$

The kinetic energy of rotation of the diatomic molecule is then given by

$$\begin{aligned}
\varepsilon_r &= \tfrac{1}{2} m_1 (v_{1\theta}{}^2 + v_{1\phi}{}^2) + \tfrac{1}{2} m_2 (v_{2\theta}{}^2 + v_{2\phi}{}^2) \\
&= \tfrac{1}{2} m_1 d_1{}^2 (\dot{\theta}^2 + \sin^2 \theta\, \dot{\phi}^2) + \tfrac{1}{2} m_2 d_2{}^2 (\dot{\theta}^2 + \sin^2 \theta\, \dot{\phi}^2) \\
&= (I/2)(\dot{\theta}^2 + \sin^2 \theta\, \dot{\phi}^2)
\end{aligned} \tag{5-30}$$

where I represents the moment of inertia about a perpendicular axis through the center of mass. The rotational energy does not usually contain a potential-energy term; however, a molecule possessing a permanent electric or magnetic moment, when placed in a field, will have a potential energy depending on its orientation with respect to the field direction. Assuming no potential-energy term depending on θ and ϕ, the rotational distribution function will depend only on the velocity components. The rotational velocity space is two-dimensional; the element, whether referred to nucleus 1 or 2, is proportional to $d\dot{\theta} \sin \theta\, d\dot{\phi}$. Since the formula (5-30) for ε_r does not depend in any way on the translational coordinates or velocity components, the exponential of the Maxwell-Boltzmann law factors into two independent exponentials, one depending on translational quantities only and the other only on the rotational components of velocity. This means that the distribution functions for the translational and rotational degrees of freedom are independent, as has already been mentioned in Sec. 5-1. The rotational distribution function of a diatomic molecule is then given by

$$\Phi_r \, d\dot\theta \, \sin\theta \, d\dot\phi = \frac{e^{-\varepsilon_r/kT} \, d\dot\theta \, \sin\theta \, d\dot\phi}{\displaystyle\int_{-\infty}^{\infty} d\dot\theta \int_{-\infty}^{\infty} \sin\theta \, d\dot\phi \, e^{-\varepsilon_r/kT}} \tag{5-31}$$

and on substituting (5-30)

$$\Phi_r \, d\dot\theta \, \sin\theta \, d\dot\phi = \frac{e^{-I\dot\theta^2/2kT} \, d\dot\theta}{\displaystyle\int_{-\infty}^{\infty} d\dot\theta \, e^{-I\dot\theta^2/2kT}} \frac{e^{-I\sin^2\theta \, \dot\phi^2/2kT} \, \sin\theta \, d\dot\phi}{\displaystyle\int_{-\infty}^{\infty} \sin\theta \, d\dot\phi \, e^{-I\sin^2\theta \, \dot\phi^2/2kT}} \tag{5-32}$$

$$= \frac{e^{-I\dot\theta^2/2kT} \, d\dot\theta}{\displaystyle\int_{-\infty}^{\infty} d\dot\theta \, e^{-I\dot\theta^2/2kT}} \frac{e^{-I\Omega^2/2kT} \, d\Omega}{\displaystyle\int_{-\infty}^{\infty} d\Omega \, e^{-I\Omega^2/2kT}} \tag{5-33}$$

The angular velocities take on values from $-\infty$ to $+\infty$. The substitution $\Omega = \sin\theta \, \dot\phi$ makes it apparent that the two rotational degrees of freedom have distribution functions of the same form and that this form is the same as for the translational components of velocity. Since

$$\frac{\overline{I\dot\theta^2}}{2} = \frac{\displaystyle\int_{-\infty}^{\infty} d\dot\theta \, (I\dot\theta^2/2)e^{-I\dot\theta^2/2kT}}{\displaystyle\int_{-\infty}^{\infty} d\dot\theta \, e^{-I\dot\theta^2/2kT}} = \frac{kT}{2} \tag{5-34}$$

and

$$\frac{I\,\overline{\sin^2\theta \, \dot\phi^2}}{2} = \frac{\displaystyle\int_{-\infty}^{\infty} d\Omega \, (I\Omega^2/2)e^{-I\Omega^2/2kT}}{\displaystyle\int_{-\infty}^{\infty} d\Omega \, e^{-I\Omega^2/2kT}} = \frac{kT}{2} \tag{5-35}$$

the mean kinetic energy of rotation is

$$\bar\varepsilon_r = kT \tag{5-36}$$

for a diatomic molecule.

The vibration is treated by fixing the center of mass at the origin and keeping the molecular axis in a fixed orientation. We have then a pure vibration without translation or rotation. The variable distance between the nuclei will now be denoted by ξ and the distance from the center of mass to each of the nuclei by ξ_1 and ξ_2. Equation (5-28) is now rewritten as

$$\begin{aligned} \xi_1 &= m_2\xi/(m_1 + m_2) \\ \xi_2 &= m_1\xi/(m_1 + m_2) \end{aligned} \tag{5-37}$$

The kinetic energy of vibration is

$$\varepsilon_{vk} = \tfrac{1}{2}m_1\dot\xi_1^2 + \tfrac{1}{2}m_2\dot\xi_2^2 = \tfrac{1}{2}m^*\dot\xi^2 \tag{5-38}$$

in terms of the reduced mass m^*. We assume small displacements of the nuclei from their equilibrium positions; in this approximation the motion is simple harmonic and the potential energy is given by

$$\varepsilon_{vp} = \tfrac{1}{2}K(\xi - \xi_e)^2 = \tfrac{1}{2}m^*\omega^2(\xi - \xi_e)^2 \tag{5-39}$$

where ξ_e is the equilibrium value of ξ and K is the restoring force con-- stant. The natural frequency of oscillation $\omega/2\pi$ is related to K and m^* in the usual way $[\omega = (K/m^*)^{1/2}]$, as seen by differentiating the total energy with respect to the time. Since (5-38) and (5-39) depend neither on translational nor rotational coordinates and velocities, the vibrational distribution function is independent of the distribution functions for the other degrees of freedom. The independence of the rotational and vibra- tional motions and distribution functions is actually not exact because the centrifugal forces arising from rotation have an effect on the vibration. Thus the equilibrium distance and the effective force constant depend slightly on the angular velocities of rotation. If the molecule is "stiff" or nearly rigid, i.e., if K and ω are large, the centrifugal effects are small at ordinary temperatures, and it is usually a good approximation to neglect them.*

The vibrational phase space† of the diatomic molecule is two-dimen- sional, and the element is proportional to $d\xi \, d\dot{\xi}$. The distribution func- tion for vibration is given by

$$\Phi_v \, d\xi \, d\dot{\xi} = \frac{e^{-(\varepsilon_{vp}+\varepsilon_{vk})/kT} \, d\xi \, d\dot{\xi}}{\int_{-\infty}^{\infty} d\xi \int_{-\infty}^{\infty} d\dot{\xi} \, e^{-(\varepsilon_{vp}+\varepsilon_{vk})/kT}} \tag{5-40}$$

$$= \frac{e^{-m^*\omega^2(\xi-\xi_e)^2/2kT} \, d\xi}{\int_{-\infty}^{\infty} d\xi \, e^{-m^*\omega^2(\xi-\xi_e)^2/2kT}} \frac{e^{-m^*\dot{\xi}^2/2kT} \, d\dot{\xi}}{\int_{-\infty}^{\infty} d\dot{\xi} \, e^{-m^*\dot{\xi}^2/2kT}} \tag{5-41}$$

The integration is extended from $-\infty$ to $+\infty$ in spite of the fact that the displacements and velocities have been assumed to be small. No signifi- cant error is made, however, because the exponential drops off rapidly on either side of the maximum. The average energies are obtained from

$$\bar{\varepsilon}_{vk} = \frac{m^*\overline{\dot{\xi}^2}}{2} = \frac{\int_{-\infty}^{\infty} d\dot{\xi} \, (m^*\dot{\xi}^2/2)e^{-m^*\dot{\xi}^2/2kT}}{\int_{-\infty}^{\infty} d\dot{\xi} \, e^{-m^*\dot{\xi}^2/2kT}} = \frac{kT}{2} \tag{5-42}$$

$$\bar{\varepsilon}_{vp} = \frac{m^*\omega^2\overline{(\xi-\xi_e)^2}}{2} = \frac{\int_{-\infty}^{\infty} d\xi \, [m^*\omega^2(\xi-\xi_e)^2/2]e^{-m^*\omega^2(\xi-\xi_e)^2/2kT}}{\int_{-\infty}^{\infty} d\xi \, e^{-m^*\omega^2(\xi-\xi_e)^2/2kT}}$$

$$= \frac{kT}{2} \tag{5-43}$$

whence
$$\bar{\varepsilon}_v = \bar{\varepsilon}_{vk} + \bar{\varepsilon}_{vp} = kT \tag{5-44}$$

The mean total energy of the diatomic molecule is the sum of the mean translational energy $3kT/2$ (cf. Eq. (2-17)), the mean rotational energy

---

* We also neglect the effect of the vibration on the rotational moment of inertia.
† This term is defined in Appendix 5-2.

kT, and the mean vibrational energy kT.   Thus

$$\bar{\varepsilon} = 7kT/2 \tag{5-45}$$

The mean energy associated with each translational degree of freedom is $kT/2$ (cf. Eq. (5-6)), that associated with each rotational degree of freedom is also $kT/2$ (cf. Eqs. (5-34) and (5-35)), and with the one vibrational degree of freedom is kT.   The vibrational degree of freedom contributes doubly because there is a potential energy term with the same mean value as the kinetic energy.

5-4. THE EQUIPARTITION THEOREM AND SPECIFIC HEATS

The generalization of the results of the previous section to a system with more degrees of freedom, such as a polyatomic molecule or a solid, is embodied in the theorem of *equipartition of energy*.   This theorem may be stated as follows:* *Let the total energy of the system, e.g., one polyatomic molecule, be expressed in terms of the position coordinates and velocity components for all the degrees of freedom; then, for each squared term appearing in this expression, the system (molecule) possesses a mean energy of $kT/2$.* Quadratic cross terms in the vibrational energy are not counted; if "normal coordinates" are used, these terms do not appear.   The proof of the theorem is readily given.   Let $\alpha\zeta^2$ be a squared term for the coordinate or velocity component ζ.   The coefficient α may be a function of the other coordinates.   The distribution function for ζ is evidently

$$e^{-\alpha\zeta^2/kT} \frac{d\zeta}{\displaystyle\int_{-\infty}^{\infty} d\zeta\, e^{-\alpha\zeta^2/kT}} \tag{5-46}$$

The mean value of $\alpha\zeta^2$ is

$$\overline{\alpha\zeta^2} = \frac{\displaystyle\int_{-\infty}^{\infty} d\zeta\, (\alpha\zeta^2)\, e^{-\alpha\zeta^2/kT}}{\displaystyle\int_{-\infty}^{\infty} d\zeta\, e^{-\alpha\zeta^2/kT}} = \frac{kT}{2} \tag{5-47}$$

Examples of (5-47) have already been given in Eqs. (5-9), (5-34), (5-35), (5-42), and (5-43).   The mean energy of a nonlinear polyatomic molecule with N atoms is the sum of the mean translational energy $3kT/2$, the mean rotational energy $3kT/2$, and the mean vibrational energy $(3N - 6)kT$. If the molecule is nonlinear, there are three degrees of freedom of rotation; i.e., a set of coordinate axes fixed in the molecule can be oriented

---

* The equipartition theorem is sometimes stated as follows: "Each degree of freedom of the system contributes $kT/2$ to the mean energy."   This statement of the theorem implies a definition of "degree of freedom" differing from the accepted usage in mechanics.   Needless confusion is avoided by simply referring to "squared terms" rather than to "degrees of freedom" redefined to mean the number of squared terms in the energy.   A more general statement of the theorem is to be found in Prob. 5-9.

with respect to space-fixed axes by means of nine direction cosines of which only three are independent. The number of vibrational degrees of freedom is equal to the total number $3N$ minus the six degrees of freedom of translation and rotation.

These results can now be used to obtain the specific heat. The specific heat per mole at constant volume is given by $C_v = dU/dT$ where U is the total thermal energy per mole of the gas, including all the degrees of

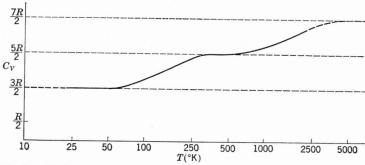

Fig. 5-2. Specific heat per mole at constant volume of ordinary hydrogen versus absolute temperature.

freedom in which thermal energy can be stored. Consider a diatomic gas; then, according to (5-45) or the equipartition theorem,

$$U = 7RT/2 \quad \text{and} \quad C_v = 7R/2 \quad (5\text{-}48)$$

Thus C_v is predicted to be independent of temperature and the same for all diatomic gases (≈ 7 calories per mole per °C). This result of the equipartition theorem is *contradicted by experiment*, which shows that C_v varies with T and approaches the predicted value $7R/2$ only at very high temperatures. At very low temperatures it is found that C_v decreases toward the monatomic gas value of $3R/2$. Figure 5-2 shows the specific heat-versus-temperature curve for hydrogen. Other diatomic gases show similar behavior except that the low temperature approach to $3R/2$ cannot be observed. At the lowest temperatures, $C_v = 3R/2$; then the curve rises to $5R/2$ and stays constant at this value over a limited temperature range (which includes room temperature for many gases); finally, there is a second rise toward the predicted $7R/2$. The transition regions occur at different temperatures for different gases.

These results indicate that classical kinetic theory and statistical mechanics fail to account for the energy associated with internal degrees of freedom. This failure is essentially due to the "quantization" of the vibration and rotation. According to the quantum theory, only certain discrete energies of vibration and rotation are possible for a molecule. A certain minimum energy is needed to start rotation, i.e., to excite the molecule to its first rotational energy state or level. At temperatures so low that kT is much less than this minimum, the chance of rotational excitation in a collision is very small, very few molecules will possess rotational energy, and the rotation will not contribute appreciably to the internal energy and specific heat. When kT is of the order of the minimum energy (transition region), a significant fraction of the molecules are excited, and, ultimately, at temperatures for which kT is much larger than the minimum, the discreteness of the energy states is unimportant and the equipartition theorem gives the correct result. In the case of vibration, a similar explanation holds except that the molecule possesses vibrational energy even in its lowest quantum state. This residual "zero-point energy" does not vanish even at the absolute zero. If kT is much less than the separation between consecutive vibrational energy levels, the chance of vibrational excitation in a collision is very small and nearly all molecules are in the lowest quantum state. Thus the rate of change of the vibrational energy with increasing temperature is negligibly small, and the vibration does not contribute appreciably to the specific heat. In the other limiting case ($kT \gg$ level spacing), the quantization is again unimportant and the vibrational specific heat is given correctly by the equipartition theorem. Since the vibrational level spacing is always greater than the minimum energy needed to excite rotation, the transition region for vibration occurs at higher temperatures than for rotation. Therefore, the first rise from $3R/2$ to $5R/2$ in Fig. 5-2 is attributed to rotation, and the second rise from $5R/2$ to $7R/2$ to vibration. The exact shape of the specific heat curve can be accounted for by quantum theory.*

Except in the high-temperature limit, kinetic theory and classical statistical mechanics give incorrect results when applied to internal degrees of freedom. This difficulty does not exist for the translational degrees of freedom which remain unquantized in the quantum theory. Since the greatest part of kinetic theory is concerned only with translation, it is practically unaffected by the failure of the equipartition theorem. The inadequacy of the classical theory of specific heats provided an important impetus toward the development of the early quantum theory.

PROBLEMS

(For additional problems, see Appendixes 5-1 and 5-2.)

5-1. The probability, or error, integral is defined by

$$\Phi(x) = \frac{2}{\pi^{\frac{1}{2}}} \int_0^x e^{-x^2} \, dx$$

* See R. H. Fowler, "Statistical Mechanics," Cambridge University Press, London, 1936, chap. 3.

Express the probability that a molecule has a speed exceeding a certain value v_0 in terms of the probability integral.

5-2. Gas leaks out slowly through a small hole in a container into an evacuated region. Find the root-mean-square speed of the escaping molecules and show that their mean energy is $2kT$. What significance has this result?

5-3. Find the number of molecules colliding with a surface per unit area per unit time with normal components of velocity exceeding a certain value v_0.

5-4. Calculate the total x momentum transferred per unit area per unit time across the yz plane in a gas in equilibrium. Interpret the result.

5-5. Calculate the total y momentum transferred per unit area per unit time across the yz plane in a gas in equilibrium. Interpret the result.

5-6. Show that the normalized distribution function for the translational kinetic energy, i.e., the fraction of molecules having kinetic energies between ε_k and $\varepsilon_k + d\varepsilon_k$, is given by

$$\frac{2\pi}{(\pi kT)^{3/2}} e^{-\varepsilon_k/kT}\varepsilon_k^{1/2}\, d\varepsilon_k$$

What is the most probable energy?

5-7. A gas of molecules possessing a permanent electric dipole moment μ is placed in a uniform electric field E. The potential energy of a molecule in the field is given by $V(\theta) = -\mu E \cos\theta$ where θ denotes the angle between the direction of the dipole moment and the direction of the field. Obtain the distribution function for orientation, i.e., the probability that a molecule will have a moment oriented between θ and $\theta + d\theta$. Show that the average component of the dipole moment in the direction of the field is

$$\mu\,\overline{\cos\theta} = \mu\left(\coth\frac{\mu E}{kT} - \frac{kT}{\mu E}\right) \to \mu^2 E/3kT \qquad \text{if } \mu E \ll kT$$

5-8. What specific heats are predicted by the equipartition theorem for the linear triatomic molecule CO_2 and the nonlinear molecule H_2O?

5-9. Assume a quite-general dependence of the energy on the coordinate or velocity component ζ given by $\varepsilon(\zeta)$ where $\varepsilon(\zeta) \to +\infty$ as $\zeta \to \pm\infty$. Show that

$$\overline{\zeta\, \partial\varepsilon/\partial\zeta} = kT$$

5-10. Interpret the velocity distribution function

$$F(v_x,v_y,v_z) = \left(\frac{m}{2\pi kT}\right)^{3/2} e^{-\frac{m}{2kT}[(v_x-a)^2+(v_y-b)^2+(v_z-c)^2]}$$

where a, b, and c are independent of velocity.

APPENDIX 5-1

Barometric Derivation of Maxwell's Law

The first step is the derivation of the barometric formula for the variation of atmospheric pressure with altitude, assuming the gravitational field to be homogeneous and the temperature uniform. For simplicity, we also assume a pure gas.   Consider a vertical column of gas of unit cross-sectional area extending from $z = 0$ at the earth's surface to an indefinite height.   We regard the atmosphere as a continuous fluid of mass density $\rho = nm$ in hydrostatic equilibrium.   The layer of fluid between z and $z + dz$ is subject to a force $p(z)$ on its lower surface and $p(z + dz) = p(z) + dp$ on its upper surface where $dp < 0$ if $dz > 0$. Then

$$-dp = \rho g\, dz = nmg\, dz \qquad (5\text{-}49)$$

where g is the acceleration of gravity (assumed to be constant).   Assuming the perfect-gas law and inserting $n = p/kT$ in (5-49), one finds

$$\frac{-dp}{p} = \frac{mg}{kT}\, dz \qquad (5\text{-}50)$$

and assuming uniform temperature, integration gives

$$p = p(0)e^{-mgz/kT}$$
and
$$n = n(0)e^{-mgz/kT} \qquad (5\text{-}51)$$

where $p(0)$ is the pressure and $n(0)$ the density at the earth's surface. Equation (5-51) is the barometric formula; it is not accurate because of temperature gradients in the atmosphere.   It is evident that Eq. (5-51) is a special case of the more general formula for the density of a gas at uniform temperature in an external field of force

$$n = ce^{-V(x,y,z)/kT} \qquad (5\text{-}52)$$

where $V(x,y,z)$ is the potential energy of a molecule at the point x,y,z and c is a constant.

We now seek the velocity distribution of the molecules which is compatible with the density distribution (5-51) and the assumption of uniform temperature.   For simplicity we assume a one-dimensional gas—i.e., one in which the molecules move only in a vertical direction—and we begin by neglecting collisions between molecules.   A molecule leaving the $z = 0$ plane with velocity v_0 will rise to a height $z = v_0^2/2g$ and then fall back to the $z = 0$ plane, where it is elastically reflected.   If all molecules left the ground with the same velocity, the density would drop abruptly to zero at the height $v_0^2/2g$; also the temperature would decrease linearly with altitude, reaching absolute zero at the "top of the atmosphere." Let $f(v_0)\, dv_0$ be the velocity distribution function of the molecules leaving the ground.   Then the number of molecules that leave unit area of the ground per unit time with velocities between v_0 and $v_0 + dv_0$ is

$$dN = n(0)v_0 f(v_0)\, dv_0 \qquad (5\text{-}53)$$

This group of molecules will have turning points between $z = v_0^2/2g$ and $(v_0 + dv_0)^2/2g$.   The number of molecules crossing unit area of the plane

$z = v_0{}^2/2g = z_0$ in an upward direction per unit time is $n(z_0)\bar{v}(z_0)$ where $\bar{v}(z_0)$ represents the mean speed of the molecules at height z_0. The corresponding number crossing the plane $z = z_0 + dz_0 = (v_0 + dv_0)^2/2g$ is $n(z_0 + dz_0)\bar{v}(z_0 + dz_0)$. Since the mean speed is determined by the temperature, which is assumed to be independent of z,

$$\bar{v}(z_0 + dz_0) = \bar{v}(z_0) = \bar{v} = \text{constant}$$

The number per unit area per unit time which cross the lower plane but fail to reach the upper plane is

$$dN = [n(z_0) - n(z_0 + dz_0)]\bar{v} = -\bar{v}(dn/dz_0)\, dz_0$$
$$= \frac{mg\bar{v}}{kT}\, n(0)e^{-mgz_0/kT}\, dz_0 \tag{5-54}$$

using the barometric formula for $n(z)$. Equations (5-53) and (5-54) represent the same group of molecules. Hence

$$dN = n(0)f(v_0)v_0\, dv_0 = \frac{m\bar{v}}{kT}\, n(0)e^{-mgz_0/kT}g\, dz_0 \tag{5-55}$$

Since $mgz_0 = mv_0{}^2/2$ and $g\, dz_0 = v_0\, dv_0$, we find

$$f(v_0) = (m\bar{v}/kT)e^{-\frac{1}{2}mv_0{}^2/kT} \tag{5-56}$$

which is a one-dimensional form of the Maxwell distribution law ($m\bar{v}/kT$ is a constant). We find that the molecules leaving the ground are distributed according to the Maxwell law; it is readily seen that the same distribution of velocities exists at any height.

The effect of one-dimensional collisions on the one-dimensional distribution is seen to be nil. This is because the molecules simply exchange their velocities in such a collision, the final velocity of each being identical with the initial velocity of the other. Since the molecules are of the same species, the collision has no effect on the distribution. Two questions that arise in connection with the foregoing are (1) why does not the atmosphere collapse, all molecules falling to the ground under the influence of gravity, and (2) how is it possible for the molecules at every height to have the same average speed and kinetic energy? The answer to the first question is that all molecules, in the absence of collisions, would fall to the ground and rebound elastically although diffusely. Molecules are continually being emitted from the ground with velocities distributed according to Maxwell's law. In the absence of collisions, these initial velocities would carry the molecules to great heights (at ordinary temperatures, Eq. (2-19) gives a root-mean-square speed $\sim 10^4 - 10^5$ cm/sec). The effect of collisions is to transfer the upward motion from some molecules to others; the same is true of the downward motion, and, as we have seen, the collisions have no effect on the velocity distribution. The second question arises because, on the one hand, a uniform temperature requires the same mean kinetic energy at all heights, and, on the other hand, the molecules, as they rise, gain potential energy at the expense of their kinetic energy. Although it is true that molecules lose kinetic energy as they rise, this does not affect the *mean* kinetic energy because the slowest molecules drop out of the rising beam and only the faster molecules survive at the greater heights. The two effects just compensate if the velocities are distributed according to Maxwell's law.

In conclusion, we observe that the "barometric derivation" is unrigorous in several respects. A kinetic-theory justification of the hydrostatic equation (5-49) has not been given; this requires a separate and extended proof. The thermodynamic requirement of uniform temperature was assumed, as was the perfect-gas law. Finally, no proper account was taken of the three-dimensional nature of the collisions.

PROBLEMS

A5-1. Derive Eq. (5-52) by the hydrostatic method.

A5-2. Prove that two like molecules exchange their velocities in a one-dimensional collision.

A5-3. Show that the velocity distribution at any height above the ground is also given by Eq. (5-56).

APPENDIX 5-2

Statistical-Mechanical Derivation of the Maxwell-Boltzmann Law

A brief discussion of the mathematical method of the Lagrange multiplier is given first. Consider the problem of finding stationary values (e.g., maxima) of the function $F(x,y,z)$ when the variables are not independent but are related by the condition $f(x,y,z) = 0$. If x, y, and z were independent, we should have $\partial F/\partial x = \partial F/\partial y = \partial F/\partial z = 0$; however, these equations do not hold when the variables are related. Suppose that $f(x,y,z) = 0$ can be solved for z and that the solution $z(x,y)$ is inserted in $F(x,y,z(x,y))$. The condition for a stationary value is

$$\left(\frac{\partial F}{\partial x}\right)_y = \left(\frac{\partial F}{\partial x}\right)_{yz} + \left(\frac{\partial F}{\partial z}\right)_{xy}\left(\frac{\partial z}{\partial x}\right)_y = 0 \qquad (5\text{-}57)$$

and since

$$\left(\frac{\partial z}{\partial x}\right)_y = -\frac{(\partial f/\partial x)_{yz}}{(\partial f/\partial z)_{xy}} \qquad (5\text{-}58)$$

we obtain (dropping subscripts)

$$\frac{\partial F/\partial x}{\partial f/\partial x} = \frac{\partial F/\partial z}{\partial f/\partial z} \qquad (5\text{-}59)$$

and in a similar way

$$\frac{\partial F/\partial y}{\partial f/\partial y} = \frac{\partial F/\partial z}{\partial f/\partial z} \qquad (5\text{-}60)$$

Solving (5-59), (5-60), and $f(x,y,z) = 0$ simultaneously gives the coordinates x_m, y_m, z_m of the maximum or stationary value. In the method of Lagrange one defines a new function

$$G(x,y,z,\lambda) \equiv F(x,y,z) - \lambda f(x,y,z) \tag{5-61}$$

and maximizes (or minimizes) $G(x,y,z,\lambda)$, treating x, y, and z as independent. This gives

$$\begin{aligned}
\partial G/\partial x &= \partial F/\partial x - \lambda \partial f/\partial x = 0 \\
\partial G/\partial y &= \partial F/\partial y - \lambda \partial f/\partial y = 0 \\
\partial G/\partial z &= \partial F/\partial z - \lambda \partial f/\partial z = 0
\end{aligned} \tag{5-62}$$

$$\therefore \lambda = \frac{\partial F/\partial x}{\partial f/\partial x} = \frac{\partial F/\partial y}{\partial f/\partial y} = \frac{\partial F/\partial z}{\partial f/\partial z} \tag{5-63}$$

Equations (5-63) are identical with (5-59) and (5-60). Also, setting $\partial G/\partial \lambda = 0$ reproduces the equation of condition $f(x,y,z) = 0$. It has thus been shown that the original problem of maximizing $F(x,y,z)$ subject to the condition $f(x,y,z) = 0$ is equivalent to the more convenient problem of maximizing $G(x,y,z,\lambda)$ directly with respect to x, y, z, and λ, without any equation of condition, i.e., treating x, y, and z as independent variables. The parameter λ is known as the *Lagrange multiplier*. The result obtained here can be readily generalized to a function $F(x_1 \cdots x_n)$ of the n variables $x_1 \cdots x_n$, which are not all independent but are connected by m equations of condition: $f_1(x_1 \cdots x_n) = 0, \ldots,$ $f_m(x_1 \cdots x_n) = 0$ where $m < n$. We introduce m Lagrange multipliers $\lambda_1 \cdots \lambda_m$ and define the new function

$$\begin{aligned}
G(x_1 \cdots x_n, \lambda_1 \cdots \lambda_m) \equiv F(x_1 \cdots x_n) + \lambda_1 f_1(x_1 \cdots x_n) \\
+ \cdots + \lambda_m f_m(x_1 \cdots x_n) \quad (5\text{-}64)
\end{aligned}$$

The condition for a stationary value of F is that the partial derivatives of G with respect to $x_1 \cdots x_n$, $\lambda_1 \cdots \lambda_m$ be equal to zero. Thus there are $n + m$ equations

$$\begin{aligned}
\frac{\partial G}{\partial x_i} &= \frac{\partial F}{\partial x_i} + \lambda_1 \frac{\partial f_1}{\partial x_i} + \cdots + \lambda_m \frac{\partial f_m}{\partial x_i} = 0 \qquad i = 1, 2, \ldots n \\
\frac{\partial G}{\partial \lambda_j} &= f_j = 0 \qquad j = 1, 2, \ldots m
\end{aligned} \tag{5-65}$$

to determine the $n + m$ unknowns $x_1 \cdots x_n$, $\lambda_1 \cdots \lambda_m$. It is assumed that at least one of the Jacobian determinants of the functions $f_1 \cdots f_m$ with respect to m of the variables $x_1 \cdots x_n$ is different from zero.*

---

* Cf. R. Courant, "Differential and Integral Calculus," vol. II, p. 198, Interscience Publishers, Inc., N.Y., 1937.

The statistical-mechanical derivation is based on the concept of a *phase space*. Consider a bead sliding on a straight wire as an example of a one-dimensional motion. The dynamical state of the bead at any instant is specified by the coordinate x and momentum p_x. In a graph of p_x versus x, the dynamical state of the bead at any instant is represented by a point and the dynamical history by a sequence of points forming a smooth curve if there are no abrupt changes in the motion. The mathematical "space" of two dimensions, whose coordinates are x and p_x, is referred to as a phase space. A molecule of a monatomic gas has three degrees of freedom; thus, three position coordinates x, y, z and three momentum components p_x, p_y, p_z are required to specify its dynamical state. The phase space in this case is a mathematical "space" of six dimensions with coordinates x, y, z, p_x, p_y, and p_z. The dynamical state of a molecule at a particular instant is represented by a point in the phase space and the dynamical state of the entire gas by a large collection of points. Between collisions, the representative point of a molecule traces out a continuous path in the phase space; when a collision occurs, the representative point jumps to another region of the phase space, since the velocity components are abruptly altered. The element of "volume" is defined by $d\tau = dx\,dy\,dz\,dp_x\,dp_y\,dp_z$ in analogy to the usual definition.

The phase space is now divided into small cells of equal "volume." These cells are considered to be so small that molecules whose representative points lie within the same cell have indistinguishable physical properties but at the same time are assumed to be large enough to contain many representative points. A *microstate* of the gas at any instant is specified by a particular distribution of the representative points of the molecules among the different cells. An interchange of representative points between different cells leads to a new microstate, since the molecules have exchanged their dynamical variables.* On the other hand, an interchange of representative points within the same cell does not lead to a new microstate, since the change of dynamical properties is negligible. A *macrostate* of the gas at any instant is specified by the numbers of representative points in each cell, i.e., by the set of integers $\{N_1, N_2, \ldots\}$ where N_i denotes the number of points in the ith cell. We now assume that a gas is in equilibrium when it is in the macrostate of greatest probability, and we seek to determine the distribution numbers N_i for the equilibrium macrostate. Since each macrostate corresponds to many possible microstates, the probability $W(N_1, N_2, \ldots)$ of the macrostate $\{N_1, N_2, \ldots\}$ is equal to the number of microstates

---

* It is especially to be noted that the molecules are here assumed to be distinguishable in principle. In the quantum statistics the particles are assumed to be indistinguishable in principle, and an exchange of particles between cells becomes a meaningless operation which does not lead to a new microstate.

compatible with the given macrostate multiplied by the a priori probability of a microstate. It is here assumed that all microstates have the same probability of occurrence. This assumption is equivalent to the assumption that equal "volumes" of phase space have equal a priori probabilities; i.e., a representative point is as likely to be found in one cell as in another, since we have assumed all cells to be of the same size. The probability of a microstate is then given by $g^{N_1}g^{N_2} \cdots = g^N$ where N is the total number of molecules in the gas and g is a geometric probability equal to the "volume" of the cell divided by the total accessible "volume." The probability g that a representative point lies in a particular cell is here assumed to be independent of the number of points in the cell. The assumptions made in this paragraph may seem to be highly arbitrary. No explanation has been offered as to why the phase space, as defined, should have the basic property that equal "volumes" have equal a priori probabilities. A justification of these assumptions in terms of more fundamental statistical-mechanical theory is outside the scope of this text.

The number of microstates compatible with the macrostate $\{N_1,$ $N_2, \ldots\}$ is equal to the number of combinations of N things taken $N_1, N_2, \ldots$ at a time, i.e., to the number of ways N objects can be divided into a group of N_1 objects, another of N_2 objects, another of N_3, etc. This number is equal to

$$\frac{N!}{N_1!N_2!N_3! \cdots} \tag{5-66}$$

Hence the probability of a macrostate is given by

$$W(N_1,N_2, \ldots) = \frac{N!}{N_1!N_2! \cdots} g^N \tag{5-67}$$

Our problem is to maximize* W with respect to the variables N_i, which are not independent. There are two equations of condition, one expressing conservation of the total number of molecules and the other expressing conservation of the total energy, since all collisions are assumed to be elastic. Thus

$$\sum_i N_i - N = 0 \tag{5-68}$$

and

$$\sum_i N_i\varepsilon_i - E = 0 \tag{5-69}$$

where ε_i is the energy of a molecule in the ith cell and E is the total energy. Since W and $\log W$ are simultaneously maximized, we may replace (5-67)

---

* The mathematical proof that the stationary value obtained for W is actually a maximum is left as an exercise for the reader.

by

$$\log W = \log N! - \log N_1! - \log N_2! \cdots + N \log g$$
$$= C - \sum_i \log N_i! \tag{5-70}$$

where C is a constant. Because the N_i are all large by hypothesis, the factorials can be approximated by Stirling's formula (Eq. (4-83)):

$$N_i! \simeq N_i^{N_i+\frac{1}{2}} e^{-N_i} (2\pi)^{\frac{1}{2}}$$

giving
$$\log N_i! \simeq (N_i + \tfrac{1}{2}) \log N_i - N_i + \tfrac{1}{2} \log 2\pi$$
$$\simeq N_i \log N_i - N_i \tag{5-71}$$

where insignificant terms have been dropped. Substituting (5-71) in (5-70) one obtains

$$\log W = C - \sum_i N_i \log N_i + \sum_i N_i = C' - \sum_i N_i \log N_i \quad (5\text{-}72)$$

Since the integers N_i are large, we make little error by treating them as continuous variables (an increment of unity represents a small relative change). We now minimize the function

$$F(N_1, N_2, \ldots) = \sum_i N_i \log N_i \tag{5-73}$$

subject to the conditions

$$f_1(N_1, N_2, \ldots) = \sum_i N_i - N = 0$$

and
$$f_2(N_1, N_2, \ldots) = \sum_i N_i \varepsilon_i - E = 0$$

Introducing the Lagrange multipliers α and β, we obtain from Eqs. (5-65)

$$\frac{\partial F}{\partial N_j} + \alpha \frac{\partial f_1}{\partial N_j} + \beta \frac{\partial f_2}{\partial N_j} = 0 \qquad j = 1, 2, \ldots$$

whence
$$\log N_j + 1 + \alpha + \beta \varepsilon_j = 0$$

and
$$N_j = e^{-(1+\alpha+\beta\varepsilon_j)} = A e^{-\beta\varepsilon_j} \tag{5-74}$$

where A and β are constants independent of j. A is proportional to the "volume" $\Delta\tau$ of the cells. We now make the cells infinitesimal in size and label each cell by the values of the coordinates x, y, z, p_x, p_y, p_z at its center. Then (5-74) becomes

$$N(x, y, \ldots, p_z) = A' e^{-\beta\varepsilon(x, y, \ldots, p_z)} d\tau \tag{5-75}$$

and the total number of molecules is given by

$$N = \sum_j N_j = A' \int e^{-\beta\varepsilon(x, y, \ldots, p_z)} d\tau \tag{5-76}$$

where the integral is extended over all the accessible part of the phase space. The distribution function that gives the probability that a molecule is found between x and $x + dx$, y and $y + dy$, and z and $z + dz$ with momentum components between p_x and $p_x + dp_x$, p_y and $p_y + dp_y$, and p_z and $p_z + dp_z$ is denoted by $\Phi(x,y, \ldots ,p_z) \, dx \, dy \cdots dp_z$. This is evidently the same as the probability that the representative point lies in the cell of "volume" $d\tau$ about the point x, y, $\ldots$, p_z. Thus

$$\Phi(x,y, \ldots ,p_z) \, d\tau = \frac{N(x,y, \ldots ,p_z)}{N} = \frac{e^{-\beta\varepsilon(x,y, \ldots ,p_z)} \, d\tau}{\int e^{-\beta\varepsilon(x,y, \ldots ,p_z)} \, d\tau} \quad (5\text{-}77)$$

where $d\tau = dx \, dy \, dz \, dp_x \, dp_y \, dp_z$. It is shown in Sec. 5-1 that $\beta = 1/kT$. The distribution function (5-77) is known as the *Maxwell-Boltzmann function*. According to this law of distribution, the energy ε of a cell in phase space determines the population of the cell: comparing two cells of equal size, the one of smaller energy will contain the greater number of representative points. This result may perhaps seem to conflict with the initial assumption that equal-sized cells in phase space have equal a priori probabilities. The difference between the a priori and the ultimate probabilities arises from the condition of energy conservation (Eq. (5-69)). If this had not been taken into account, the ultimate and a priori probabilities would have been found to be the same, i.e., the representative points would have been uniformly distributed over the accessible region of the phase space.

PROBLEMS

A5-4. Show that a uniform distribution of representative points would have been found instead of Eq. (5-74) if the energy condition had been omitted.

A5-5. Generalize the foregoing derivation by permitting the cells to be of different sizes with different geometric probabilities g_1, g_2, $\ldots$. Show that Eq. (5-74) is replaced by the relation

$$N_j = Ag_j e^{-\beta\varepsilon_j} \quad (5\text{-}74')$$

where A and β are constants independent of j.

A5-6. If the gas is not at rest but in a state of uniform mass motion in the x direction, show that there are three subsidiary conditions and three Lagrange multipliers. Interpret the resulting distribution function.

A5-7. Prove that the stationary value found for W is actually a maximum.

CHAPTER 6

IMPERFECT GASES AND INTERMOLECULAR FORCES

In this chapter we take up a number of effects which demonstrate that molecules are not simply little billiard balls and which require for their explanation a more sophisticated molecular model. Imperfect-gas behavior is discussed in Sec. 6-1, and the equation of state is expanded in a series of small corrections to the perfect-gas law (virial expansion). The well-known equation of van der Waals is considered in detail, and its limitations are indicated. In Sec. 6-2 we first give a general definition of the pressure in the interior of a perfect gas and then include the additional stress (static pressure) arising from the intermolecular forces in an imperfect gas. The static pressure, which is simply related to the second virial coefficient of the virial expansion, is calculated by direct integration, assuming the molecules to be point centers of force and the force fields to be spherically symmetric. A general expression is then obtained for the second virial coefficient in terms of the intermolecular potential function. The van der Waals equation is shown to correspond to a molecular model of weakly attracting rigid spheres; the case of strongly attracting rigid-sphere molecules is also considered. The origin of the van der Waals attraction between neutral, nonpolar molecules is discussed; some general remarks are made about the nature of the intermolecular forces (discussed in greater detail in Chap. 12), and four simple models of intermolecular force fields are introduced. The greater part of Sec. 6-3 is devoted to an elementary treatment of the viscosity of an imperfect gas according to the model of weakly attracting rigid-sphere molecules (van der Waals–Sutherland) and another model representing the molecules as point centers of force which repel according to an inverse power of the distance. Using mean-free-path methods, one obtains a very simple and fairly satisfactory representation of the temperature dependence of the viscosity coefficient from both models.

6-1. THE VIRIAL COEFFICIENTS AND THE VAN DER WAALS EQUATION

In preceding chapters it has been assumed that the molecules of a gas could be adequately represented as small, rigid, elastic spheres. When account is taken of the force fields between molecules, as well as of the finite size of the molecules themselves, the gas is referred to as *imperfect*. One indication of imperfect-gas behavior has already been found in Sec. 3-5 in connection with the temperature-dependence of the viscosity coefficient. The theory of imperfect gases will be approached here through the *equation of state*, which expresses the relation between the three state variables: pressure p, volume V, and absolute temperature T. Experiment shows that actual gases deviate from the perfect-gas law or equation of state and that the deviations become more noticeable as the critical temperature is approached. The effects of intermolecular forces depend on the average separation of the molecules and therefore decrease with decreasing density. The effects due to finite molecular size also decrease with decreasing density. One therefore expects the perfect-gas law to hold in the limit of very low molecular densities—that is, for high temperatures and low pressures. Since a series expansion in powers of the density is thus indicated, we write the equation of state of an imperfect gas in the form

$$\frac{pV}{NkT} = 1 + \frac{B'N}{V} + C'\left(\frac{N}{V}\right)^2 + \cdots \tag{6-1}$$

where N is the total number of molecules. It is customary to rewrite (6-1), applied to 1 mole of gas, in the form

$$\frac{pV}{RT} = 1 + \frac{B(T)}{V} + \frac{C(T)}{V^2} + \cdots \tag{6-2}$$

where B and C are functions of the temperature. B and C are referred to as the *second* and *third virial coefficients*. It is possible to represent experimental data over a wide range of temperatures and pressures by means of the *virial expansion* (6-2) with a small number of terms that diminish rapidly in size. The first-order departures from perfect-gas behavior are represented by the second virial coefficient B. At low temperatures, B is found to be negative for all gases;* as the temperature is raised, B becomes positive and approaches a maximum that has been observed in the case of He. The temperature at which B vanishes is called the *Boyle temperature*. At this temperature, Boyle's law holds up to fairly high pressures, and the deviations from perfect-gas behavior begin with the third virial term. In the theory of imperfect gases, an attempt is made to understand and account for the observed departures from the perfect-gas law on the basis of simple assumptions about intermolecular forces. Conversely, one uses the observed data, e.g., the observed variation of B with T, to learn more about the nature of the intermolecular forces and the "sizes" of molecules.

* Graphs of $B(T)$ versus T for neon and argon are shown in Fig. 12-1.

Although the formulation of the equation of state in the previous paragraph is the most general and satisfactory one, it is nevertheless of interest to discuss the simple, well-known equation of van der Waals and to indicate its limitations. We shall first give a rough theoretical argument to justify the form of the equation; a more detailed derivation will follow in Sec. 6-2. Two main effects are taken into account in the van der Waals equation: (1) the effect of the finite size of the molecules in reducing the available volume and (2) the effect of intermolecular attractive forces in contributing a negative normal stress, or tension. The first effect is taken into account by replacing the volume V in the perfect-gas law by the available volume $V - b$ where b is of the order of magnitude of the total volume occupied by the molecules themselves, i.e.,

$$b \approx \tfrac{4}{3}\pi \left(\frac{d}{2}\right)^3 N \tag{6-3}$$

Here the molecules are treated as rigid elastic spheres of diameter d surrounded by attractive fields of force. The second correction arises from the cohesion between the molecules. The stress across an imaginary surface in the gas is due mainly to the transport of momentum, as in a perfect gas,* but in addition there is a small negative pressure or tension contributed by the molecules near one side of the surface interacting with the molecules near the other side. For low densities, this tension is expected to be jointly proportional to the densities of interacting pairs of molecules, i.e., to $(N/V)^2$, and can be written in the form $-a/V^2$ where $a > 0$. Then the total pressure is given by

$$p = \frac{NkT}{V - b} - \frac{a}{V^2}$$

or
$$\left(p + \frac{a}{V^2}\right)(V - b) = NkT \tag{6-4}$$

Equation (6-4) is van der Waals' equation of state and a and b are referred to as van der Waals' constants. Just as b is determined by the molecular diameter, a is determined by the law of force between the molecules. Let us assume an attraction varying as the inverse sth power of the distance r between centers. The form of a can then be deduced by a simple dimensional argument. Assuming the cohesion to be a static effect, i.e., to be independent of the state of motion of the molecules, we expect a to be independent of velocity and mass. The dependence of the cohesive stress on density makes a vary as N^2. In addition, a will depend on the constants of the force law and on the molecular diameter. Writing $F = -cr^{-s}$ for the law of force, we have

$$a = N^2 f(c,s,d) \tag{6-5}$$

---

* This will be explained more fully at the beginning of Sec. 6-2.

where $f(c,s,d)$ is to be obtained by dimensional analysis. Since a/V^2 is a pressure, the dimensions of a are given by $[FL^4]$, where $[F]$ stands for force and $[L]$ for length. The dimensions of c are $[FL^s]$. Setting

$$a\ [FL^4] \propto N^2 c^p d^q\ [F^p L^{ps} L^q] \tag{6-6}$$

it is evident that $p = 1$ and $q = 4 - s$. Therefore

$$a \propto N^2 c/d^{s-4} \tag{6-7}$$

The calculation of the next section shows that Eqs. (6-3) and (6-7) are correct apart from numerical factors of the order of unity. However, the use of Eq. (6-4), together with Eqs. (6-3) and (6-7), can only be justified for sufficiently weak attractive fields and sufficiently low densities.

The van der Waals constants a and b can be determined by a variety of experimental methods. The most common and, for our purposes, least satisfactory method is to use critical-point data. The van der Waals isotherms* (see Fig. 6-1) for high values of T differ but slightly from the

hyperbolas of an ideal gas; however, when T is small, the isotherms go through a minimum and then a maximum with increasing V. The transition between the two types of curves occurs when the maximum and minimum coincide; thus the transition curve has a horizontal tangent at its inflection point. It is shown in texts on thermodynamics that the transition curve represents the isotherm at the critical temperature and that its point of inflection is the critical point. It is then a simple exercise to express the critical data p_c, V_c, and T_c in terms of a and b. The critical ratio per mole $p_c V_c/RT_c$ is found to have the value $\frac{3}{8}$. This is in disagreement with ob-

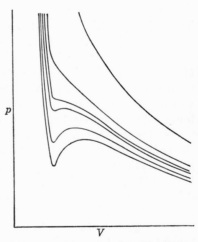

FIG. 6-1. The van der Waals isotherms.

servation: the critical ratios for simple nonpolar molecules are found to be very close to 0.30 and for other molecules to be less. Since the assumptions underlying van der Waals' equation do not hold in the neighborhood of the critical point, the disagreement is hardly surprising.†

Values of a and b can be determined at low densities from pressure,

* Curves of constant T in a p versus V diagram.

† A further discrepancy is found in the critical volumes: although $V_c = 3b$ is predicted, the volumes observed are closer to $2b$.

volume, and temperature measurements, e.g., from an experimental isotherm. Corresponding to a particular point on an isotherm, a local set
of a, b values can be obtained from the ordinate and slope, which are
inserted respectively in the van der Waals equations for p and $(\partial p/\partial V)_T$.
Another procedure is to measure the coefficient $(\partial p/\partial T)_V$ with a constant-
volume gas thermometer; since $(\partial p/\partial T)_V = R/(V - b)$, one can determine a local set of a, b values from this relation combined with van der
Waals' equation. The values of a and b determined by these methods
are found not to be constant, as one would expect from Eqs. (6-3) and
(6-7), but to vary slowly with the temperature. The van der Waals
equation, expanded in virial form, is

$$pV = RT \left(1 + \frac{b}{V} + \frac{b^2}{V^2} \cdots \right) - \frac{a}{V} \tag{6-8}$$

giving for the virial coefficients

$$B(T) = b - (a/RT) \qquad C(T) = b^2, \ldots \tag{6-9}$$

The third and higher virial coefficients are incorrect in principle, as will
be explained in the following section. The formula for $B(T)$ predicts
negative values at low temperatures, changing to positive when $T = a/bR$
(Boyle temperature), and an asymptotic approach to a constant value b
at high temperatures. This behavior is easily interpreted in terms of the
van der Waals model of weakly attracting, rigid-sphere molecules. At
temperatures so low that kT is much less than the potential energy of the
molecules "at contact," the encounters between molecules are of relatively long duration and the influence of the attractive forces is relatively
large. The term in a/RT then makes the principal contribution to $B(T)$.
In the other limit of high temperatures, the encounters are brief, the molecules are only slightly deflected by the attractive forces, and the effects
of repulsion, represented by the first term b, are predominant.

It has already been pointed out that when van der Waals' equation is
fitted to experimental data, the values of a and b are found to vary with
the temperature. The most marked deviations of the experimental
points from the hyperbolic curve of $B(T)$ versus T given by Eq. (6-9)
occur at high temperatures. Instead of an asymptotic approach to the
constant value b, the data indicate the approach toward a maximum, and
points well beyond this maximum have been observed for He. The discrepancy is accounted for by the unrealistic representation of molecular
repulsion in the van der Waals model. The rigid-sphere representation
implies that when two molecules come into "contact," an infinite repulsion sets in abruptly and the molecules are prevented from coming closer
together, regardless of their relative velocity. Actual molecules are
"softer" than rigid spheres; i.e., they repel each other at close distances

of approach but with finite forces acting over a finite range of distances. This means that, instead of a sharp diameter d, there is an effective diameter that depends on the repulsive law of force and the relative velocity and thus on the temperature. The effective diameter is a distance comparable to the separation at which the mean kinetic energy $3kT/2$ is equal to the potential energy of repulsion. At high temperatures, the attractive forces can be neglected and the principal effect is the decrease of effective diameter with increasing temperature. As the molecules move faster, they approach more closely in collisions, and the effective diameter is reduced. Thus the effective volume of the molecules decreases, and the van der Waals b should also decrease with increasing temperature. This is in accord with experiment and accounts qualitatively for the maximum of $B(T)$ at high temperature. It is clear that quantitative information about the repulsive law of force can be obtained from the observed temperature variation of b at high temperatures. Information about the attractive forces can be obtained from the observed values of van der Waals' a (cf. Eq. (6-7)). The temperature-dependence of a will be discussed in the next section. The general connection between the second virial coefficient and the intermolecular law of force will also be presented in the next section.

6-2. THEORY OF THE SECOND VIRIAL COEFFICIENT

Stresses in the Interior of a Gas. In Sec. 2-3, the pressure in a perfect gas was found by calculating the momentum imparted to unit area of the wall per unit time through molecular impacts. We shall now define the pressure in the interior of a perfect gas at rest in a container with reference to an imaginary plane being crossed by molecules in both directions: *the total normal component of momentum transported across unit area per unit time is the pressure.* This will now be shown to equal the pressure on the walls as calculated in Sec. 2-3. Let the z axis be normal to the plane. Then the number of molecules crossing the area dS in the time interval dt with velocities in a narrow range dv_x, dv_y, dv_z is equal to the volume $v_z \, dt \, dS$ of the cylinder containing the molecules that approach dS during the interval dt in the specified range of directions multiplied by the density $nF(v_x,v_y,v_z) \, dv_x \, dv_y \, dv_z$ of such molecules. The total normal momentum transported per unit area per unit time by all molecules crossing from both sides is

$$P_{zz} = \iiint mv_z \cdot v_z \cdot nF(v_x,v_y,v_z) \, dv_x \, dv_y \, dv_z \qquad (6\text{-}10)$$

$$= nm \int_{-\infty}^{\infty} \Psi(v_x) \, dv_x \int_{-\infty}^{\infty} \Psi(v_y) \, dv_y \int_{-\infty}^{\infty} v_z^2 \Psi(v_z) \, dv_z$$

$$= nm\overline{v_z^2} = nkT \qquad (6\text{-}11)$$

using Eqs. (5-12) and (5-6).   Thus P_{zz} is the same as the pressure exerted by a perfect gas on the walls of its container.   It is to be noted that the momentum transports from opposite sides do not cancel but that the total transport is twice that from either side.   The molecules crossing from below carry $+z$ momentum in the $+z$ direction, and those crossing from above carry $-z$ momentum in the $-z$ direction.   Those in the former group contribute $+z$ momentum to the gas above the plane; those in the latter group deplete the gas above the plane of $-z$ momentum.   But taking away $-z$ momentum has the same effect as adding $+z$ momentum; therefore the two transports have effects in the same direction.*   This is expressed mathematically by the fact that the integrand of Eq. (6-10) is an even function of v_z.

It is of interest to calculate the shearing stress in a perfect gas at rest. According to the convention adopted in Sec. 3-4, the shearing stress P_{zy} represents a force in the y direction exerted over a plane perpendicular to the z axis.   Since P_{zy} is equal to the total y momentum transferred per unit time across unit area of the plane, Eq. (6-10) can be used if the normal momentum mv_z is replaced by the tangential momentum mv_y. Thus

$$P_{zy} = \iiint mv_y \cdot v_z \cdot nF(v_x,v_y,v_z) \, dv_x \, dv_y \, dv_z$$
$$= nm \int_{-\infty}^{\infty} \Psi(v_x) \, dv_x \int_{-\infty}^{\infty} v_y \Psi(v_y) \, dv_y \int_{-\infty}^{\infty} v_z \Psi(v_z) \, dv_z = 0$$

(6-12)

since the last two integrals vanish because of odd integrands.   Therefore the shearing stresses vanish in a perfect gas at rest.   Since the Maxwell law of distribution of velocities is valid also for an imperfect gas,† this result continues to hold and is, in fact, a special case of the theorem that in a fluid at rest the tangential stresses vanish.   The Maxwell law cannot apply to a gas in viscous flow, for the shearing stresses do not vanish in this case.   This will be discussed more fully in Chap. 11.

The stress across an imaginary plane in a solid arises from the interaction of the molecules on one side with those on the other side.   The normal stress is defined as the normal component of the interaction force per unit area of the plane.   This type of stress is absent in perfect gases, since the molecules are assumed to exert no forces on each other, but it is present to a small extent in imperfect gases.   The total pressure in an imperfect gas then consists of two parts: the *kinetic pressure* p_k, which arises from the transfer of momentum by moving molecules, and the *static pressure* p_s, which is due to the intermolecular forces.   Since the Maxwell velocity distribution holds for an imperfect gas, the kinetic pressure is the same as for a perfect gas; thus $p_k = nkT$.   The static

---

* A similar situation is found in electrolysis: currents of oppositely charged ions moving in opposite directions are added, not subtracted.

† This is proved in works on statistical mechanics (see the Bibliography).

pressure may be positive or negative depending on whether the inter-molecular repulsions or attractions are more important at a given temperature. It is immediately evident that a relation exists between the static pressure and the virial coefficients. Thus

$$p = p_k + p_s = (RT/V) + p_s \qquad (6\text{-}13)$$

for 1 mole of gas and, substituting from Eq. (6-2),

$$\frac{pV}{RT} = 1 + \frac{Vp_s}{RT} = 1 + \frac{B}{V} + \frac{C}{V^2} + \cdots \qquad (6\text{-}14)$$

whence

$$p_s = RT\left(\frac{B}{V^2} + \frac{C}{V^3} + \cdots\right) \qquad (6\text{-}15)$$

The first term on the right side of (6-15) varies quadratically with the density and corresponds to binary interactions only. The higher terms result from interactions in which three or more molecules are simultaneously within range of each other's force fields. We assume that the density of the gas is sufficiently low that only binary interactions need to be taken into account; i.e., we ignore simultaneous interactions of a molecule with more than one other molecule. The first-order value of p_s calculated under this assumption is denoted by $p_s^{(1)}$ and is related to the second virial coefficient by

$$B = V^2 p_s^{(1)}/RT \qquad (6\text{-}16)$$

Derivation of the Formula for $B(T)$. We represent the molecules as point centers of force surrounded by spherically symmetric fields of short range. These fields are attractive except for close distances of approach when a strong repulsion is encountered. We denote the potential energy of an interacting pair of molecules by $u(r)$ with the condition that $u(\infty) = 0$. The force is given by $F = -du/dr$ and is negative for attraction and positive for repulsion. We consider the interaction between a pair of molecules located in the volume elements $d\tau_1$ and $d\tau_2$ at a certain instant. If there were but two molecules in the container of volume V, the probability of finding a specified one of them in the element $d\tau_1$ and the other in $d\tau_2$ a distance r away would be

$$Ce^{-u(r)/kT} \, d\tau_1 \, d\tau_2 \qquad (6\text{-}17)$$

where the spatial distribution function of Eqs. (5-52) and (5-2) has been introduced.* Normalizing this probability to unity gives

$$C \int_V d\tau_1 \int_V d\tau_2 \, e^{-u(r)/kT} \approx C \int_V d\tau_1 \int_V d\tau_2 = CV^2 = 1 \qquad (6\text{-}18)$$

The exponential has been replaced by unity, since $u(r)$ is negligibly small for distances exceeding $\sim 10\text{Å}$, i.e., over most of the box. Now if there

* Ultimate justification of (6-17) comes from statistical mechanics.

are altogether N molecules in the container, the molecule in $d\tau_1$ can be selected in N ways and that in $d\tau_2$ in $N - 1$ ways. The total probability of finding one molecule in $d\tau_1$ and another in $d\tau_2$ is then given by

$$\frac{N(N-1)}{V^2} e^{-u(r)/kT} d\tau_1 d\tau_2 \approx n \, d\tau_1 \, n \, d\tau_2 \, e^{-u(r)/kT} \qquad (6\text{-}19)$$

In the absence of intermolecular forces, this would reduce to $n \, d\tau_1 \, n \, d\tau_2$.

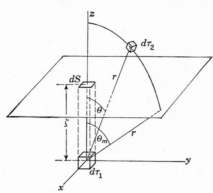

The probabilities for different pairs, which are added in obtaining (6-19), are mutually exclusive by hypothesis (low density). The same result is obtained by multiplying the number of pairs $N(N - 1)/2$ by twice (6-17), since there are two ways to arrange each pair. The average force between the two elements is

$$-du/dr \cdot n^2 e^{-u(r)/kT} \, d\tau_1 \, d\tau_2 \qquad (6\text{-}20)$$

FIG. 6-2. Coordinate system used in calculating the static pressure, i.e., the part of the stress due to intermolecular forces.

We locate the element $d\tau_1$ at the origin and the interface across which the stress is to be calculated at the plane $z = \zeta$. The coordinates of $d\tau_2$ are r, θ, ϕ, and, since $d\tau_2$ and $d\tau_1$ are on opposite sides of the interface, the possible values of θ and r are contained within the intervals: $0 \leq \theta \leq \theta_m$ and $\zeta \leq r < \infty$ where $\theta_m = \cos^{-1} \zeta/r$ (see Fig. 6-2). The component normal to the interface of the force between $d\tau_1$ and $d\tau_2$ summed over all locations of $d\tau_2$, i.e., over all possible positions of the second molecule above the interface, is

$$dF = -n^2 \, d\tau_1 \iiint (du/dr) \cos \theta \, e^{-u(r)/kT} r^2 \, dr \sin \theta \, d\theta \, d\phi$$

$$= -2\pi n^2 \, d\tau_1 \int_\zeta^\infty dr \, r^2 (du/dr) e^{-u(r)/kT} \int_0^{\theta_m} d\theta \sin \theta \cos \theta$$

$$= -\pi n^2 \, d\tau_1 \int_\zeta^\infty dr \, (r^2 - \zeta^2)(du/dr) \, e^{-u(r)/kT} \qquad (6\text{-}21)$$

Equation (6-21) represents the average force exerted on any molecule that happens to be in $d\tau_1$ averaged over all positions of the interacting molecule on the other side of the interface. We set $d\tau_1 = dS \, d\zeta$ where $dS = dx \, dy =$ element of area in the interface and $d\zeta =$ height of the element. Dividing (6-21) by dS and integrating over ζ from 0 to ∞, one obtains the total normal force per unit area of the interface, i.e., the static pressure $p_s^{(1)}$. Thus

$$p_s^{(1)} = -\pi n^2 \int_0^\infty d\zeta \int_\zeta^\infty dr \, (r^2 - \zeta^2)(du/dr) \, e^{-u(r)/kT} \qquad (6\text{-}22)$$

It is advantageous to invert the order of integration. Then

$$p_s^{(1)} = -\pi n^2 \int_0^\infty dr \frac{du}{dr} e^{-u(r)/kT} \int_0^r d\zeta \, (r^2 - \zeta^2)$$

$$= -\frac{2\pi n^2}{3} \int_0^\infty dr \, r^3 \frac{du}{dr} e^{-u(r)/kT} \tag{6-23}$$

$$= \frac{2\pi n^2 kT}{3} \int_0^\infty r^3 \frac{d}{dr} e^{-u(r)/kT} \, dr$$

$$= -\frac{2\pi n^2 kT}{3} \int_0^\infty r^3 \frac{d}{dr} (1 - e^{-u(r)/kT}) \, dr \tag{6-24}$$

The last step makes possible a reformulation through integration by parts. If $u(r)$ vanishes at infinity as an inverse power of the distance r^{-q}, the integral of Eq. (6-23) will not converge unless $q > 3$. We assume $q > 3$ in the following. Then an integration of (6-24) by parts gives

$$p_s^{(1)} = -\frac{2\pi n^2 kT}{3} \left\{ r^3 [1 - e^{-u(r)/kT}] \Big|_0^\infty - 3 \int_0^\infty r^2 [1 - e^{-u(r)/kT}] \, dr \right\}$$

$$= 2\pi n^2 kT \int_0^\infty dr \, r^2 [1 - e^{-u(r)/kT}] \tag{6-25}$$

The integrated term vanishes at the lower limit, where the force is repulsive, and also at the upper limit, since it approaches $r^3 u(r)/kT$ and $u(r)$ vanishes faster than r^{-3}. Introducing (6-25) into (6-16), we obtain as a general expression for the second virial coefficient*

$$B = 2\pi L \int_0^\infty dr \, r^2 [1 - e^{-u(r)/kT}] \tag{6-26}$$

Equation (6-26) is valid for intermolecular forces of any strength provided that $u(r)$ vanishes at infinity more rapidly than r^{-3}.

Let us now assume the van der Waals model of weakly attracting rigid-sphere molecules of diameter d. Then for $0 \le r < d$ the potential energy $u(r)$ is positively infinite; the criterion of weak attraction is that $|u(r)| \ll kT$ for $r > d$. Then

$$B = 2\pi L \left(\int_0^d dr \, r^2 + \int_d^\infty dr \, r^2 \{1 - [1 - u(r)/kT \cdots]\} \right)$$

$$= \frac{2\pi L d^3}{3} + \frac{2\pi L}{kT} \int_d^\infty dr \, r^2 u(r)$$

$$= \frac{2\pi L d^3}{3} - \frac{2\pi L^2}{RT} \int_d^\infty dr \, r^2 |u(r)| \tag{6-27}$$

$$= b - \frac{a}{RT}$$

* Alternative derivations by statistical mechanical methods may be found in R. H. Fowler, "Statistical Mechanics," Cambridge University Press, London, 1936, chap. 9.

This is of the same form as the second virial coefficient obtained from van der Waals' semiempirical equation of state (cf. Eq. (6-9)). The explicit formulas for the van der Waals a and b are

$$b = 2\pi L d^3 / 3 \tag{6-28}$$

$$a = 2\pi L^2 \int_d^\infty dr\, r^2 |u(r)| \tag{6-29}$$

Thus b is equal to four times the total volume of the molecules regarded as spheres of diameter d; this is in agreement with the preliminary estimate of Eq. (6-3). Experimental values of b can be used to estimate Ld^3 in place of Eq. (3-32); this gives another method of finding L and d. The molecular diameters determined from van der Waals' b agree closely with those determined by other methods. If the attraction is given by a simple inverse power law, namely $u(r) = -c'r^{-q}$ with $q > 3$, the resulting formula for a is

$$a = 2\pi L^2 c' \int_d^\infty r^{2-q}\, dr = \frac{2\pi L^2 c'}{(q-3)d^{q-3}} \tag{6-30}$$

In order to compare this with the preliminary estimate (6-7), we replace the potential energy constants by the force constants. Since

$$F = -\frac{du}{dr} = -\frac{qc'}{r^{q+1}} = -\frac{c}{r^s} \tag{6-31}$$

the resulting expression is

$$a = \frac{2\pi L^2 c}{q(q-3)d^{q-3}} = \frac{2\pi L^2 c}{(s-1)(s-4)d^{s-4}} \tag{6-32}$$

which agrees, apart from a numerical factor, with Eq. (6-7) (since the formulas of this section refer to one mole, N is to be replaced by L).

The model of weakly attracting rigid spheres has been shown to lead to the same formula: $B(T) = b - (a/RT)$ with a and b independent of temperature, as is obtained from the virial expansion of van der Waals' equation. The assumption of a weak attraction, i.e., $|u(r)| \ll kT$ for $r > d$, is unduly restrictive. Values of a determined at room temperature T indicate that $|u(d)| \approx kT$ in many cases, e.g., N_2. We therefore investigate the model of rigid spheres attracting in accordance with an inverse power law, without assuming the attraction to be small. The potential energy of interaction is given by

$$\begin{aligned} u(r) &= +\infty & r &< d \\ u(r) &= -u^*(d/r)^q & r &> d, \qquad q > 3 \end{aligned} \tag{6-33}$$

where $u^* = c'd^{-q}$ represents the magnitude of the mutual potential energy of two molecules in contact. We substitute (6-33) in (6-26), expand the exponential in series, and integrate term by term.   Then

$$B = 2\pi L \left[\int_0^d dr\, r^2 - \int_d^\infty dr\, r^2 (e^{u^*d^q/kTr^q} - 1) \right]$$

$$= \frac{2}{3}\pi L d^3 - 2\pi L \int_d^\infty dr\, r^2 \sum_{j=1}^\infty \frac{1}{j!} \left(\frac{u^*d^q}{kTr^q}\right)^j$$

$$= \frac{2}{3}\pi L d^3 \left[1 - \sum_{j=1}^\infty \frac{3}{j!(jq-3)} \left(\frac{u^*}{kT}\right)^j \right] \qquad (6\text{-}34)$$

$$= \frac{2}{3}\pi L d^3 - \frac{2\pi L d^3 u^*}{(q-3)kT} - 2\pi L d^3 \sum_{j=2}^\infty \frac{1}{j!(jq-3)} \left(\frac{u^*}{kT}\right)^j$$

$$= \frac{2}{3}\pi L d^3 - \frac{2\pi L^2 c'}{(q-3)d^{q-3}} \frac{1}{RT} - 2\pi L d^3 \sum_{j=2}^\infty \frac{1}{j!(jq-3)} \left(\frac{u^*}{kT}\right)^j \quad (6\text{-}35)$$

In the case of weak attraction ($u^* \ll kT$), the contribution from the sum over j in (6-35) is negligible, and the first two terms are just the van der Waals terms previously obtained (Eqs. (6-28) and (6-30)).   The additional terms represented by the sum from $j = 2$ to ∞ indicate a temperature-dependence of van der Waals' a.   The temperature-dependence of b has been discussed in Sec. 6-1.   The observed temperature variations of a and b then reflect the inadequacy of assuming weak attractions and rigid-sphere repulsions.

Nature of the van der Waals Attractive Forces.   The calculation of the third and higher virial coefficients is taken up in more advanced texts.*   The van der Waals third virial coefficient (Eq. (6-9)) not only takes no account of the attractive forces but gives the wrong result for rigid spheres.   This section will be concluded with a brief discussion of the nature of the van der Waals attractive forces between neutral molecules, commonly referred to as London *dispersion forces*.   It is assumed that neither of the two interacting molecules possesses a permanent electric dipole moment, and the effects of higher moments are neglected.   All atoms and molecules have instantaneous dipole moments, but these fluctuate too rapidly to be observed.   The absence of a permanent moment means that the instantaneous moments average to zero.   Thus in a hydrogen atom the electron and proton at any instant form a dipole, but when the motion of the electron is averaged over many periods, the average value of the dipole moment is found to be zero.   The force does

---

* J. O. Hirschfelder, C. F. Curtiss, and R. B. Bird, "Molecular Theory of Gases and Liquids," John Wiley & Sons, Inc., New York, 1954; T. L. Hill, "Statistical Mechanics," McGraw-Hill Book Company, Inc., 1956.

not arise from a direct interaction between the instantaneous dipole moments in the two molecules; this interaction would vanish on averaging over the uncorrelated electronic motions.   However, it is known that molecules are polarizable, i.e., that they acquire induced dipole moments in the presence of an electric field.   The instantaneous moment of each molecule gives rise to an electric field at the site of the other molecule and, since the molecules are polarizable, a dipole moment is induced in the other molecule.   The interaction between the instantaneous dipole in one molecule and the dipole it induces in the other leads to an attraction between the two molecules.   The induced dipole moment is proportional to the inducing moment; hence the interaction energy depends on the square of the instantaneous moment, and this, of course, does not average to zero.

It can be readily seen that the potential energy of attraction varies with the inverse sixth power of the distance.   The electric field at molecule 2 due to an instantaneous moment μ_1 in molecule 1 is proportional to μ_1/r^3.   The induced moment μ_2 is proportional to the inducing field, and the constant of proportionality α_2 is called the *polarizability* of molecule 2; thus $\mu_2 \propto \alpha_2 \mu_1/r^3$.   The interaction energy between either dipole and the field due to the other is proportional to $\mu_1 \mu_2/r^3$ and thus to $\alpha_2 \mu_1^2/r^6$.   If the instantaneous dipole is located in molecule 2, one obtains an interaction energy proportional to $\alpha_1 \mu_2^2/r^6$.   Although the angular dependence of the interactions has not been considered in this argument, it is nevertheless sufficient to show that the interaction energy depends on the square of the instantaneous moment and varies inversely with the sixth power of the distance.   This power law satisfies the condition $q > 3$ which was stipulated earlier in this section.   The mean-square instantaneous moment is obtained from quantum theory.

6-3. INTERMOLECULAR FORCES AND VISCOSITY

The intermolecular force consists of a short-range repulsion and a longer-range attraction.   The short-range repulsion prevents two molecules from coalescing, interpenetrating each other, and effectively occupying the same space at the same time.   The observed volumes of liquids and solids indicate that very little interpenetration of atoms, molecules, or ions takes place, and the low compressibilities show that the forces resisting interpenetration are very strong.   Evidence for the attractive forces is provided by the existence of the liquid state, by the Joule-Thomson effect,* and by the imperfect-gas behavior discussed in the preceding sections.   The repulsion sets in when the electron distributions of the two molecules begin to overlap; it originates partly in the electrostatic

---

* See any textbook on thermodynamics.

repulsion of partially shielded nuclei but is mainly associated with effects of the Pauli exclusion principle on the electronic energy.*   The origin of the attractive force between neutral nonpolar molecules has been discussed in Sec. 6-2.   The precise analytic form of the intermolecular potential energy is not known for any pair of molecules.   The calculations of transport properties become intractable unless the simplifying assumption of central fields, i.e., spherical symmetry, is made.   Four simple models of intermolecular force fields are commonly used in kinetic theory: (1) rigid elastic spheres, (2) weakly attracting rigid elastic spheres, (3) point centers of inverse power repulsion, (4) combinations of inverse power attraction and repulsion.   The limitations of the first two models have been indicated.   The first model has been extensively applied to the transport properties of gases in earlier chapters.   The second model was introduced to explain the equation of state for imperfect gases.

In the third model, the molecules are represented as point centers of force which repel according to an inverse power of the distance: $F = cr^{-s}$. Both s and c are to be determined from experiment.   This representation of the intermolecular repulsion allows for the fact that actual molecules are "softer" than rigid spheres.   The value of s determines the steepness of the $F(r)$ versus r curve; it may be said to measure the "hardness" of the molecules.   The rigid-sphere model can be regarded as a limiting case with $s = \infty$: if the diameter is d, then $F \propto \lim_{s \to \infty} (d/r)^s$.   The absence of an attractive term makes this model unrealistic; nevertheless it is often used in transport calculations because of its simplicity.   According to the fourth model, the intermolecular force is given by

$$F(r) = ar^{-\alpha} - br^{-\beta} \qquad \alpha > \beta \qquad (6\text{-}36)$$

where a and b are positive constants.   The condition $\alpha > \beta$ ensures that the repulsive first term will predominate for small r and the attractive second term for large r.   Since the dispersion force between neutral nonpolar molecules varies as r^{-7}, β is known for this case; however, α must be determined to fit experimental data.   The values of α do not agree with the values of s obtained from the third model when applied to the same experimental data.   The values of s are found to be smaller, obviously because the third model compensates for the lack of attractive forces by making the molecules "extra soft."   The fourth model provides a reasonable representation of the intermolecular force; furthermore, the three adjustable parameters a, b, and α make it possible to fit a greater amount of experimental data than with the other models.   Figure 6-3 shows graphs of the intermolecular potential functions for the four models.

* See J. C. Slater, "Introduction to Chemical Physics," McGraw-Hill Book Company, Inc., New York, 1939.

Viscosity Coefficient from the Model of Weakly Attracting Rigid Spheres. We turn to an elementary consideration of the viscosity of an imperfect gas. The mean-free-path treatment given in Chap. 3 was based on the first model of rigid elastic spheres. An accurate treatment of the viscosity of an imperfect gas requires advanced methods beyond the scope of this chapter.* However, the mean-free-path method can be

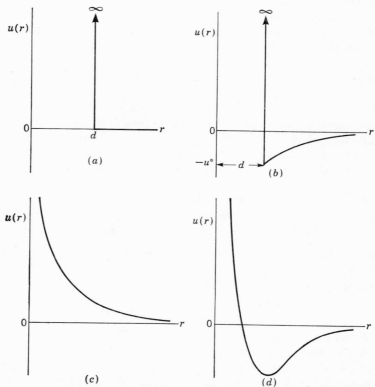

FIG. 6-3. Intermolecular potential functions for (a) rigid elastic spheres, (b) weakly attracting rigid elastic spheres (van der Waals–Sutherland model), (c) point centers of inverse power repulsion, (d) point centers of inverse power attraction and a shorter-range inverse power repulsion.

adapted to the case of an imperfect gas if the intermolecular fields of models *two* and *three* are assumed. In this way one obtains a very simple and fairly satisfactory theoretical representation of the temperature-dependence of the viscosity coefficient. Let us first consider the van der Waals model of weakly attracting rigid spheres. Two effects of the attractive forces are to be distinguished. The first effect is to enhance

* Such a treatment is presented in Chap. 11 (Sec. 11-2).

IMPERFECT GASES AND INTERMOLECULAR FORCES

the probability of a collision by bending the trajectories of two approaching molecules toward each other, with the result that some molecules collide which would have missed each other in the absence of the forces. The collision frequency being enhanced, the mean free path λ is reduced and the viscosity coefficient, which is proportional to λ, is reduced in the same proportion. The second effect involves encounters of two molecules which do not actually collide but which pass close enough to experience significant deflections from their original directions of motion. Although the collision frequency is not directly affected by these encounters, it is clear that they must contribute to the transport of momentum. It obviously cannot matter whether given deflections and momentum changes are produced by actual glancing collisions of spheres or by action-at-a-distance encounters.

Although a complete calculation would have to take both effects into account, the second effect can be neglected in comparison with the first *provided that the attraction is weak*. This is because small-angle, i.e., slight, deflections contribute only second-order terms to the transport (cf. Eq. (8-49)). If the forces are weak, the angles of deflection in the second effect are small and are readily seen to be proportional to the force constant (cf. Prob. 6-7). The change in the viscosity coefficient is then second-order in the force constant. Since the angles of deflection in the first effect are large because rigid-sphere collisions are involved, the change in the viscosity coefficient in this case is first-order in the force constant. We assume a weak attraction and neglect the second effect. The evaluation of the first effect requires calculating the new target area or collision cross section, which is then inserted in the mean free path and viscosity formulas in place of the "billiard-ball" cross section πd^2. Consider for simplicity a case in which one molecule is fixed and other molecules approach the first with velocity v and are deflected. Let the *impact parameter* b denote the perpendicular distance from the center of the fixed molecule to the straight-line path that the center of the moving molecule would describe if the fixed molecule were not present to deflect it. In the absence of intermolecular forces a collision will ensue if and only if $b \leq d$ where d is the molecular diameter. The collision frequency is determined as in Sec. 3-2 by counting the molecules whose centers are in a right circular cylinder of length v and cross-sectional area equal to the target area or collision cross section σ. In general, $\sigma = \pi b_{\max}^2$ where $b_{\max}$ is the largest value of the impact parameter for which a collision can occur; i.e., a collision occurs if $b \leq b_{\max}$ and does not occur if $b > b_{\max}$. The billiard-ball model gives $b_{\max} = d$; however, if there are attractive forces, values of b greater than d will also lead to collision, and $\sigma = \pi b_{\max}^2 > \pi d^2$.

The calculation of $b_{\max}$ will be carried out in Chap. 8. A straightforward solution of the dynamical problem gives the result (see Eq. (8-42)):

$$\sigma = \pi b_{\text{max}}^2 = \pi d^2 [1 + (u^*/\varepsilon)] \tag{6-37}$$

where $\varepsilon = m^* v_r^2/2 =$ the initial kinetic energy of relative motion of the two molecules (v_r is the relative velocity of approach and m^* is the reduced mass), and u^* represents the magnitude of the potential energy of attraction when the molecules are in contact (cf. Eq. (6-33)). Equation (6-37) is independent of the form of the potential energy $u(r)$. Of course, $u(\infty) = 0$ and $u^* \equiv |u(d)|$. We require the cross section averaged over the distribution of molecular velocities. Without further calculation it is apparent that

$$\bar{\sigma} = \pi d^2 [1 + (\gamma u^*/kT)] \tag{6-38}$$

will represent the effective cross section as a function of temperature with γ a positive numerical constant of order unity. Equations (6-37) and (6-38) show that the target area is increased by the attractive force, and that the increase depends on the relative velocity of approach of the two molecules and thus on the temperature. The increase is small for fast molecules and high temperatures, since a fast molecule, spending little time in the field, is deflected only slightly, and the value of b_{max} is therefore close to d. It should be pointed out that in the accurate treatment of viscosity a somewhat different definition of the effective cross section is used;* this would alter the result only through the value of the constant γ. The initial assumption of weak attraction is expressed by: $u^* \ll kT$. Denoting the mean free path and viscosity coefficient of the rigid sphere model by $\lambda_{\text{r.s.}}$ and $\eta_{\text{r.s.}}$, respectively, we obtain the proportions

$$\frac{\eta}{\eta_{\text{r.s.}}} = \frac{\lambda}{\lambda_{\text{r.s.}}} = \frac{\pi d^2}{\bar{\sigma}} = \frac{1}{1 + (\gamma u^*/kT)} \tag{6-39}$$

Since $\eta_{\text{r.s.}}$ varies with temperature as $T^{1/2}$, the predicted temperature dependence of η is

$$\eta \propto \frac{T^{1/2}}{1 + (S/T)} \tag{6-40}$$

where S is a positive constant to be determined by experiment. The temperature dependence of the viscosity coefficient has already been discussed in Sec. 3-5, where it was pointed out that η increases more rapidly with temperature than $T^{1/2}$ and that the temperature dependence is different for different gases. These results of experiment are in agreement with Eq. (6-40), which was first proposed by Sutherland.† For many gases, Eq. (6-40) gives a good representation of the temperature

---

* See Eq. (8-49).
† W. Sutherland, *Phil. Mag.*, vol. 36, p. 507, 1893.

dependence of η at ordinary temperatures. However, it fails when extended to very low or very high temperatures.* The agreement with experiment in some cases is not too meaningful, since the values found for S are so large that the assumption of a weak attraction is not justified (e.g., $S \approx 270$ in the case of CO_2). Furthermore, the values of u^* deduced from the observed values of S do not agree well with values obtained from van der Waals' equation of state. A satisfactory theory requires dropping the assumption of a weak attraction, but this greatly complicates the calculation. In any case, the intermolecular repulsion is not properly represented in this model. The considerations of this section are applicable also to diffusion coefficients. Obviously,

$$\frac{D}{D_{r.s.}} = \frac{\lambda}{\lambda_{r.s.}} = \frac{1}{1 + (\gamma' u^*/kT)} = \frac{1}{1 + (S'/T)} \tag{6-41}$$

where γ' and S' can be shown to differ slightly from γ and S.

Viscosity Coefficient from the Model of Point Centers of Inverse Power Repulsion. Let us consider, finally, the variation of η with T predicted by the third model of molecules as point centers of force repelling according to an inverse power of the distance. Since contact collisions do not occur in this model, it is necessary to extend or generalize the concepts of collision frequency, collision diameter and cross section, and the free path. The generalized definitions of the cross section and the collision frequency will be taken up in Chap. 8. For the purpose of ascertaining the temperature dependence of η, no precise formulation is required; all reasonable definitions of the collision diameter or cross section lead to the same result as that determined by dimensional considerations. The generalized collision diameter d can depend only on the mass m of the molecules, the mean value of the relative velocity $\bar{v}_r = \sqrt{2}\,\bar{v}$, and the law of force $F = cr^{-s}$. Thus d is a function of m, $\bar{v}$, c, and s. The dimensions of c are given by $[MLT^{-2}L^s]$ where $[M]$ stands for mass, $[L]$ for length, and $[T]$ for time. Setting

$$d\,[L] \propto m^p \bar{v}^q c^n\,[M^p L^q T^{-q} M^n L^{(s+1)n} T^{-2n}] \tag{6-42}$$

one obtains the three equations:

$$p + n = 0 \qquad q + 2n = 0 \qquad q + (s+1)n = 1$$

which have solutions:

$$n = \frac{1}{s-1} \qquad p = -\frac{1}{s-1} \qquad q = -\frac{2}{s-1} \tag{6-43}$$

Thus

$$d \propto \left(\frac{c}{m\bar{v}^2}\right)^{1/(s-1)} \propto \bar{v}^{-2/(s-1)} \tag{6-44}$$

---

* The range of application of (6-40) can be extended by allowing S to be different for different temperature intervals. The formula then becomes semiempirical.

The viscosity coefficient η is proportional to $\bar{v}d^{-2}$ according to Eq. (3-30). Hence

$$\eta \propto \bar{v}^{1+[4/(s-1)]} \propto T^{\frac{1}{2}+[2/(s-1)]} \qquad (6\text{-}45)$$

The rigid-sphere result is obtained by setting $s = \infty$. It is seen that a repulsion softer than for rigid spheres makes the viscosity increase more rapidly with temperature. Evidently, as the molecules move faster at higher temperatures, they approach each other more closely in encounters and the effective diameter is reduced, the mean free path lengthened, and the viscosity increased. Alternatively, if a free path is regarded as terminated when the deflection in an encounter exceeds a certain minimum angle, then as the velocities increase with rising temperature, the deflections become smaller, and fewer exceed the minimum angle. Therefore, the free paths are lengthened, and the viscosity is increased. It is of interest to note that Eq. (6-44) is obtained directly if the effective diameter d is defined to be the average distance of closest approach during an encounter. At closest approach, the difference between the incident energy and the centrifugal energy is equal to the potential energy.* Since the mean value of this difference is proportional to $m\bar{v}^2$ and the potential energy is proportional to $cd^{-(s-1)}$, we obtain

$$cd^{-(s-1)} \propto m\bar{v}^2$$

$$d^{s-1} \propto \frac{c}{m\bar{v}^2} \qquad (6\text{-}46)$$

$$d \propto \left(\frac{c}{m\bar{v}^2}\right)^{1/(s-1)}$$

which is the same as Eq. (6-44).

Equation (6-45) predicts a faster rise of η with T than $T^{\frac{1}{2}}$ and also a possibly different temperature dependence for different gases, since the values of s may be different. This is in accord with experiment. The same qualitative behavior is obtained from the effects of the attractive forces, although the Sutherland formula (6-40) does not have the same form as (6-45). It is difficult to know how much of the observed departure from the $T^{\frac{1}{2}}$ law of the rigid-sphere model is to be attributed to the softness of the repulsion and how much to the existence of an attraction. In applying (6-45) to different gases, values of s are determined which range from about 5 for the larger molecules to 14.6 for helium.† In the case of helium, the power law (6-45) gives very much better agreement with experiment than the Sutherland formula (6-40). The lowest values

---

* See Sec. 8-1.

† The range of application of (6-45) can be extended in semiempirical fashion by allowing s to be different for different temperature intervals. Then s is found to decrease with decreasing T.

of s, which apparently indicate that the repulsive force varies less rapidly with r than the attractive dispersion force, cannot be taken literally. As has already been pointed out, the values of s are too small because the model compensates for the lack of attractive forces by making the molecules "extra soft."

PROBLEMS

6-1. Express the critical data p_c, V_c, and T_c in terms of van der Waals' a and b. Show that $V_c = 3b$ and $p_c V_c / R T_c = \frac{3}{8}$.

6-2. The molecular diameter d of argon and Avogadro's number L were estimated in Prob. 3-6 from the density of solid argon and the viscosity η of the gas. The value of η given was for $T = 273°K$. Redetermine d and L using data at different temperatures:

   a. $\eta = 0.839 \times 10^{-4}$ dyne-sec/cm² at 100°K
   b. $\eta = 5.30 \times 10^{-4}$ dyne-sec/cm² at 1000°K

Why are the results different?

6-3. Write a formula for the molecular diameter d in terms of the viscosity coefficient η and van der Waals' b, using the rough equation (3-31) and also the more accurate relations given in Prob. 3-6. Since b varies with temperature, one selects the value of b appropriate to the temperature at which η is measured. For the case of argon at 0°C, the appropriate values are $b = 41$ cm³/mole and $\eta = 2.10 \times 10^{-4}$ dyne-sec/cm². Determine d and L and compare with the results of Prob. 3-6.

6-4. Show that the second virial coefficient for the case of the square-well potential

$$u(r) = \infty \qquad 0 \le r < d$$
$$u(r) = -u^* \qquad d < r < md \qquad u^* > 0$$
$$u(r) = 0 \qquad r > md$$

is given by

$$B = b[1 - (m^3 - 1)(e^{u^*/kT} - 1)]$$

6-5. Show with the aid of Eq. (6-23) that the second virial coefficient for the case of point centers of inverse power repulsion

$$u(r) = c'r^{-q} \qquad c' > 0, \qquad q > 3$$

is given by

$$B = \frac{2\pi L}{3} \left(\frac{c'}{kT}\right)^{3/q} \Gamma\left(\frac{q-3}{q}\right)$$

where Γ denotes the gamma function. Show that the rigid-sphere result is obtained in the limit $q \to \infty$ by using

$$u(r) = \lim_{q \to \infty} u^*(d/r)^q$$

6-6. Equation (6-28) for b can be obtained more simply from considerations of geometric probability. Let $V = $ volume, $V' = $ effective volume, $v = $ volume occupied by one molecule, and $v' = $ effective volume of each molecule. Let

P_N = a priori geometric probability of having N point molecules in V and P'_N = a priori geometric probability of having N molecules of finite size in V. Then, omitting a constant factor, we set $P_N = V^N$ and $P'_N = V'^N$.

   a. Show that

$$P'_N = V^N \left(1 - \frac{v'}{V}\right)\left(1 - 2\frac{v'}{V}\right) \cdots \left[1 - (N-1)\frac{v'}{V}\right]$$

   b. Assuming that $Nv' \ll V$ and retaining only first-order terms, show that

$$V'^N \simeq V^N \left[1 - \frac{N(N-1)v'}{2V}\right]$$

   c. Assuming that $N \gg 1$ and setting $V' = V - b$, show that

$$b = Nv'/2 = 4Nv = 2\pi Nd^3/3$$

   6-7. Show that if a particle is scattered by a center of force, the angle of deflection for slight deflections is given approximately by

$$\chi \simeq \frac{b}{2E}\int_{-\infty}^{\infty} \frac{F[b(1 + x'^2)^{1/2}]}{(1 + x'^2)^{1/2}}\, dx'$$

where b is the impact parameter, E the kinetic energy of approach along the x axis, $F[r]$ the central force, and $x' = x/b$. Thus, to this approximation, χ is proportional to the force constant appearing in $F[r]$.

   Hint: Since $\chi \simeq p_y/p$, one determines p_y from the impulse integral, making the approximation that the particle moves with uniform velocity along its original path (x axis).

CHAPTER 7

THERMAL DIFFUSION

An entire short chapter is devoted to the special subject of thermal diffusion in gases because of the unusual theoretical and practical interest pertaining to this topic and the lack of an extended, elementary discussion in the other textbooks in this field. We follow the elementary approach developed by Frankel and elaborated by Furry, which is based on the momentum-transfer method of Maxwell and Stefan. The two molecular models of weakly attracting rigid spheres and point centers of inverse power repulsion are used in an elementary way to make simple predictions about the effect. Although the chapter is mainly devoted to theory, a short account is given of the two-bulb type of experiment and of the thermal-diffusion separation column of Clusius and Dickel.

7-1. ELEMENTARY THEORY OF THERMAL DIFFUSION

The phenomenon of thermal diffusion is peculiarly sensitive to the precise form of the molecular-interaction law. Thus, while a small alteration of the force law makes but a small change in the usual transport phenomena, e.g., in the temperature-dependence of the viscosity coefficient, a small change in the force law can cause the thermal-diffusion effect to reverse its direction in certain cases. Thermal diffusion arises when a gas mixture is in a state of nonuniform temperature; it leads to a state of nonuniform composition. If a homogeneous binary mixture in a closed tube is heated at one end and cooled at the other, a relative drift motion of the two components will take place with one component, usually the lighter gas, tending to concentrate at the hotter end and the other at the cooler end. A concentration gradient is therefore established in the same direction as the temperature gradient. As the concentration gradient develops, ordinary mutual diffusion will take place in the opposite sense to the thermal diffusion. Eventually, if the temperatures are maintained constant, a steady state is reached with a nonvanishing concentration gradient for which the transport by mutual diffusion just balances the transport by thermal diffusion. Thermal diffusion is different from the types of diffusion considered previously in that the relative drift motion of the component gases is caused by a temperature gradient

117

instead of a concentration, or density, gradient. The thermal-diffusive transport is proportional to the temperature gradient.

Thermal diffusion in gases was predicted by Enskog and Chapman,[*] independently, on the basis of a refined mathematical theory of transport phenomena; its existence has been subsequently confirmed in numerous experiments. Although a rigorous theory of thermal diffusion requires advanced methods, it is possible, as was first pointed out by Frankel,[†] to give an elementary explanation that brings out the characteristic features of the phenomenon in a particularly simple way. The approach is similar to the momentum-transfer method of treating mutual diffusion. The basic idea is that the temperature gradient causes a net transfer of momentum from one gas to the other in the direction of the gradient. This results in partial pressure gradients for both gases in opposite senses, i.e., in a concentration gradient. Ordinarily, the direction of momentum transfer is determined by the unlike collisions of greatest relative velocity, i.e., usually by those in which a light molecule coming from the warmer region collides with a heavy molecule coming from the colder part of the gas. Such collisions lead to a net transfer of momentum from the light to the heavy molecules in a direction opposite to the temperature gradient. Since the light molecules lose momentum in this sense, their partial pressure must increase in the opposite sense, i.e., in the same sense as the temperature gradient. Thus, in the usual case, the partial pressure and concentration of light molecules increase toward the hotter part of the gas. One may think of the effect of the unlike collisions as a "resistance" pushing the light molecules toward the warmer region, its force being balanced by a partial pressure "head" in the steady state.

For simplicity, we assume, following Frankel, that the molecules of one gas are so heavy that their motion can be neglected and that the molecules of the other gas are divided into two one-dimensional streams moving parallel and antiparallel to the temperature gradient. Let the temperature gradient be along the z axis in the $+z$ direction. Let n_1^+ be the number density and v_1^+ the speed of the stream of light molecules moving in the $+z$ direction, and n_1^- and v_1^- the corresponding quantities for the other stream. In the steady state, $n_1^+v_1^+ = n_1^-v_1^-$, since the net molecular flow vanishes. Writing this as $n_1^+m_1v_1^+ = n_1^-m_1v_1^-$, we see that both streams carry the same amount of momentum per unit volume. Let M_{12}^+ and M_{12}^- be the momentum transfers per unit volume per unit time from each of the light streams to the heavy gas. The number of unlike encounters per cubic centimeter per second for each of the streams is given by $n_1^{\pm}n_2v_1^{\pm}\sigma_{12}(v_1^{\pm})$ where n_2 is the density of heavy molecules

* Cf. S. Chapman and T. G. Cowling, "The Mathematical Theory of Nonuniform Gases," Cambridge University Press, London, 1939.

† S. Frankel, *Phys. Rev.*, vol. 57, p. 660, 1940; cf. also W. H. Furry, *Amer. Jour. Phys.*, vol. 16, p. 63, 1948.

and $\sigma_{12}(v_1{}^{\pm})$ represents the effective cross section for momentum transfer in an unlike collision, which is in general a function of the relative velocity. The average momentum lost per unlike encounter is proportional to $m_1 v_1{}^{\pm}$. The following approximate expression for the momentum transfer is thus obtained (cf. Eq. (4-14)):

$$M_{12}{}^{\pm} \approx m_1 v_1{}^{\pm} \cdot n_1{}^{\pm} n_2 v_1{}^{\pm} \sigma_{12}(v_1{}^{\pm}) \tag{7-1}$$

whence
$$\frac{M_{12}{}^{+}}{M_{12}{}^{-}} = \frac{n_1{}^{+} m_1 v_1{}^{+}}{n_1{}^{-} m_1 v_1{}^{-}} \frac{v_1{}^{+} \sigma_{12}(v_1{}^{+})}{v_1{}^{-} \sigma_{12}(v_1{}^{-})} = \frac{v_1{}^{+} \sigma_{12}(v_1{}^{+})}{v_1{}^{-} \sigma_{12}(v_1{}^{-})} \tag{7-2}$$

Equation (7-2) expresses the important fact that since both streams carry the same momentum per cubic centimeter, the momentum transfers are in the ratio of the collision frequencies per molecule and are thus determined by the product $v_1 \sigma_{12}(v_1)$. From the assumed direction of the temperature gradient $(dT/dz > 0)$, it follows that the $(^{+})$ superscript refers to the colder stream and the $(^{-})$ to the warmer. Hence $v_1{}^{+} < v_1{}^{-}$. The direction of the net momentum transfer is therefore determined by the velocity dependence of the product $v_1 \sigma_{12}(v_1)$; if this increases with increasing v_1, as seems nearly always to be the case, it follows that $v_1{}^{+} \sigma_{12}(v_1{}^{+}) < v_1{}^{-} \sigma_{12}(v_1{}^{-})$ and $M_{12}{}^{+} < M_{12}{}^{-}$. Then the net light-to-heavy momentum transfer $M_{12}{}^{-} - M_{12}{}^{+}$ is in the $-z$ direction, i.e., in the direction of the warmer stream of light molecules and opposite to the temperature gradient. As pointed out in the last paragraph, this implies a partial pressure gradient of the light molecules in the same sense as the temperature gradient. Hence the light molecules tend to concentrate in the hotter region.

In the general case in which account is taken of the three-dimensional nature of the molecular motions as well as the distribution in velocities and the molecules of one gas are not assumed to be infinitely heavy, the momentum transfer is expressed by an integral over the velocity distribution functions. The integrand contains the magnitude of the relative velocity of approach v_r in the combination $v_r \sigma_{12}(v_r)$ (see Sec. 8-2). Thus the direction of the net momentum transfer is again determined, as in the simple treatment above, by the behavior of the function $v \sigma_{12}(v)$ as v increases. If $v_r \sigma_{12}(v_r)$ increases with increasing v_r, then the encounters with the largest values of v_r make the greatest contribution to the momentum transfer. We now consider the velocity dependence of the cross section σ_{12} on the basis of the three models considered previously. On the rigid-sphere model, σ is, of course, a constant and $v \sigma_{12}(v)$ increases linearly with v. The model of weakly attracting rigid spheres makes σ_{12} decrease with increasing v, as is apparent from Eq. (6-37) and also from the remarks following Eq. (6-38).* It is readily seen that the prod-

---

* The cross section of Eq. (6-37) is not the effective cross section for transfer of momentum, but we shall overlook this difference (cf. Prob. 8-8).

uct $v\sigma_{12}(v)$ increases with increasing v except for speeds so low that $m^*v^2/2 < u^*$. If the attraction is weak or the temperature high ($u^* \ll kT$), there will be very few encounters for which $m^*v^2/2 < u^*$ and the direction of momentum transfer will be determined by the faster encounters for which $v\sigma_{12}(v)$ is an increasing function of v.

The representation of molecules as point centers of inverse power repulsion provides interesting results. The effective diameter has been obtained as a function of velocity in Eqs. (6-44) and (6-46). For the force law $F = cr^{-s}$, the result was $d \propto v^{-2/(s-1)}$. Hence

$$v\sigma_{12}(v) \propto vd^2 \propto vv^{-4/(s-1)} = v^{(s-5)/(s-1)} \qquad (7\text{-}3)$$

Although the cross section decreases with increasing velocity, the product $v\sigma_{12}(v)$ is an increasing function of v if $s > 5$. However, if the molecules are so soft that $s < 5$, $v\sigma_{12}(v)$ becomes a decreasing function of v. In the special case of the inverse fifth power repulsion, $v\sigma_{12}(v)$ is independent of velocity. We have already observed that the values of s which are obtained from the temperature variation of the viscosity coefficient range from about five to fifteen. The force law in the present instance refers to the interaction of unlike rather than like molecules; however, there appear to be very few cases in which $s < 5$ is required by the experimental data.* Referring to Eq. (7-2), one notes that for $s < 5$ the thermal-diffusion effect would be reversed, since $M_{12}{}^+ > M_{12}{}^-$, and the net light-to-heavy momentum transfer would be in the $+z$ direction instead of the $-z$ direction. The light molecules would then concentrate in the cooler region. In the special case $s = 5$, $M_{12}{}^+ = M_{12}{}^-$, and there would be no resultant momentum transfer between the two gases. A partial pressure gradient could not be supported, and the thermal-diffusion effect would vanish. These results follow also from a rigorous treatment.

Assuming from now on that $v_r\sigma_{12}(v_r)$ increases with increasing relative velocity v_r, the encounters with the largest values of v_r will determine the direction of momentum transfer. We have already remarked that the largest values of v_r occur when a light molecule coming from the warmer region encounters a heavy molecule coming from the cooler region, leading to a light-to-heavy momentum transfer opposite in direction to the temperature gradient. Suppose now that the two gases have equal molecular weights; on the basis of the arguments just advanced, which depend on a molecular mass difference, one would expect no thermal diffusion. That this is not the case, however, can be seen by a simple extension of the considerations presented above. In general, the molecules of the two constituents have different "sizes" and therefore different

---

* One such instance is an isotopic NH_3 mixture at temperatures below 20°C. See W. Watson and D. Woernley, *Phys. Rev.*, vol. 63, p. 181, 1943.

mean free paths. Considering those molecules that are proceeding away from the hotter region, we see that in spite of equal molecular weights the average speeds of the two species must be different because the molecules with longer mean free paths have undergone fewer collisions and thus have better preserved the higher speeds acquired in the warmer region. The largest values of v_r now occur when a molecule of the species with the longer mean free path, coming from the hotter region, encounters a molecule of the other species moving in the opposite direction. A net momentum transfer from the species of greater to lesser λ takes place in the opposite sense to the temperature gradient. Hence thermal diffusion will occur and the species that has the longer mean free path will be concentrated in the hotter region. Usually the difference between the two mean free paths is associated with a difference in molecular diameters. Thermal diffusion tends to concentrate the smaller molecules in the warmer region.

An interesting possibility arises if the "mass effect" and "size effect" act in opposite directions, i.e., if the heavier molecules are smaller than the lighter ones. When the mass difference is very small and the size difference large, it is possible for the size effect to predominate, with the result that the smaller, heavier molecules concentrate in the warmer region. Mixtures of carbon dioxide (CO_2) and cyclopropane ($CH_2CH_2CH_2$) show a thermal-diffusion effect of this type.* The size effect is absent in the case of an isotopic mixture. A further effect comes about when the unlike-molecule-collision cross section σ_{12} differs materially from the average of the like-molecule cross sections. Suppose the like-molecule cross sections to be nearly equal and σ_{12} to be much smaller; then collisions occur mainly between molecules of the same species. The component of lower concentration has then the longer mean free path and tends to accumulate in the hotter region. If this were the only effect, the direction of the thermal diffusion would reverse at 50 per cent concentration. If σ_{12} is much greater than the like-molecule cross sections, the collisions will occur mainly between molecules of different species. The component of higher concentration then tends to accumulate in the hotter region because of its greater mean free path. This effect will be referred to as the "concentration effect." It is also absent in the case of an isotopic mixture.

7-2. THERMAL DIFFUSION AND ISOTOPE SEPARATION

The standard equation of diffusion, when there is both a concentration gradient and a temperature gradient along the z direction, is written in

* B. Leaf and F. T. Wall, *Jour. Phys. Chem.*, vol. 46, p. 820, 1942.

the form

$$G_1 = -nD_{12}\frac{dc_1}{dz} + \frac{nD_T}{T}\frac{dT}{dz} \tag{7-4}$$

where G_1 is the diffusive flow or transport per unit area per unit time of type-1 molecules under the stipulated standard condition of zero net flow, i.e., $G_1 + G_2 = 0$. The fractional molecular concentration $c_1 = n_1/(n_1 + n_2) = n_1/n$ appears in the first (ordinary diffusion) term, D_{12} represents the mutual diffusion coefficient, and D_T is called the *coefficient of thermal diffusion*. Apart from the appearance of the second term, which represents the thermal diffusive transport of gas 1, Eq. (7-4) differs from Eq. (4-1) in the form of the first term, which was previously written as $-D_{12}\,dn_1/dz$. The two forms are equivalent as long as the total density n is uniform, but they differ when a temperature gradient exists, since the density n varies with the temperature and $dn/dz \neq 0$. In Eq. (7-4), all the temperature variation is taken into account in the second term. The new way of expressing the mutual-diffusion term ensures that it will vanish when applied to a pure gas in a temperature gradient. We rewrite (7-4) in the form

$$G_1 = -nD_{12}\left(\frac{dc_1}{dz} - \frac{k_T}{T}\frac{dT}{dz}\right) \tag{7-5}$$

where $k_T \equiv D_T/D_{12}$ is called the *thermal-diffusion ratio*. When a steady state is reached in a closed tube, both G_1 and G_2 vanish and

$$dc_1 = k_T\,dT/T \tag{7-6}$$

Before integrating this equation, one should ascertain whether k_T can be treated as constant along the tube. Since the thermal-diffusion effect depends on the net rate of transfer of momentum between the two gases, it is clear that if either species is very rare, the momentum transfer and the thermal-diffusive transport will both be very small. Both the momentum transfer (see Eq. (4-15)) and the thermal-diffusion coefficient are proportional to $n_1 n_2$ or $c_1 c_2$. In addition to this relatively large dependence on concentration, there is the small concentration effect discussed at the end of Sec. 7-1. Furthermore, D_T and k_T depend slightly on temperature. It is customary to define the *thermal-diffusion factor* α by

$$k_T \equiv \alpha c_1 c_2 = \alpha c_1(1 - c_1) \tag{7-7}$$

In contrast to k_T, α does not vanish at the extreme concentrations, and its slight dependence on the temperature and concentration can be neglected for the purpose of integrating Eq. (7-6). Inserting (7-7) in (7-6) and integrating, one obtains for the steady state

$$\log\,(c_1/1 - c_1) - \alpha \log T = \text{const.} \tag{7-8}$$

The three coefficients D_T, k_T, and α are ordinarily defined to be positive when the lighter component is concentrated in the warmer region. The sign convention in Eqs. (7-4) through (7-8) then corresponds to a choice of gas 1 as the lighter gas.

The qualitative considerations of Sec. 7-1 have already provided some information about the thermal-diffusion factor. The mass effect makes a positive contribution to α in nearly all cases. This is always true on the rigid-elastic-sphere model. The model of attracting rigid spheres leads to a positive α provided that $kT \gtrsim u^*$; however, if $kT \lesssim u^*$, the direction of the net momentum transfer is reversed and α becomes negative. This model then predicts a temperature dependence of α, with α decreasing with decreasing temperature. Confining our attention to isotopic mixtures for which the mass effect alone is present, experiment confirms the qualitative prediction, but negative values of α have been found in only a few cases. One such instance is the isotopic NH_3 mixture already mentioned, for which α is observed to be positive above and negative below room temperature. A strong attraction between NH_3 molecules is thus indicated. The model of molecules as point centers of inverse power repulsion ($F = cr^{-s}$) leads to positive α when $s > 5$ and negative α when $s < 5$ if the mass effect alone is considered. The direction of momentum transfer is determined by the value of s and cannot change with the temperature. The exact theory shows that α is proportional to $(s - 5)/(s - 1)$ and is independent of temperature. The dependence on s, which might have been anticipated from Eq. (7-3), shows that α is greatest for the case of rigid elastic spheres ($s = \infty$). The model is then incapable of explaining the inversion observed in isotopic NH_3 mixtures and the temperature-dependence of α found in other cases. In order to fit the formula for α to data taken over a range of temperatures, the value of s must be adjusted to decrease as T decreases, e.g., in the case of isotopic NH_3, s drops below 5 as T decreases below 20°C. This semiempirical adjustment of s to fit thermal-diffusion data is in qualitative agreement with the adjustment of s required to fit viscosity data over a range of temperatures (cf. Sec. 6-3). In both cases the molecules appear to become "softer" at lower temperatures. This is again an example of how the model compensates for the lack of attractive forces. As the temperature is lowered and the molecular speeds decrease, the influence of the attractions is relatively greater (cf. Sec. 6-1). The model compensates by making the molecules softer. The representation of molecules as point centers of attraction and repulsion (cf. Eq. (6-36)) provides a more nearly adequate model in the quantitative theory of the thermal-diffusion effect,* but in this case one must forego the simple arguments that are possible with the other models.

* See J. O. Hirschfelder, C. F. Curtiss, and R. B. Bird, "Molecular Theory of Gases and Liquids," John Wiley & Sons, Inc., New York, 1954.

It was indicated in our previous discussion of the size effect (Sec. 7-1) that α can become negative in nonisotopic mixtures if the heavier molecule is smaller than the lighter molecule, provided that the relative mass difference is very small and the size difference large. In nonisotopic mixtures there is also the possibility of an inversion as the composition of the mixture is varied; this arises from the concentration effect discussed in Sec. 7-1, and it can only be observed if the mass effect is small and is approximately canceled by the size effect. This appears to be the case in ammonia-neon mixtures, in which it has been found that α changes sign at a concentration of 25 per cent NH_3.[*]

The partial separation of the components of a binary mixture by thermal diffusion can be observed with the aid of two bulbs connected by a tube of small diameter. The bulbs are maintained at different temperatures, and, when a steady state has been reached, the composition of the gas mixture in the bulbs is determined. The results can be expressed in terms of the separation factor f defined in Eq. (2-29). Rewriting Eq. (7-8) as

$$c_1/1 - c_1 = \text{const.} \times T^\alpha \qquad (7\text{-}9)$$

and inserting (7-9) in (2-29), we obtain for the separation factor in this case

$$f = \frac{c_1'/1 - c_1'}{c_1/1 - c_1} = \left(\frac{T'}{T}\right)^\alpha \qquad (7\text{-}10)$$

where c_1' is the concentration in one bulb at temperature T' and c_1 the concentration in the other bulb at temperature T. The thermal-diffusion factor α can be obtained from the measured value of f with the aid of Eq. (7-10), which gives

$$\alpha = \log f/\log (T'/T) \qquad (7\text{-}11)$$

The experimental results are frequently stated in terms of the *separation* S, defined as the difference in composition in the two bulbs: $S \equiv c_1' - c_1$. In a typical experiment, S is found to be of the order of a few per cent or less. Whereas this type of experiment is of theoretical interest, since the measurement of α can provide information about the intermolecular force laws, the separations achieved are too small to be of practical importance. An absurdly simple modification of the experimental arrangement, however, leads to a continuous, cumulative separation process with a greatly enhanced value of the separation factor, as was first shown by Clusius and Dickel.[†]

The thermal-diffusion separation column of Clusius and Dickel con-

---

[*] K. E. Grew, *Phil. Mag.* vol. 35, p. 30, 1944.
[†] K. Clusius and G. Dickel, *Naturwiss.*, vol. 26, p. 546, 1938.

sists of a cooled, closed tube with an electrically heated wire along its axis, maintained in a vertical position. Thermal diffusion takes place along the radially directed temperature gradient. In addition to the horizontal diffusion, there occurs a vertical convection with the hot gas near the wire rising and the cool gas near the wall descending. The convective circulation causes a portion of the gas in the rising stream to encounter continually fresh portions of the descending stream with which it is not in equilibrium. This results in a continuous change of composition.* The lighter component concentrates in the hot stream and accumulates at the top of the column while the heavier component goes to the bottom. A vertical concentration gradient is thus established which attains an equilibrium value when the separation process is balanced by the remixing effects of convection and ordinary diffusion. It is helpful in understanding the *modus operandi* of the column to imagine that thermal diffusion and convection take place alternately instead of simultaneously. Let the column be of rectangular cross section with one vertical wall heated and the opposite wall cooled; then the gas is divided into two streams, one rising next to the hot wall and the other descending adjacent to the cold wall. For simplicity, we divide the two streams into equal-sized portions, each portion being of uniform composition and moving as a unit. We suppose that thermal diffusion takes place until the equilibrium concentration is reached, that convection then carries each unit into the place vacated by the preceding unit, that thermal diffusion then brings about a new equilibrium concentration, etc. The successive changes of composition can then be easily visualized with the aid of Fig. 7-1, which pertains to a hypothetical case in which the thermal-diffusive separation S is 8 per cent (independent of composition) and the initial concentration 50 per cent. The numbers in the boxes denote percentage concentration of the light component. The theory of the separation column is somewhat lengthy and involved, and the reader is referred for further details to the comprehensive review article by Jones and Furry.† Unfortunately, the theory is not yet sufficiently precise to permit a quantitative determination of α from the measured separation. One is obliged to use the nonconvective two-bulb apparatus mentioned earlier for measurements of α. However, the sign of α can obviously be determined with the separation column. The most important application of the column is to the separation of isotopes. As an example of the results achieved, Clusius and Dickel separated the neon isotopes Ne^{20} and Ne^{22} and also the chlorine isotopes Cl^{35} and Cl^{37} (in the form of HCl), both to within 1 per cent of purity for both isotopes and in significant amounts. Five columns were used in series with a total length of 36 m.

* The counter-current type of process is extensively used in chemical engineering.
† R. C. Jones and W. H. Furry, *Rev. Mod. Phys.*, vol. 18, p. 151, 1946.

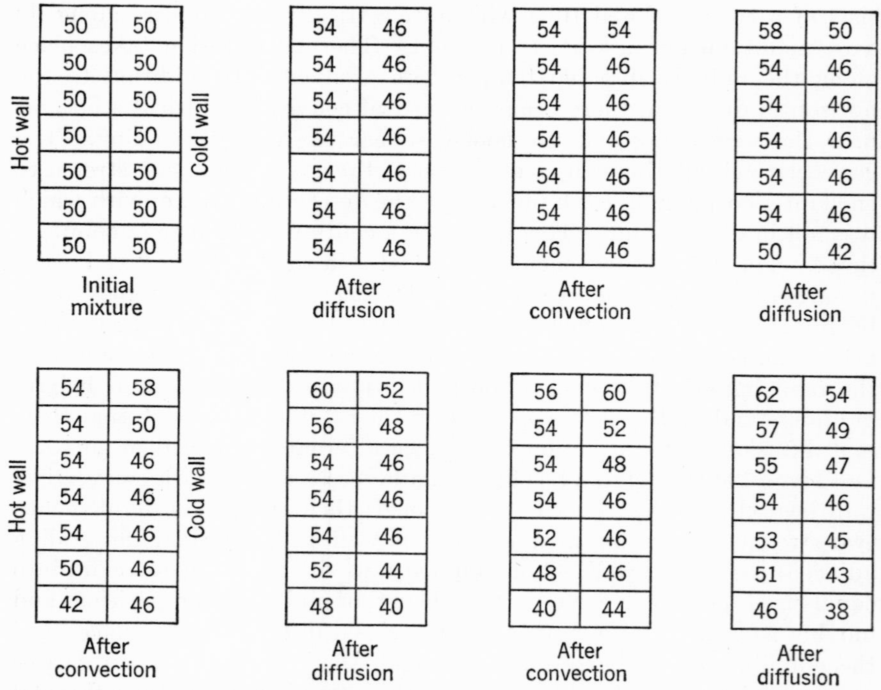

Initial mixture (Hot wall | Cold wall)

50	50
50	50
50	50
50	50
50	50
50	50
50	50

After diffusion

54	46
54	46
54	46
54	46
54	46
54	46
54	46

After convection

54	54
54	46
54	46
54	46
54	46
54	46
46	46

After diffusion

58	50
54	46
54	46
54	46
54	46
54	46
50	42

After convection (Hot wall | Cold wall)

54	58
54	50
54	46
54	46
54	46
50	46
42	46

After diffusion

60	52
56	48
54	46
54	46
54	46
52	44
48	40

After convection

56	60
54	52
54	48
54	46
52	46
48	46
40	44

After diffusion

62	54
57	49
55	47
54	46
53	45
51	43
46	38

FIG. 7-1. Composition changes in a Clusius-Dickel separation column of rectangular cross section, assuming that thermal diffusion and convection take place alternately instead of simultaneously. The boxes denote equal-sized portions of gas assumed to be of uniform composition and to move as a unit. The numbers in the boxes give the percentage of the light component. The separation S is taken to be 8 per cent and the initial concentration 50 per cent. (Adapted from K. E. Grew and T. L. Ibbs, "Thermal Diffusion in Gases," by permission of the Cambridge University Press.)

The method can be applied on a laboratory scale to separate many isotopic mixtures.

PROBLEMS

7-1. Show that the standard equation of diffusion can be expressed in the form

$$c_1 c_2 (u_1 - u_2) = -D_{12} \frac{dc_1}{dz} + \frac{D_T}{T} \frac{dT}{dz}$$

where u_1 and u_2 are the diffusive transport velocities defined in Sec. 4-2.

7-2. Show that for weakly attracting rigid spheres the product $v\sigma_{12}(v)$ increases with increasing v if $m^* v^2/2 > u^*$.

7-3. Make the figure analogous to Fig. 7-1 for a case in which $S = 4$ per cent and the initial concentration of the light component is 40 per cent.

7-4. The theory of thermal diffusion leads to the following formula for α in the case of an isotopic mixture of molecules treated as point centers of repulsion ($F = cr^{-s}$):

$$\alpha = \frac{105}{118} C(s) \frac{s - 5}{s - 1} \frac{m_2 - m_1}{m_2 + m_1}$$

where $C(s)$ is a slowly varying function* of s and $C(\infty) = 1$. Since $C(s)$ changes monotonically from 0.874 to 0.906 as s goes from 10 to 15, we may write the approximate formula for "hard molecules"

$$\alpha \approx \frac{4}{5} \frac{s - 5}{s - 1} \frac{m_2 - m_1}{m_2 + m_1}$$

and determine s from the temperature dependence of η given in Eq. (6-45).

   a. In the temperature range 400–600°K, the viscosity of neon varies as $T^{0.64}$. Determine α for the isotopic mixture $Ne^{20} - Ne^{22}$. Experiment gives $\alpha = 0.031$ for this range of T.
   b. In the neighborhood of 450°K, the viscosity of O_2 varies as $T^{0.73}$. Determine α for the isotopic mixture $O_2^{16,16} - O_2^{16,18}$. The experimental value of α is 0.0145 for this temperature.

---

* $C(s)$ is tabulated in the Jones and Furry review article, *loc. cit.*

CHAPTER 8

COLLISION DYNAMICS, CROSS SECTIONS, MUTUAL DIFFUSION, AND CHEMICAL KINETICS

This chapter lays part of the foundation for more advanced developments. The first two sections deal with fundamental aspects of the dynamics of molecular encounters in which the molecules are represented as point centers of force; the last two sections provide important applications of the theory presented in the first two sections to the mutual diffusion problem and to the chemical kinetics of bimolecular reactions. Section 8-1 reviews the classical dynamics of two-particle central-field encounters, and all the basic dynamical formulas used in this and later chapters are derived in this section. Section 8-2 deals with the definition and evaluation of scattering and transport cross sections and gives detailed results for rigid-sphere collisions and also some useful results for weakly attracting rigid spheres. A number of useful formulas are obtained for the collision rate, or the rate at which encounters take place between point-center-of-force molecules per unit volume of the gas. In Sec. 8-3 we give a revised calculation of the mutual-diffusion coefficient by the momentum-transfer method, in which the rigid-sphere model is not assumed and a careful calculation is made of the momentum transfer M_{12}, taking the distribution of molecular velocities into account. The result agrees exactly with the first approximation of the Enskog-Chapman theory. Section 8-4 contains a brief review of the elements of chemical kinetics for the case of bimolecular reactions. The simple collision theory of these reactions is developed on the basis of a classical potential-barrier model for the formation of the "activated complex." The derivation, somewhat more general than that usually given, leads to the customary formula for the rate constant of a simple second-order bimolecular reaction. This is discussed and compared with experiment.

8-1. COLLISION DYNAMICS

The further development of the subject requires an analysis of molecular collisions, or encounters. It will be assumed that the molecules can be represented as point centers of force and that they interact in pairs with conservative forces directed along the line joining the pair. The rigid-sphere model can be considered a special case in which the inter-action potential is given by $u(r) = \lim\limits_{q \to \infty} u^* (d/r)^q$. The dynamical prob-lem is treated in two frames of reference. In the most general molecular encounter, both molecules are in motion with respect to the container. A reference frame at rest with respect to the container will be referred to as the *rest frame* (or laboratory system), and the results must ultimately be referred to this system. The *center-of-mass frame* (or C system) moves along with the center of mass of the two colliding molecules; i.e., it is at rest with respect to the center of mass, which is itself moving with uni-form velocity through the container. This system is particularly simple kinematically and most convenient for the application of the conservation laws. It will be shown that the two-particle encounter in the C system reduces to the simpler case of a single particle deflected in a central field of force. This two-dimensional problem can in turn be replaced by an equivalent one-dimensional problem.

Dynamics of a Particle in a Central Field of Force. The dynamical problem of a particle in a central field of force will be treated first; the results can then be adapted to the two-particle encounter by changes in notation. A central force is always directed toward a fixed point. A conservative central force can be derived from a potential that is a func-tion only of the distance of the particle from the fixed point. The radius vector from the fixed point to the particle and the instantaneous-velocity vector of the particle define a plane. Since the force vector lies in this plane, the components of acceleration and velocity normal to the plane both permanently vanish. The trajectory in a central field is therefore confined to a plane. Let r, ϕ be plane polar coordinates specifying the position of the particle with the center of force at the origin. Let a_r and a_ϕ denote the radial and transverse components of the acceleration. It is readily found that (see Prob. 8-1)

$$a_r = \ddot{r} - r\dot{\phi}^2 \qquad a_\phi = 2\dot{r}\dot{\phi} + r\ddot{\phi} \qquad (8\text{-}1)$$

Denoting the central force by $F(r)$, the equations of motion are given by

$$ma_r = F(r) \qquad ma_\phi = 0 \qquad (8\text{-}2)$$

The *angular momentum* of the particle is defined as the moment of its linear-momentum vector about an axis through the origin perpendicular to the plane. Since the radial component of the momentum has zero moment, the angular momentum is obtained from the transverse momen-tum mv_ϕ multiplied by the "lever arm" r. Since $v_\phi = r\dot{\phi}$, the angular momentum is given by

$$p_\phi = mv_\phi r = mr^2\dot{\phi} \qquad (8\text{-}3)$$

which agrees with the elementary definition. Differentiation of (8-3) with respect to the time gives

$$\dot{p}_\phi = 2mr\dot{r}\dot{\phi} + mr^2\ddot{\phi}$$
$$= mra_\phi \qquad\qquad (8\text{-}4)$$
$$= 0$$

using (8-1) and (8-2). This leads to the important result that in a central field of force the angular momentum is unchanged throughout the motion. Since the force has been assumed to be conservative, i.e., derivable from a potential, the sum of the kinetic and potential energies also remains unchanged during the motion. Accordingly, the angular momentum and the total energy are referred to as *constants of the motion*.

Let the potential function be $u(r)$; then $F(r) = -du/dr$. The first equation of motion becomes

$$m\ddot{r} - mr\dot{\phi}^2 = -du/dr \qquad\qquad (8\text{-}5)$$

The term $mr\dot{\phi}^2$ is commonly referred to as the centrifugal force. It is convenient to introduce the *centrifugal potential* defined by

$$u_c(r) = p_\phi{}^2/2mr^2 \qquad\qquad (8\text{-}6)$$

and $\qquad\qquad du_c/dr = -p_\phi{}^2/mr^3 = -mr\dot{\phi}^2 \qquad\qquad (8\text{-}7)$

with the aid of (8-3). Substitution in Eq. (8-5) gives

$$m\ddot{r} = -d(u + u_c)/dr \qquad\qquad (8\text{-}8)$$

Equation (8-8) can be interpreted as the one-dimensional equation of motion of a particle of mass m moving along a straight line (the r axis) in a field determined by the effective potential $u(r) + u_c(r)$. On multiplying both sides of Eq. (8-8) by $\dot{r}$ and integrating with respect to the time, one obtains

$$m\int\dot{r}\ddot{r}\,dt = -\int d(u + u_c)/dr\,\dot{r}\,dt$$
$$m\int\dot{r}\,d\dot{r} = -\int d(u + u_c) \qquad\qquad (8\text{-}9)$$
$$m\dot{r}^2/2 + u_c(r) + u(r) = \text{const.}$$

But from Eqs. (8-3) and (8-6),

$$u_c(r) = mr^2\dot{\phi}^2/2 \qquad\qquad (8\text{-}10)$$

and substituting this in (8-9),

$$(m/2)(\dot{r}^2 + r^2\dot{\phi}^2) + u(r) = \text{const.} \qquad\qquad (8\text{-}11)$$

Equation (8-11) expresses the conservation of energy; the first term is the kinetic energy, and it consists of a radial part $m\dot{r}^2/2$ and a transverse part that is equal to the centrifugal potential. It has now been established that the two equations of motion (8-2) lead to the two conservation laws for energy and angular momentum, respectively. The remaining discussion is based on these two laws.

In all cases of interest, the field vanishes when the particle is infinitely far from the center of force. The trajectory of a particle scattered in a central field will have two asymptotes, one along the initial direction of approach at infinity and the other along the final direction of motion when the particle has receded to an infinite distance. The *angle of deflection* χ is defined as the angle between the asymptotes measured from the initial to the final direction of motion. For a particle of given mass entering a given field of force, the trajectory and the angle of deflection will be determined by the velocity of approach at infinity v_0 and by the *impact parameter* b, which is defined as the perpendicular distance from the center of force to the asymptote along the direction of approach (cf. Sec. 6-3 for an equivalent definition). A particular trajectory can be characterized by the values of the parameters v_0 and b or by assigning values to the two constants of the motion. Since $u(\infty) = 0$, the total energy is equal to the kinetic energy at infinity: $mv_0{}^2/2$. The initial linear momentum of approach is mv_0. Hence the angular momentum is equal to $mv_0 b$, since the lever arm is equal to the impact parameter. The conservation laws can now be explicitly written out:

$$p_\phi = mr^2\dot\phi = mv_0 b \tag{8-12}$$

$$\frac{m\dot r^2}{2} + \frac{p_\phi{}^2}{2mr^2} + u(r) = \frac{mv_0{}^2}{2} \tag{8-13}$$

Of particular importance is the point on the trajectory where the particle is closest to the center of force. We seek to determine the polar coordinates r_m, ϕ_m of this point of closest approach. Denoting the polar equation of the orbit by $r = r(\phi)$, the condition for closest approach is $dr(\phi)/d\phi = 0$, since the radius vector r is a minimum. If $r(\phi)$ is known explicitly, this suffices to determine r_m and ϕ_m. However, useful formulas for r_m and ϕ_m can be obtained without solving the equations of motion for $r(\phi)$. Since $dr/d\phi = \dot r/\dot\phi$ and $\dot\phi$ cannot be infinite, an alternative condition is that $\dot r = 0$, i.e., the radial component of velocity vanishes. This condition can also be obtained from the equivalent one-dimensional problem. The point of closest approach in the two-dimensional problem corresponds to the turning point of the one-dimensional motion. The turning point is reached when the effective potential energy $u(r) + u_c(r)$ becomes equal to the total energy $mv_0{}^2/2$. From Eq. (8-13), $m\dot r^2/2 = 0$ and $\dot r = 0$ at the turning point. Then

$$\frac{p_\phi{}^2}{2mr_m{}^2} + u(r_m) = \frac{mv_0{}^2}{2} \tag{8-14}$$

and on substituting $p_\phi = mv_0 b$ one obtains

$$\frac{b^2}{r_m{}^2} = 1 - \frac{u(r_m)}{\frac{1}{2}mv_0{}^2} \tag{8-15}$$

This relation between the impact parameter b and the distance of closest approach r_m will be used later.

In order to determine ϕ_m, one first rewrites (8-13) with the aid of (8-12) in the form

$$\frac{\dot{r}^2}{v_0^2} = 1 - \frac{b^2}{r^2} - \frac{u(r)}{\frac{1}{2}mv_0^2} \tag{8-16}$$

From (8-12)

$$\frac{\dot{\phi}^2}{v_0^2} = \frac{b^2}{r^4}$$

whence

$$\left(\frac{dr}{d\phi}\right)^2 = \left(\frac{\dot{r}}{\dot{\phi}}\right)^2 = \frac{r^4}{b^2}\left[1 - \frac{b^2}{r^2} - \frac{u(r)}{\frac{1}{2}mv_0^2}\right] \tag{8-17}$$

It is readily seen from Eq. (8-17) that the orbit is symmetric about a line from the center of force through the point of closest approach (the *apse*

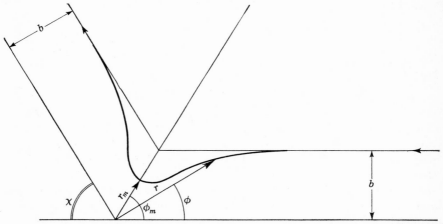

FIG. 8-1. Trajectory of a particle in a central field of force combining an attraction with a shorter-range repulsion: b is the impact parameter, χ is the angle of deflection, and (r_m, ϕ_m) are the polar coordinates of the point of closest approach.

line). Let the angle ϕ in (8-17) be measured from this line; then at $\phi = 0$, we have the condition equations $r = r_m$ and $dr/d\phi = 0$. Now both (8-17) and the condition equations are invariant to the transformation $\phi' = -\phi$, which reflects the orbit in the line $\phi = 0$. Hence the orbit is symmetric about this line. We now measure ϕ from the direction of incidence as shown in Fig. 8-1. It is apparent from the figure that the angle of deflection χ is related to ϕ_m by

$$\chi = \pi - 2\phi_m \tag{8-18}$$

In order to determine ϕ_m we take the square root of both sides of (8-17) obtaining

$$d\phi = \pm \frac{br^{-2}\,dr}{\{1 - (b^2/r^2) - [u(r)/\frac{1}{2}mv_0^2]\}^{\frac{1}{2}}} \tag{8-19}$$

and integrate from infinity to the point of closest approach. Since $dr/d\phi$ < 0 along the incoming trajectory, the negative square root is used. Then

$$\phi_m = \int_0^{\phi_m} d\phi = -\int_\infty^{r_m} \frac{br^{-2}\,dr}{\{1 - (b^2/r^2) - [u(r)/\frac{1}{2}mv_0^2]\}^{1/2}} \tag{8-20}$$

We obtain, finally, for the angle of deflection,

$$\chi = \pi - 2b \int_{r_m}^\infty \frac{r^{-2}\,dr}{\{1 - (b^2/r^2) - [u(r)/\frac{1}{2}mv_0^2]\}^{1/2}} \tag{8-21}$$

Dynamics of an Encounter between Two Particles. We turn now to the actual two-particle collision. Let $\mathbf{r}_1$ and $\mathbf{r}_2$ be vectors in the rest frame from a fixed origin to the two particles. We introduce the vector $\mathbf{r}_c$ from the origin to the center of mass of the particles

$$\mathbf{r}_c \equiv \frac{m_1\mathbf{r}_1 + m_2\mathbf{r}_2}{m_1 + m_2} \tag{8-22}$$

and also the separation vector $\mathbf{r}$, whose magnitude is the interparticle distance r,

$$\mathbf{r} \equiv \mathbf{r}_1 - \mathbf{r}_2 \tag{8-23}$$

Then $\dot{\mathbf{r}}$ represents the relative-velocity vector and $\ddot{\mathbf{r}}$ the relative acceleration. The equations of motion are

$$m_1\ddot{\mathbf{r}}_1 = \mathbf{F}_1(r) \tag{8-24}$$
$$m_2\ddot{\mathbf{r}}_2 = \mathbf{F}_2(r) = -\mathbf{F}_1(r) \tag{8-25}$$

where the law of action and reaction has been used. The forces are here assumed to be along the line joining the two particles and to depend only on the interparticle distance. On differentiating twice with respect to the time, Eq. (8-22) becomes

$$\ddot{\mathbf{r}}_c = \frac{m_1\ddot{\mathbf{r}}_1 + m_2\ddot{\mathbf{r}}_2}{m_1 + m_2} = \frac{\mathbf{F}_1(r) + \mathbf{F}_2(r)}{m_1 + m_2} = 0 \tag{8-26}$$

Since the acceleration of the center of mass vanishes, we obtain the familiar result that the center of mass is in uniform rectilinear motion. Next we divide (8-24) by m_1 and (8-25) by m_2 and subtract, obtaining

$$\ddot{\mathbf{r}} = \ddot{\mathbf{r}}_1 - \ddot{\mathbf{r}}_2 = \left(\frac{1}{m_1} + \frac{1}{m_2}\right)\mathbf{F}_1(r) \tag{8-27}$$

and, introducing the reduced mass m^*,

$$\mathbf{F}_1(r) = m^*\ddot{\mathbf{r}} \tag{8-28}$$

Since $\mathbf{F}_1(r)$ is in the direction of $\mathbf{r}$, this equation for the relative motion has the same form as the equation of motion of a single particle of mass

m^* in a central field of force.   The separation vector $\mathbf{r}$ and the relative velocity $\dot{\mathbf{r}}$ define a plane that contains both particles and their center of mass.   Since $\mathbf{F}_1(r)$ lies in this plane, the relative acceleration $\ddot{\mathbf{r}}$ is in the plane, and the normal components of $\dot{\mathbf{r}}$ and $\ddot{\mathbf{r}}$ are both permanently zero. Hence the *relative* motion is confined to a plane containing the center of mass.   The plane is itself translated with the constant velocity of the center of mass.   Alternatively, one can say that in the C system the orbits of both particles lie in a plane through the center of mass and the relative motion in this same plane is equivalent to the motion of a single particle of mass m^* in the central field $\mathbf{F}_1(r)$.

The results obtained earlier in this section can now be adapted to the two-particle encounter.   The mass m is to be replaced in all formulas by the reduced mass m^*.   The coordinate r represents the interparticle distance and $u(r)$ the intermolecular potential energy.   The initial velocity v_0 is now to be interpreted as the initial *relative* velocity and the impact parameter b as the *hypothetical* distance of closest approach if both particles were to continue undeflected along their original trajectories (r_m is the *actual* distance of closest approach).   The relative kinetic energy of approach at infinity (initial relative energy) $\frac{1}{2}m^*v_0{}^2$ is conserved throughout the encounter.   Thus the kinetic energy of the center of mass and the relative energy are separately conserved.   The relative angular momentum $p_\phi = m^*v_0b$ is also conserved.   It will be shown below that the relative kinetic energy is equal to the total kinetic energy of the particles referred to the C system and the relative angular momentum is equal to the total angular momentum of the particles in the C system. Finally, the angle of deflection χ is redefined as the angle between the initial and final directions of the relative velocity $\dot{\mathbf{r}}$.

The collision will now be examined from the point of view of an observer in the C system.   The velocity of the center of mass $\mathbf{v}_c = \dot{\mathbf{r}}_c$ and the relative velocity $\mathbf{v}_r = \dot{\mathbf{r}}$.   Time differentiation of Eqs. (8-22) and (8-23) relates these velocities to the particle velocities $\mathbf{v}_1$ and $\mathbf{v}_2$ in the rest frame. The relations have already been given in Eqs. (5-19).   We now introduce the velocities of the two particles referred to the C system: $\mathbf{v}_{1c}$ and $\mathbf{v}_{2c}$. Then, using (5-21), one finds

$$\mathbf{v}_{1c} = \mathbf{v}_1 - \mathbf{v}_c = \left(\frac{m_2}{m_1 + m_2}\right)\mathbf{v}_r$$

$$\mathbf{v}_{2c} = \mathbf{v}_2 - \mathbf{v}_c = -\left(\frac{m_1}{m_1 + m_2}\right)\mathbf{v}_r$$

$$(8\text{-}29)$$

The momenta of the two particles in the C system are given by

$$m_1\mathbf{v}_{1c} = m^*\mathbf{v}_r$$
$$m_2\mathbf{v}_{2c} = -m^*\mathbf{v}_r$$

$$(8\text{-}30)$$

The two momenta are equal and opposite before, after, and at all times during the encounter. Before collision, the particles approach along parallel lines a distance b apart, each with momentum m^*v_0 where v_0 is the magnitude of the initial relative velocity. The moment of momentum of this "momentum couple" is m^*v_0b. The total angular momentum of the particles in the C system is therefore equal to the relative angular momentum. We next observe that

$$
\begin{aligned}
m_1v_{1x}^2 + m_2v_{2x}^2 &= m_1(v_{cx} + v_{1cx})^2 + m_2(v_{cx} + v_{2cx})^2 \\
&= (m_1 + m_2)v_{cx}^2 + m_1v_{1cx}^2 + m_2v_{2cx}^2 \\
&\qquad\qquad\qquad + 2v_{cx}(m_1v_{1cx} + m_2v_{2cx})
\end{aligned}
\tag{8-31}
$$

The last term of (8-31) vanishes in accordance with (8-30). Adding similar expressions for y and z components, one obtains the energy equation

$$
\tfrac{1}{2}m_1v_1^2 + \tfrac{1}{2}m_2v_2^2 = \tfrac{1}{2}(m_1 + m_2)v_c^2 + \tfrac{1}{2}m_1v_{1c}^2 + \tfrac{1}{2}m_2v_{2c}^2 \tag{8-32}
$$

which expresses the well-known theorem that the total kinetic energy in the rest frame is equal to the kinetic energy of the particles in the C system plus the kinetic energy of the total mass moving with the velocity of the center of mass. It is readily seen from (8-29) that

$$
\tfrac{1}{2}m_1v_{1c}^2 + \tfrac{1}{2}m_2v_{2c}^2 = \tfrac{1}{2}m^*v_r^2 \tag{8-33}
$$

which establishes that the kinetic energy of the particles referred to the C system is equal to the relative kinetic energy.

We now consider the relations between the initial and final velocities and momenta. *Unprimed* quantities will henceforth refer to *initial* values rather than values at arbitrary times, and *primed* quantities to *final* values after the encounter. Since the kinetic energy of the center of mass is unchanged in the encounter, the conservation of energy gives

$$
\tfrac{1}{2}m^*v_r^2 = \tfrac{1}{2}m^*v_r'^2 \tag{8-34}
$$

from which it follows that the *relative velocity is changed in direction but not in magnitude by the encounter*. After the encounter

$$
\begin{aligned}
m_1\mathbf{v}_{1c}' &= m^*\mathbf{v}_r' \\
m_2\mathbf{v}_{2c}' &= -m^*\mathbf{v}_r'
\end{aligned}
\tag{8-35}
$$

Thus
$$
\begin{aligned}
m_1|\mathbf{v}_{1c}'| &= m^*|\mathbf{v}_r'| = m^*|\mathbf{v}_r| = m_1|\mathbf{v}_{1c}| \\
|\mathbf{v}_{1c}'| &= |\mathbf{v}_{1c}| \quad \text{and} \quad |\mathbf{v}_{2c}'| = |\mathbf{v}_{2c}|
\end{aligned}
\tag{8-36}
$$

These results can be summarized as follows: An observer at rest in the C system sees the particles approaching with equal and opposite momenta along parallel paths and departing also with equal and opposite momenta along parallel paths. The velocity of each particle is changed in direction but not in magnitude by the encounter, as observed in the C system. Obviously, both particles approach along the direction of $\mathbf{v}_r$ and depart along the direction of $\mathbf{v}_r'$. Hence, in the C system, both particles are deflected through the same angle, and this angle is identical with the deflection χ defined previously as the angle between $\mathbf{v}_r$ and $\mathbf{v}_r'$. It should be emphasized that in the rest frame, in general, the particles do not emerge in opposite directions and the speeds are altered by the encounter.

We take up finally the change in momentum of each particle produced by the encounter. Let $\delta(m_1\mathbf{v}_1)$ be the change in momentum of particle 1, i.e., the momentum transferred from particle 2 to particle 1. Then

$$
\begin{aligned}
\delta(m_1\mathbf{v}_1) &= m_1\mathbf{v}_1' - m_1\mathbf{v}_1 \\
&= m_1(\mathbf{v}_{1c}' - \mathbf{v}_{1c}) \\
&= m^*(\mathbf{v}_r' - \mathbf{v}_r)
\end{aligned}
\tag{8-37}
$$

using (8-30) and (8-35). Obviously, $\delta(m_2\mathbf{v}_2) = -\delta(m_1\mathbf{v}_1)$. The components of the momentum transfer $\delta(m_1\mathbf{v}_1)$ taken parallel ($\parallel$) and perpendicular ($\perp$) to $\mathbf{v}_r$ are

$$
\begin{aligned}
\delta(m_1\mathbf{v}_1)_\parallel &= m^*(v_r \cos\chi - v_r) \\
&= -m^*v_r(1 - \cos\chi)
\end{aligned}
\tag{8-38}
$$
$$
\delta(m_1\mathbf{v}_1)_\perp = m^*v_r \sin\chi
\tag{8-39}
$$

Equation (8-38) will be used in calculating the momentum transfer in the treatment of mutual diffusion in Sec. 8-3.

8-2. CROSS SECTIONS AND COLLISION RATES

The collision cross section as first introduced in Sec. 3-2 referred to the cross section of the sphere of influence in the case of a collision between two rigid-elastic-sphere molecules. In this section the definition of the collision cross section will be extended to the case of an encounter between particles interacting with central forces. Another type of cross section, known as the *transport cross section*, will also be introduced. We first review the scattering of rigid elastic spheres. As in Sec. 3-2, one molecule of diameter d_2 is held fixed in the path of a homogeneous beam of molecules of diameter d_1. The beam molecules are assumed to be moving in the same direction with the same speed. By the *intensity* of the beam is meant the number of beam particles crossing unit area of a plane at right angles to the beam in unit time. The number of beam molecules N scattered in unit time by the fixed or target molecule is equal to σI where σ is the cross section of the sphere of influence and I the intensity of the beam. In our previous notation, $\sigma = \pi d_{12}{}^2$ where $d_{12} = (d_1 + d_2)/2$ and $I = nv$ where n is the number density and v the velocity of the beam. If the beam molecules are of negligible size ($d_1 \to 0$), σ is the actual target area of the fixed molecule, i.e., its area of cross section. Considering a uniform beam of unit cross section, the probability that a molecule of this beam is scattered is just N/I. But this probability is geometrically determined as the ratio of the target area σ to the total area available, i.e., unit area. Thus $\sigma = N/I$. *The generalized collision or scattering cross section for an action-at-a-distance encounter between point molecules can be defined by this relation, i.e., as the ratio of the number of beam molecules scattered per unit time by one fixed molecule to the intensity of the beam.*

Before taking up the general case, it is instructive to consider the scattering of weakly attracting rigid-sphere molecules and to deduce the cross section for this case (cf. Eq. (6-37)). As pointed out in Sec. 6-3, one can neglect the contribution to the transport of those deflections in which the spheres do not come into contact, provided the forces are sufficiently weak. We consider only the scattering produced by contact collisions. Since the centers of the molecules are a distance d_{12} apart at contact, those and only those trajectories in the force field will lead to a contact collision for which the distance of closest approach $r_m \leqq d_{12}$. The value of r_m is determined by the initial velocity v_0 and the impact parameter b according to Eq. (8-15). The maximum impact parameter for which a contact collision can occur is then given by

$$b_{\max} = d_{12}\left[1 - \frac{u(d_{12})}{\frac{1}{2}mv_0{}^2}\right]^{\frac{1}{2}} \tag{8-40}$$

where m is the mass of the beam molecules. Those and only those molecules in the beam whose lines of approach pass inside a circle of radius $b_{\max}$ will suffer a contact collision. The number of collisions per unit time with the fixed molecule is equal to the number of beam molecules crossing the circle, i.e., $\pi b_{\max}^2 I$. The cross section for contact collisions is therefore

$$\sigma = \pi b_{\max}^2 = \pi d_{12}{}^2\left[1 - \frac{u(d_{12})}{\frac{1}{2}mv_0{}^2}\right] \tag{8-41}$$

If the target molecule is itself in motion, the beam kinetic energy $\frac{1}{2}mv_0{}^2$ is replaced by the initial kinetic energy of relative motion $\frac{1}{2}m^*v_r{}^2$ where v_r is the relative velocity of approach. The result for contact collisions in an *attractive* field of force is

$$\sigma = \pi d_{12}{}^2[1 + (u^*/\varepsilon)] \tag{8-42}$$

where $u^* = |u(d_{12})|$ and $\varepsilon = \frac{1}{2}m^*v_r{}^2$. If the molecules are alike $(d_1 = d_2 = d)$, Eq. (8-42) is identical with Eq. (6-37), which has already been discussed in Sec. 6-3. It is easily seen that the cross section for contact collisions in the case of *repelling* rigid-sphere molecules is

$$\begin{aligned} \sigma &= \pi d_{12}{}^2[1 - (u^*/\varepsilon)] & \varepsilon > u^* \\ \sigma &= 0 & \varepsilon < u^* \end{aligned} \tag{8-43}$$

Equation (8-43) will be found useful in the treatment of bimolecular reactions in Sec. 8-4.

Our approach to the general action-at-a-distance encounter between point molecules is through the definition of the *differential scattering cross section*. We again consider a homogeneous beam incident upon a single fixed-target molecule that acts as a center of force deflecting the beam molecules. Because of the spherical symmetry of the force field, the deflection pattern will have an axis of symmetry along the line of approach through the center of force. The differential scattering cross section measures the distribution-in-angle of the scattered particles. Let the origin be located at the target molecule, or center of force, and let the polar axis be taken along the direction of approach of the beam. Because of the axial symmetry, the angular distribution is independent of azimuth and depends only on the polar angle of deflection χ. *The differential scattering cross section $d\sigma$ is defined as the number of molecules scattered into the element of solid angle $d\omega$ per unit time divided by the incident intensity.* Because of symmetry, the element of solid angle is integrated over azimuth and $d\omega$ is taken to be the solid angle between the cones defined by an arbitrary polar angle χ and $\chi + d\chi$, i.e., $d\omega = 2\pi \sin \chi \, d\chi$. Then

$$d\sigma = S(\chi) \, 2\pi \sin \chi \, d\chi \qquad (8\text{-}44)$$

specifies the number scattered per unit time with deflections between χ and $\chi + d\chi$ per unit incident intensity. The angular distribution function $S(\chi)$ is often referred to as the differential scattering cross section. For a given velocity of the beam, there is a one-to-one correspondence between the angle of deflection and the impact parameter such that impact parameters between b and $b + db$ correspond to deflections between χ and $\chi - d\chi$ (obviously $d\chi/db < 0$ for forces decreasing with increasing distance). The number of molecules deflected between χ and $\chi + d\chi$ per unit time is equal to the number in the incident beam whose lines of approach pass through an annulus of width db and area $2\pi b \, db$ (see Fig. 8-2). Since this number is just $2\pi I b \, db$, it follows that

$$d\sigma = 2\pi b \, db \qquad (8\text{-}45)$$

Thus the differential cross section is equal to the area of the "impact parameter ring." The angular distribution function is given by

$$S(\chi) = \frac{b}{\sin \chi} \left| \frac{db}{d\chi} \right| \qquad (8\text{-}46)$$

The evaluation of $db/d\chi$ is a dynamical problem that has been essentially solved in the previous section. Equation (8-21) gives χ as a function of b and r_m which can be explicitly found when the force field is specified. Eliminating r_m with the aid of (8-15), one obtains χ as a function of b and the velocity of approach v_0.

The *total scattering cross section* σ is obtained by integrating the differential cross section over the complete solid angle of 4π.   Thus

$$\sigma = 2\pi \int_0^\pi S(\chi) \sin \chi \, d\chi \qquad (8\text{-}47)$$

This integral diverges in the case of force fields of the usual type, which extend to infinity, e.g., inverse power attractions or repulsions.   For such fields there is no upper limit to the impact parameter, since deflections occur no matter how large the value of b is.   The effective area of the

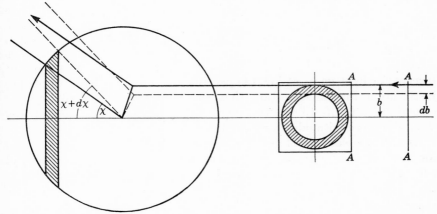

FIG. 8-2. Scattering of a homogeneous beam by a fixed center of force, the field being spherically symmetric.   The impact-parameter annulus of area $2\pi b\,db$ is shown together with the corresponding element of solid angle $d\omega = 2\pi \sin \chi \, d\chi$.   Only the asymptotes of the trajectory are shown.

molecule would then be infinite.   This difficulty did not arise in connection with the cross-section equations (8-42) and (8-43) because only contact collisions were taken into account.   The small-angle scattering that leads to the divergence of the σ integral is given incorrectly by classical theory.   In quantum theory, the angular distribution is obtained statistically without reference to impact parameters or trajectories, which are not meaningful because of limitations imposed by the principle of indeterminacy.   In the case of force fields vanishing more rapidly than r^{-3} at infinity, the integral of Eq. (8-47) is convergent when the quantum mechanical distribution $S(\chi)$ is inserted.   This includes the intermolecular force fields introduced in Chap. 6.   The total cross section *measured* in the scattering of a beam of fast particles is $\pi b_{\max}^2$ where $b_{\max}$ corresponds to the minimum angle of deflection measured in the experiment.   The total scattering cross section is, however, of secondary interest in kinetic theory since the integral of Eq. (8-47) nowhere appears in the treatment of transport phenomena.   The theory leads instead to the two integrals

$$\sigma_D = 2\pi \int_0^\infty (1 - \cos \chi)b \; db$$

$$= 2\pi \int_0^\pi S(\chi)(1 - \cos \chi) \sin \chi \; d\chi \qquad (8\text{-}48)$$

and

$$\sigma_\eta = 2\pi \int_0^\infty \sin^2 \chi \; b \; db$$

$$= 2\pi \int_0^\pi S(\chi) \sin^3 \chi \; d\chi \qquad (8\text{-}49)$$

The generalized *transport cross section* σ_D comes into the first-approximation treatment of mutual diffusion, as will be shown in the next section,* and the cross section σ_η appears instead in the first approximation to the coefficients of viscosity and heat conduction. Because of the extra factors $1 - \cos \chi$ and $\sin^2 \chi$, which vanish as χ^2 for infinitesimal deflections, the integrals (8-48) and (8-49) converge for the usual intermolecular force fields in the classical case, and quantum corrections are insignificant (except for light gases at low temperatures). Equation (8-49) provides justification for the assertion that small deflections contribute only second-order terms to the transport in the discussion of the van der Waals–Sutherland model in Sec. 6-3.

As an example of the foregoing, we shall determine the function $S(\chi)$ for the scattering of rigid elastic spheres by a fixed sphere. Instead of using Eqs. (8-21) and (8-46), it will be instructive to employ an alternative method. The line joining the centers of the spheres when they are in contact will be referred to as the *line of centers;* its length is

$$d_{12} = (d_1 + d_2)/2$$

Let θ and ϕ be spherical coordinates of the line of centers with the line of head-on approach as polar axis. Since an elastic reflection takes place, the directions of approach and departure make equal angles θ with the line of centers; i.e., the angle of reflection is equal to the angle of incidence. It is seen from Fig. 8-3 that $\chi = \pi - 2\theta$ is the angle of deflection. Consider those collisions for which the line of centers is within the element of solid angle $d\omega = \sin \theta \; d\theta \; d\phi$. The number of such collisions that occur in unit time is equal to the number of incident molecules whose centers are to be found in an oblique cylinder of base $dS = d_{12}^2 \; d\omega$ and slant length v_0. This number is equal to the volume of the cylinder $v_0 \cos \theta \; dS$ multiplied by the beam density n. Dividing by the incident intensity nv_0, the number of collisions per unit time per unit intensity with θ in the range $d\theta$ and ϕ in the range $d\phi$ is

$$d^2\sigma = \cos \theta \; dS = d_{12}^2 \cos \theta \sin \theta \; d\theta \; d\phi \qquad (8\text{-}50)$$

---

* We note that σ_D is an effective cross section for momentum transfer. The factor $1 - \cos \chi$ takes on its greatest value, 2, for a head-on collision ($b = 0$) in which the momentum transfer is greatest, and its least value, 0, when the impact parameter $b = \infty$ and no momentum is transferred.

and the number per unit time per unit incident intensity with line of centers between θ and $\theta + d\theta$ is

$$d\sigma = 2\pi d_{12}{}^2 \sin \theta \cos \theta \, d\theta$$
$$= 2\pi b \, db \qquad (8\text{-}51)$$

since the impact parameter $b = d_{12} \sin \theta$. Obviously, Eq. (8-51) could have been obtained directly from (8-45); the alternative "line-of-centers"

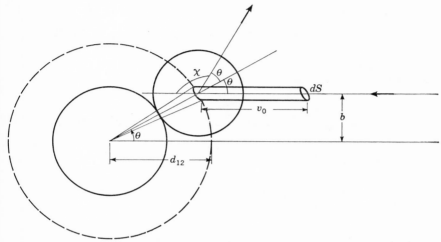

FIG. 8-3. Collision between rigid elastic spheres: θ is the polar angle of the line of centers, and χ is the angle of deflection.

approach has been used because it is frequently referred to in the literature. Substituting $\theta = (\pi - \chi)/2$ in (8-51), the differential scattering cross section (with an appropriate change of sign, since $d\chi/db < 0$), is obtained as

$$d\sigma = (d_{12}/2)^2 \, 2\pi \sin \chi \, d\chi \qquad (8\text{-}52)$$

whence $S(\chi) = (d_{12}/2)^2$. Since $S(\chi)$ is a constant, the angular distribution is spherically symmetrical or isotropic.* It is to be emphasized that this result holds only if the target sphere is held fixed and not if it is free to recoil. This will be explained in the next paragraph.

The discussion has so far been restricted to the case of a fixed scatterer or center of force. But in most actual scattering experiments the scatterer is free to move, and, if initially at rest, it is set in motion by the encounter. In the encounters that take place in gases, both molecules are initially in motion and either may be regarded as the scatterer. It is therefore necessary to extend the cross-section definitions to genuine

* In an isotropic scattering $d\sigma$ is directly proportional to the element of solid angle $2\pi \sin \chi \, d\chi$.

two-particle encounters. It has been shown in Sec. 8-1 that the two-particle encounter in the center-of-mass frame of reference (C system) is equivalent dynamically to a single particle moving in the field of a fixed center of force. The cross-section definitions can be adapted to the relative motion by replacing the beam velocity by the relative velocity and the impact parameter by the relative impact parameter defined in Sec. 8-1. It has been shown that in the C system both particles are deflected through the same angle and that this is also the angle through

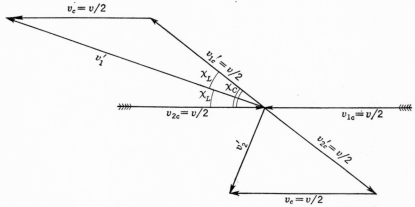

FIG. 8-4. Vector-velocity diagram for an encounter between particles of equal mass with initial speeds $v_1 = v$ and $v_2 = 0$.

which the relative velocity is turned by the encounter. In the rest frame, the angles of deflection are not the same as in the C system. Consider the usual scattering experiment in which the scatterers are initially at rest. Since the angles of deflection in the laboratory frame are different from those in the C system, the angular distributions will also be different. Denoting the angle between the initial and final directions of motion of the scattered particle, as measured in the laboratory, by χ_L and the angle of deflection in the C system by χ_C, it is readily found that (see Prob. 8-6)

$$\tan \chi_L = \frac{\sin \chi_C}{\cos \chi_C + (m_1/m_2)} \tag{8-53}$$

where m_1 and m_2 are the masses of the incident and struck particles, respectively. As $m_2 \to \infty$, we approach the case of a fixed target, and $\chi_L = \chi_C$, since the laboratory and C systems become identical. If $m_2 = m_1$ the right-hand side of (8-53) is equal to $\tan \frac{1}{2}\chi_C$; thus

$$\chi_L = \frac{1}{2}\chi_C \qquad m_2 = m_1 \tag{8-54}$$

This may be seen more easily from Fig. 8-4. Let $S_L(\chi_L)$ and $S_C(\chi_C)$ be the angular distribution functions in the two reference frames. Then, since

$$d\sigma = S_L(\chi_L)\ 2\pi\ \sin\ \chi_L\ d\chi_L = S_C(\chi_C)\ 2\pi\ \sin\ \chi_C\ d\chi_C \qquad (8\text{-}55)$$

it follows that

$$S_L(\chi_L) = S_C(\chi_C)\ \frac{\sin\ \chi_C}{\sin\ \chi_L}\ \frac{d\chi_C}{d\chi_L} \qquad (8\text{-}56)$$

where $d\chi_C/d\chi_L$ can be evaluated with the aid of (8-53).   It is readily seen that, if $m_2 = m_1$,

$$S_L(\chi_L) = 4\ \cos\ \chi_L\ S_C(2\chi_L) \qquad 0 \leq \chi_L \leq \tfrac{1}{2}\pi \qquad (8\text{-}57)$$

In the general scattering of rigid spheres when neither sphere is held fixed and both may be in motion, the formulas previously developed can be used for the relative scattering, since the relative motion is equivalent to a one-body problem with a fixed scatterer.   The angle χ in Eq. (8-52) then represents the angle between the initial and final directions of the relative velocity, and the result is that all directions of the relative velocity after the encounter are equally likely.   Therefore, the angular distributions of both collision partners are *spherically symmetric in the center-of-mass system*.   This result, which has already been used in deriving Eq. (4-13), is true for any initial state of motion of the spheres.   If one of the spheres is initially at rest and is free to recoil, the laboratory angular distribution is related to the isotropic center-of-mass distribution by Eq. (8-56).   When the masses are equal, the angular distribution in the laboratory, as obtained from Eq. (8-57) with $S_C = (d_{12}/2)^2$, is given by

$$S_L(\chi_L) = d_{12}{}^2\ \cos\ \chi_L \qquad 0 \leq \chi_L \leq \tfrac{1}{2}\pi \qquad (8\text{-}58)$$

where $\chi_L = \tfrac{1}{2}\pi$ is the greatest possible angle of deflection in the laboratory. The total scattering cross section is equal to $\pi d_{12}{}^2$ and is independent of the reference frame.

Derivation of Collision Rate Formulas.   We turn now to the problem of calculating the collision rate in a mixed gas in equilibrium.   This will be done for the general case of action-at-a-distance encounters.   Since the cross section, which measures the probability of an encounter, is in general a function of the relative velocity (except for rigid spheres), it is convenient to have the collision rate also as a function of relative velocity, i.e., to determine the number of encounters per unit volume per unit time for which the relative velocity is between v_r and $v_r + dv_r$ in magnitude.   We consider encounters between two groups, one having velocities in the range $\mathbf{v}_1$ to $\mathbf{v}_1 + d\mathbf{v}_1$ and the other between $\mathbf{v}_2$ and $\mathbf{v}_2 + d\mathbf{v}_2$.   Let dn_1 and dn_2 be the number densities of the two groups of molecules.   Consider the rate at which a single molecule of group 2 encounters molecules of group 1; this is the same as if the molecule of group 2 were at rest and the molecules of group 1 were approaching it with velocities between $\mathbf{v}_r$

and $\mathbf{v}_r + d\mathbf{v}_r$ where $\mathbf{v}_r = \mathbf{v}_1 - \mathbf{v}_2$ is the velocity of a group-1 molecule relative to a group-2 molecule. The rate at which such encounters occur with impact parameters between b and $b + db$ is $2\pi I b\, db$ where $I = v_r\, dn_1$. Since there are dn_2 molecules of group 2 per unit volume, the number of encounters between molecules of the two groups with impact parameters between b and $b + db$ is

$$d^7 N = 2\pi b\, db\, v_r\, dn_1\, dn_2 \tag{8-59}$$

per unit volume per unit time. Obviously, $dn_i = n_i F_i(\mathbf{v}_i)\, dv_{ix}\, dv_{iy}\, dv_{iz}$ where $F_i(\mathbf{v}_i)\, dv_{ix}\, dv_{iy}\, dv_{iz}$ represents the fraction of molecules of species i having velocity components between v_{ix}, v_{iy}, v_{iz}, and $v_{ix} + dv_{ix}, v_{iy} + dv_{iy}, v_{iz} + dv_{iz}$ (i.e., velocities between $\mathbf{v}_i$ and $\mathbf{v}_i + d\mathbf{v}_i$). If the gas is in a uniform equilibrium state, $F_i(\mathbf{v}_i)$ is the Maxwell function of Eq. (5-11). Thus

$$d^7 N = n_1 n_2\, 2\pi b\, db\, v_r F_1(\mathbf{v}_1) F_2(\mathbf{v}_2)\, dv_{1x} \cdots dv_{2z} \tag{8-60}$$

Equation (8-60) is to be summed over all velocities of both collision partners to give the total collision rate. In the summation, a collision between molecules with velocities $\mathbf{v}_a$ and $\mathbf{v}_b$ will appear once with $\mathbf{v}_1 = \mathbf{v}_a$, $\mathbf{v}_2 = \mathbf{v}_b$ and again with $\mathbf{v}_1 = \mathbf{v}_b, \mathbf{v}_2 = \mathbf{v}_a$. In unlike-molecule encounters, these are two distinct cases, but in like-molecule encounters they are identical, and the summation will therefore count each collision twice. Anticipating the application of Eq. (8-60) to like- as well as unlike-molecule collisions, we rewrite it as

$$d^7 N = \kappa n_1 n_2\, 2\pi b\, db\, v_r F_1(\mathbf{v}_1) F_2(\mathbf{v}_2)\, dv_{1x} \cdots dv_{2z} \tag{8-61}$$

where the "type number" $\kappa = \tfrac{1}{2}$ for like-molecule encounters and $\kappa = 1$ for unlike encounters.

The impact parameter is an independent parameter characterizing the encounter which can be varied independently of $\mathbf{v}_1$, $\mathbf{v}_2$, and $\mathbf{v}_r$. We can therefore integrate over b to obtain the total scattering cross section $\sigma(v_r)$, which is in general a function of v_r. The total number of encounters per unit volume per unit time between molecules of the two groups is then

$$d^6 N = \kappa n_1 n_2 v_r \sigma(v_r) F_1(\mathbf{v}_1) F_2(\mathbf{v}_2)\, dv_{1x} \cdots dv_{2z} \tag{8-62}$$

and, on inserting the Maxwell function, this becomes

$$d^6 N = \kappa n_1 n_2 \left(\frac{m_1}{2\pi kT}\frac{m_2}{2\pi kT}\right)^{3/2} v_r \sigma(v_r) e^{-(1/2kT)(m_1 v_1{}^2 + m_2 v_2{}^2)}\, dv_{1x} \cdots dv_{2z} \tag{8-63}$$

It is obviously advantageous to make the same transformation here as in Sec. 5-2. We again transform from $\mathbf{v}_1$ and $\mathbf{v}_2$ to the center-of-mass velocity $\mathbf{v}_c$ and the relative velocity $\mathbf{v}_r$. Using the transformation relations given in Eqs. (5-19) through (5-23), we find that

$$d^6N = \kappa n_1 n_2 \frac{(m_1 m_2)^{3/2}}{(2\pi kT)^3} v_r \sigma(v_r) e^{-(1/2kT)[(m_1+m_2)v_c^2 + m^* v_r^2]}$$

$$\cdot v_c^2 \, dv_c \sin\theta_c \, d\theta_c \, d\phi_c \, v_r^2 \, dv_r \sin\theta_r \, d\theta_r \, d\phi_r \quad (8\text{-}64)$$

and, on integrating over v_c, θ_c, ϕ_c, θ_r, and ϕ_r,

$$dN = \kappa n_1 n_2 \frac{(m_1 m_2)^{3/2}}{(2\pi kT)^3} (4\pi)^2 \int_0^\infty e^{-(m_1+m_2)v_c^2/2kT} v_c^2 \, dv_c$$

$$\cdot e^{-m^* v_r^2/2kT} \sigma(v_r) v_r^3 \, dv_r \quad (8\text{-}65)$$

On substituting the value of the integral from Eq. (5-25), this reduces to

$$dN = \kappa n_1 n_2 \left(\frac{m^*}{kT}\right)^{3/2} \left(\frac{2}{\pi}\right)^{1/2} e^{-m^* v_r^2/2kT} \sigma(v_r) v_r^3 \, dv_r \quad (8\text{-}66)$$

Clearly dN represents the number of encounters per unit volume per unit time for which the relative velocity is between v_r and $v_r + dv_r$ in magnitude. The total number of encounters per cubic centimeter per second is then

$$N = \kappa n_1 n_2 \left(\frac{m^*}{kT}\right)^{3/2} \left(\frac{2}{\pi}\right)^{1/2} \int_0^\infty e^{-m^* v_r^2/2kT} \sigma(v_r) v_r^3 \, dv_r \quad (8\text{-}67)$$

In the case of rigid elastic spheres, it is readily found with the aid of Eqs. (5-26) and (5-27) that this reduces to $n_1 n_2 \pi d_{12}^2 (\bar{v}_1^2 + \bar{v}_2^2)^{1/2}$ for unlike-molecule collisions. This result has already been given in (4-10).

Equation (8-66) can also be written in terms of the kinetic energy of the relative motion ε where $\varepsilon = \frac{1}{2} m^* v_r^2$. The number of encounters per unit volume per unit time for which the relative kinetic energy is between ε and $\varepsilon + d\varepsilon$ is

$$dN = \kappa n_1 n_2 \frac{2}{(kT)^{3/2}} \left(\frac{2}{\pi m^*}\right)^{1/2} e^{-\varepsilon/kT} \sigma(v_r) \, \varepsilon \, d\varepsilon \quad (8\text{-}68)$$

The total scattering cross sections appearing in Eqs. (8-66) and (8-68) are defined classically for contact collisions of rigid spheres and of rigid spheres surrounded by force fields (cf. Eqs. (8-42) and (8-43)). But in the case of long-range interactions between point molecules, e.g., the third and fourth models of Sec. 6-3, the classical definition fails, as we have already pointed out, and $\sigma(\varepsilon)$ must be obtained from the quantum theory. Equation (8-68) will be found useful in Sec. 8-4; it is particularly important in the theory of chemical kinetics.

8-3. ADVANCED TREATMENT OF MUTUAL DIFFUSION

An elementary treatment of mutual diffusion by the momentum-transfer method has been given in Sec. 4-2. The same method is used in this section, but a more careful calculation will be made of M_{12}, the momentum transferred per unit volume per unit time from gas 1 to gas 2, and the treatment will not be limited as in Sec. 4-2 to rigid-sphere molecules.   The results to be obtained are not completely rigorous, since the distribution functions are approximate rather than exact.   The first step in a rigorous calculation of M_{12} is to find the momentum transferred in a single action-at-a-distance encounter characterized by the reduced mass m^* of the collision partners, the relative velocity v_r, the impact parameter b, and the angle of deflection χ through which the relative velocity is turned.   This has already been done, and the results are given in Eqs. (8-38) and (8-39).   Because of the distribution of molecular velocities, the momentum transfer is first obtained for infinitesimal ranges of the velocities of the colliding molecules and then integrated over the distributions.   We again consider encounters between two unlike groups, one having velocities in the range $\mathbf{v}_1$ to $\mathbf{v}_1 + d\mathbf{v}_1$ and the other between $\mathbf{v}_2$ and $\mathbf{v}_2 + d\mathbf{v}_2$.   If dn_1 and dn_2 are the number densities of the two groups and $d\sigma$ is the differential cross section, the differential rate of encounter per unit volume is $d\sigma \, v_r \, dn_1 \, dn_2$.   The momentum transferred from group 1 to group 2 per cubic centimeter per second, obtained by multiplying the number of encounters by the momentum transfer in each encounter, is, using (8-37),

$$-m^*(\mathbf{v}_r' - \mathbf{v}_r)v_r \, d\sigma \, dn_1 \, dn_2 \qquad (8\text{-}69)$$

It has already been pointed out that if the intermolecular fields are spherically symmetrical, as is here assumed, the deflection pattern has an axis of symmetry along the line of head-on approach, i.e., parallel to $\mathbf{v}_r$.   On resolving (8-69) into components parallel and perpendicular to $\mathbf{v}_r$, it is evident that the perpendicular component must vanish when summed over all encounters.   Using (8-38) and (8-45), the differential momentum transfer from group 1 to group 2 per unit volume per unit time is then

$$d^7\mathbf{M}_{12} = m^*\mathbf{v}_r(1 - \cos \chi)v_r \, dn_1 \, dn_2 \, 2\pi b \, db \qquad (8\text{-}70)$$

and since $\chi = \chi(b,v_r)$ and b is variable independently of $\mathbf{v}_1$, $\mathbf{v}_2$, and $\mathbf{v}_r$, integration over b gives

$$d^6\mathbf{M}_{12} = m^*\mathbf{v}_r v_r \sigma_D(v_r) \, dn_1 \, dn_2 \qquad (8\text{-}71)$$

where the transport cross section $\sigma_D(v_r)$ has already been defined by (8-48).   Equation (8-71) gives the total momentum transfer from group 1 to group 2 per unit volume per unit time.

As in Sec. 4-2, we consider that diffusion takes place parallel to the z axis.   The concentration gradient, the partial pressure gradients and the resultant momentum transfer are then all in the z direction.   Since only the z component of $d^6\mathbf{M}_{12}$ will remain after integration, we rewrite (8-71) for the z momentum transfer:

$$d^6M_{12} = m^* v_{rz} v_r \sigma_D(v_r)\, dn_1\, dn_2 \qquad (8\text{-}72)$$

$$= m^* n_1 n_2 v_{rz} v_r \sigma_D(v_r) F_1(\mathbf{v}_1) F_2(\mathbf{v}_2)\, dv_{1x} \cdot \cdot \cdot \cdot dv_{2z} \qquad (8\text{-}73)$$

It will be seen below that M_{12} vanishes for Maxwellian distribution functions $F_1(\mathbf{v}_1)$ and $F_2(\mathbf{v}_2)$. However, since the diffusing gas mixture is in a state of nonuniform composition, the Maxwell distribution law is not applicable. In Sec. 4-2, the diffusive transport velocities of the component gases were denoted by u_1 and u_2, and it was pointed out that u_1 is identical with $\bar{v}_{1z}$. If gas 1 were flowing in a uniform stream with a uniform velocity of mass motion u_1 in the absence of gas 2, the Maxwell distribution would hold with respect to a frame of reference moving along with the gas. The distribution function, modified for the translational motion of the whole gas, would then be

$$F_1(\mathbf{v}_1) = A_1 e^{-(m_1/2kT)\,[v_{1x}{}^2 + v_{1y}{}^2 + (v_{1z}-u_1)^2]} \qquad (8\text{-}74)$$

where A_1 is the normalization constant. Equation (8-74) states that the Maxwell law holds for the random thermal-velocity components v_{1x}, v_{1y}, and $v_{1z} - u_1$. Equation (8-74) cannot be correct for the transport of gas 1 in diffusion because of the presence of the second gas and the nonuniform composition of the mixture. However, if $u_1 \ll \bar{v}_1$, we can expand (8-74) to obtain a first-order correction to the Maxwell distribution (terms in $u_1{}^2$ are neglected):

$$F_1(\mathbf{v}_1) = A_1 e^{-m_1 v_1{}^2/2kT} \left(1 + \frac{m_1 u_1 v_{1z}}{kT}\right) \qquad (8\text{-}75)$$

In mutual-diffusion experiments, the diffusive transport velocities are always very small compared to the mean speeds of thermal agitation, i.e., $u_1 \ll \bar{v}_1$. Under these circumstances, (8-75) can be used for the first approximation to the distribution function.* On integration of (8-75), the second term disappears, since the integrand is an odd function of v_{1z}; hence $A_1 = (m_1/2\pi kT)^{3/2}$ as in (5-11). As a check, we can stipulate that the first-approximation distribution function for diffusion will differ from the Maxwell function through a correction factor that is linear in v_{1z}. Writing $(1 + a_1 v_{1z})$ for this factor and determining a_1 from the condition that $\bar{v}_{1z} = u_1$, we readily find that $a_1 = m_1 u_1/kT$, in agreement with (8-75).

Substitution of (8-75) into (8-73) gives

$$d^6M_{12} = m^* n_1 n_2 A_1 A_2 v_{rz} v_r \sigma_D(v_r) e^{-(1/2kT)(m_1 v_1{}^2 + m_2 v_2{}^2)}$$
$$\cdot (1 + a_1 v_{1z})(1 + a_2 v_{2z})\, dv_{1x} \cdot \cdot \cdot \cdot dv_{2z} \qquad (8\text{-}76)$$

---

* Different first-approximation distribution functions are needed for the cases of viscosity and heat conduction. The distribution function (8-75) was first used by J. Stefan, *Wien. Ber.*, vol. 65, p. 323, 1872.

We again transform from $\mathbf{v}_1$ and $\mathbf{v}_2$ to the center-of-mass velocity $\mathbf{v}_c$ and the relative velocity $\mathbf{v}_r$. Using Eqs. (5-19) through (5-22), Eq. (8-76) becomes

$$M_{12} = m^* n_1 n_2 A_1 A_2 \int_{-\infty}^{\infty} \cdots \int_{-\infty}^{\infty} v_r \sigma_D(v_r) e^{-(1/2kT)[(m_1+m_2)v_c{}^2 + m^* v_r{}^2]}$$

$$\cdot \left[v_{rz} + (a_1 + a_2)v_{cz}v_{rz} + \frac{a_1 m_2 - a_2 m_1}{m_1 + m_2} v_{rz}^2 + a_1 a_2 \left(v_{cz}^2 v_{rz} \right. \right.$$

$$\left. \left. - \frac{m_1 m_2}{(m_1 + m_2)^2} v_{rz}^3 + \frac{m_2 - m_1}{m_1 + m_2} v_{cz} v_{rz}^2 \right) \right] dv_{cx} \cdots dv_{rz} \quad (8\text{-}77)$$

where $v_r = |\mathbf{v}_r| = (v_{rx}^2 + v_{ry}^2 + v_{rz}^2)^{1/2}$. The part of the integrand preceding the bracket is an even function of both v_{cz} and v_{rz}. Of the terms inside the brackets, all but the third term are odd functions of either v_{cz} or v_{rz} or both and therefore vanish upon integration. The uncorrected Maxwell function, which leads to the first term inside the brackets, makes no contribution to the momentum transfer. On substituting for a_1, a_2, A_1, and A_2, the sole remaining term gives

$$M_{12} = \frac{m^{*2} n_1 n_2}{kT} (u_1 - u_2) \frac{(m_1 m_2)^{3/2}}{(2\pi kT)^3} \iiint_{-\infty}^{\infty} e^{-(m_1+m_2)v_c{}^2/2kT} \, dv_{cx} \, dv_{cy} \, dv_{cz}$$

$$\cdot \iiint_{-\infty}^{\infty} e^{-m^* v_r{}^2/2kT} v_{rz}^2 v_r \sigma_D(v_r) \, dv_{rx} \, dv_{ry} \, dv_{rz} \quad (8\text{-}78)$$

The first triple integral reduces in spherical coordinates to (5-25) and is equal to $[2\pi kT/(m_1 + m_2)]^{3/2}$. The second triple integral, transformed to spherical coordinates with the aid of (5-23), is

$$\iiint_{-\infty}^{\infty} e^{-m^* v_r{}^2/2kT} \sigma_D(v_r) v_r{}^3 \cos^2 \theta_r \, v_r{}^2 \, dv_r \sin \theta_r \, d\theta_r \, d\phi_r$$

$$= \int_0^{2\pi} d\phi_r \int_0^{\pi} \cos^2 \theta_r \sin \theta_r \, d\theta_r \int_0^{\infty} e^{-m^* v_r{}^2/2kT} \sigma_D(v_r) v_r{}^5 \, dv_r \quad (8\text{-}79)$$

$$= \frac{4\pi}{3} \int_0^{\infty} e^{-m^* v_r{}^2/2kT} \sigma_D(v_r) v_r{}^5 \, dv_r$$

Substitution in (8-78) gives

$$M_{12} = \frac{4\pi m^{*2}}{3kT} \left(\frac{m^*}{2\pi kT} \right)^{3/2} n_1 n_2 (u_1 - u_2) \int_0^{\infty} e^{-m^* v_r{}^2/2kT} \sigma_D(v_r) v_r{}^5 \, dv_r \quad (8\text{-}80)$$

for the momentum transferred per unit volume per unit time from gas 1 to gas 2. Hence, using Eqs. (4-15) and (4-20),

$$f_{12} = \frac{4\pi m^{*2}}{3kT} \left(\frac{m^*}{2\pi kT} \right)^{3/2} \int_0^{\infty} e^{-m^* v_r{}^2/2kT} \sigma_D(v_r) v_r{}^5 \, dv_r \quad (8\text{-}81)$$

and $$D_{12} = \frac{kT}{n} \frac{3kT}{4\pi m^{*2}} \left(\frac{2\pi kT}{m^*}\right)^{3/2} \left[\int_0^\infty e^{-m^*v_r{}^2/2kT} \sigma_D(v_r) v_r{}^5 \, dv_r\right]^{-1} \quad (8\text{-}82)$$

It is customary to express the integral appearing in Eqs. (8-80) and (8-82) in terms of the standard Ω integral of the Enskog-Chapman theory:*

$$\Omega_D = \left(\frac{kT}{2\pi m^*}\right)^{1/2} \int_0^\infty e^{-g^2} \sigma_D(v_r) g^5 \, dg \quad (8\text{-}83)$$

where $g^2 = m^*v_r{}^2/2kT$. Equation (8-82) can then be written

$$D_{12} = \frac{3kT}{16m^*n\Omega_D} \quad (8\text{-}84)$$

Calculation of D_{12} for Two Molecular Models. Equation (8-82) was first obtained by Langevin using a similar method; the special cases of the inverse fifth power repulsion and the rigid-elastic-sphere model had been worked out previously by Maxwell and Stefan, respectively.† According to (8-82), D_{12} is independent of the concentration. Also, one observes that only the cross section for unlike encounters is involved; this was explained in Sec. 4-2. Equation (8-84) agrees exactly with the first approximation formula of the Enskog-Chapman theory; in higher approximation, a slightly different result is obtained which shows a small dependence on concentration. It is very simple to evaluate Ω_D and D_{12} for the rigid-sphere model. According to (8-48) and (8-52)

$$\sigma_D = 2\pi(d_{12}/2)^2 \int_0^\pi (1 - \cos \chi) \sin \chi \, d\chi$$
$$= \pi d_{12}{}^2 \quad (8\text{-}85)$$

Thus σ_D is just the geometric cross section of the sphere of influence and is independent of velocity. Then

$$\Omega_D = \pi d_{12}{}^2 \left(\frac{kT}{2\pi m^*}\right)^{1/2} \int_0^\infty e^{-g^2} g^5 \, dg$$
$$= \pi d_{12}{}^2 \left(\frac{kT}{2\pi m^*}\right)^{1/2} \quad (8\text{-}86)$$

since the integral is equal to unity. Hence

$$D_{12} = \frac{3}{8} \left(\frac{\pi kT}{2m^*}\right)^{1/2} \frac{1}{n\pi d_{12}{}^2} \quad (8\text{-}87)$$

* J. O. Hirschfelder, C. F. Curtiss, and R. B. Bird, "Molecular Theory of Gases and Liquids," John Wiley & Sons, Inc., New York, 1954, pp. 484, 525; S. Chapman and T. G. Cowling, "The Mathematical Theory of Nonuniform Gases," Cambridge University Press, London, 1939, p. 157.

† J. C. Maxwell, *Phil. Trans. Royal Soc.*, vol. 157, p. 49, 1867, or "Collected Works," vol. 2, p. 26; J. Stefan, *Wien. Ber.*, vol. 65, p. 323, 1872; P. Langevin, *Ann. Chim. Phys.* vol. 5, p. 245, 1905.

This result was previously stated and discussed at the end of Sec. 4-2. When (8-85) is inserted in (8-80), the resulting formula for M_{12} is found to agree with the approximate expression (4-14) except that the correct formula has an additional factor of $\frac{4}{3}$.

The calculation of D_{12} from Eq. (8-84) is somewhat lengthy when other assumptions are made about the intermolecular forces. These calculations have been carried out for the special models introduced in Sec. 6-3; details may be found in Chap. 10 of Chapman and Cowling's book.* The procedure is first to obtain χ in terms of b and v_r from Eqs. (8-21) and (8-15), then to evaluate σ_D with the aid of (8-46) and (8-48), and finally to compute Ω_D from (8-83). Except in the case of rigid spheres, it is usually necessary to perform some of the integrations numerically. One of the simpler cases is the van der Waals–Sutherland model of rigid spheres with a weak inverse power attraction, for which terms of the first degree in the force constant are retained and higher-order terms neglected. It is left as an exercise for the reader (see Probs. 8-7, 8-8, and 8-9) to work out the details for this model and to verify Eq. (6-41). A very remarkable result is found for the case in which the molecules are treated as point centers of an inverse fifth power repulsion. When the law of force $F = cr^{-s}$ is assumed, the cross section σ_D can be a function only of m^*, v_r, c, and s. From the dimensional considerations given in Eqs. (6-42) through (6-44), it is apparent that $\sigma_D(v_r)$ is proportional to $v_r^{-4/(s-1)}$. Hence

$$v_r\sigma_D(v_r) \propto v_r^{(s-5)/(s-1)} \tag{8-88}$$

Equation (8-88) is the same as Eq. (7-3). When $s = 5$, the product $v_r\sigma_D(v_r)$ is independent of v_r. The momentum-transfer integral, as obtained from Eq. (8-73), becomes, for $s = 5$,

$$\begin{aligned} M_{12} &= m^*n_1n_2\int \cdots \int v_{rz}v_r\sigma_D(v_r)F_1(\mathbf{v}_1)F_2(\mathbf{v}_2)\,dv_{1x} \cdots dv_{2z} \tag{8-89}\\ &= m^*n_1n_2v_r\sigma_D(v_r)\int \cdots \int (v_{1z} - v_{2z})F_1(\mathbf{v}_1)F_2(\mathbf{v}_2)\,dv_{1x} \cdots dv_{2z}\\ &= m^*n_1n_2v_r\sigma_D(v_r)(\bar{v}_{1z} - \bar{v}_{2z})\\ &= m^*n_1n_2v_r\sigma_D(v_r)(u_1 - u_2) \tag{8-90} \end{aligned}$$

since $u_i = \bar{v}_{iz}$ by definition. Hence

$$f_{12} = m^*v_r\sigma_D(v_r)$$

and
$$D_{12} = \frac{kT}{nm^*v_r\sigma_D(v_r)} \tag{8-91}$$

Equation (8-91), which was first obtained by Maxwell, is exact, whereas (8-84) is approximate, since it is based on the approximate distribution function (8-75). The remarkable property of the inverse fifth power force is that the result for D_{12} can be obtained without any explicit knowl-

* Chapman and Cowling, *op. cit.*

edge of the distribution function $F_i(\mathbf{v}_i)$. Maxwell evaluated $v_r \sigma_D(v_r)$ by expressing (8-21) in terms of the complete elliptic integral of the first kind and then integrating (8-48) numerically. The result is

$$v_r \sigma_D(v_r) = 2.66(c/m^*)^{1/2} \qquad (8\text{-}92)$$

and the mutual-diffusion coefficient for an inverse fifth power repulsion $F = cr^{-5}$ is given rigorously by

$$D_{12} = \frac{0.376kT}{n(m^*c)^{1/2}} \qquad (8\text{-}93)$$

Equations (8-82), (8-87), and (8-93) give the self-diffusion coefficient D_{11} when the masses are taken equal ($m^* = m/2$).

8-4. APPLICATIONS TO CHEMICAL KINETICS

The subject of chemical kinetics of gaseous reactions provides some important applications of kinetic theory. We consider only homogeneous reactions, i.e., those occurring in the body of the gas and not at solid or liquid surfaces in contact with the gas. The rate of reaction is studied as a function of the concentrations or densities, n_1, n_2, . . . , of the reacting components and the temperature. The rate of reaction can usually be expressed in the form

$$\partial n_1/\partial t = -k^* n_1{}^{s_1} n_2{}^{s_2} \cdots \qquad (8\text{-}94)$$

and $s = s_1 + s_2 + \cdots$ is called the *order* of the reaction. The *rate constant* k^* is independent of the concentrations but depends sensitively on the temperature. The value of s is usually a small integer but may be fractional. The reaction $H_2 + I_2 \rightleftarrows 2HI$ is an example of a second-order reaction: the rate of the forward reaction is proportional to the product of the densities of H_2 and I_2 molecules, and the rate of the reverse reaction is proportional to the square of the density of HI molecules. This suggests that the mechanism for the forward reaction is an encounter between an H_2 and an I_2 molecule; if conditions are energetically favorable, the two molecules unite to form a compound molecule that subsequently decomposes into two HI molecules. The rate of reaction would be proportional to the rate at which such encounters occur and thus to the product of the densities. The reverse reaction is initiated by an encounter between two HI molecules, and its reaction rate is thus proportional to the square of the HI density. Such a reaction mechanism is designated as *bimolecular*, since it is initiated by two molecules coming together.

A reaction represented by a single stoichiometric equation may take place in several steps or stages. The reaction rates of the stages determine the over-all rate of the complex reaction. Usually there is one stage that is considerably slower than the others; if this is the case, one can assume the other stages to have attained equilibrium and the over-all rate to be determined by the slowest, or "bottleneck," stage. If the mechanism of this rate-determining step is bimolecular, the complex reaction is characterized as bimolecular regardless of its order. An example is the reaction $H_2 + D_2 \rightleftarrows 2HD$, which is of order $\frac{3}{2}$. The forward reaction proceeds via the rapidly attained equilibrium $H_2 \rightleftarrows 2H$ followed by the slower bimolecular step $H + D_2 \rightarrow HD + D$, or equally well via $D_2 \rightleftarrows 2D$ followed by $D + H_2 \rightarrow HD + H$. We shall take up only the bimolecular mechanism and omit from consideration the other important (unimolecular) mechanism.* The simple collision theory presented here treats the reaction by kinetic-theory methods without taking into account the internal degrees of freedom of the reacting molecules or their geometric shapes and orientations. The internal degrees of freedom, which must properly be treated by quantum theory, are often unimportant. We assume that the collision partners are atoms or spherically symmetrical molecules. However, the direct union of two atoms to form a diatomic molecule is a process which almost never occurs in a gas, because there is no way for the molecule, formed in an unbound, excited state, to dispose of its excess energy except through the highly improbable process of radiation.

A very simple model† is used to represent the formation of the compound molecule or "activated complex." When the centers of the collision partners approach to within a distance $r = d_{12}$, it is assumed that the molecules "stick together" to form the complex. If there were no forces between the colliding molecules, the cross section σ for the formation of the complex would be simply $\pi d_{12}{}^2$. When the molecules are close together, the strongly repulsive "overlap" forces discussed in Sec. 6-3 prevent all but the most energetic molecules from approaching to within the "reaction distance" d_{12}. There is thus a potential-energy hill, or barrier, which must be surmounted before reaction can occur. The height of the potential-energy barrier, which is equal to the minimum energy required to form the complex, is referred to as the *activation energy* and is designated here by u^*. An analogous problem is that of rolling a ball up a volcanic hill with sufficient velocity to make it go over the top of the crater. Let $u(r)$ denote the spherically symmetric potential energy of mutual repulsion of the colliding molecules with $u(\infty) = 0$. Then $u(d_{12})$ will represent the activation energy u^*. The distance between centers at closest approach is determined by the initial relative velocity v_r and the impact parameter b. According to our assumptions, those and only those values of b for which the distance of closest approach would be less than d_{12} lead to formation of the activated complex. The

---

* See any book on chemical kinetics, e.g., those referred to on p. 154.
† R. D. Present, *Proc. Nat. Acad. Sci.*, vol. 41, p. 415, 1955.

cross section for complex formation is then the same as the cross section for contact collisions between rigid-sphere molecules of diameters d_1 and d_2 which repel each other with the same potential-energy function $u(r)$. This cross section, already given in Eq. (8-43), is

$$\sigma(\varepsilon) = \pi d_{12}{}^2[1 - (u^*/\varepsilon)] \qquad \varepsilon > u^* \qquad (8\text{-}95)$$
$$\sigma(\varepsilon) = 0 \qquad\qquad\qquad \varepsilon < u^*$$

where $\varepsilon = \frac{1}{2}m^*v_r{}^2$ is the initial kinetic energy of relative motion.   Equation (8-95) predicts a hyperbolic rise of the cross section beyond the threshold with an asymptotic approach to the value $\pi d_{12}{}^2$.   Since the activated complex may in some cases decompose into the initial reactants rather than into the products of the reaction, the cross section for reaction will in general be smaller than the cross section for complex formation. However, since the two cross sections will usually differ by a factor of the order of unity, this factor will be considered to be absorbed in the uncertain reaction diameter d_{12}, and σ of Eq. (8-95) will be referred to as the *reaction cross section*.   Equation (8-95) is independent of the form of $u(r)$.

We now calculate the number N of reactive encounters that take place per unit volume of the gas per unit time.   The number of such encounters for which the relative kinetic energy is between ε and $\varepsilon + d\varepsilon$ is given by Eq. (8-68) as

$$dN = \kappa n_1 n_2 \frac{2}{(kT)^{3/2}} \left(\frac{2}{\pi m^*}\right)^{1/2} e^{-\varepsilon/kT} \sigma(\varepsilon) \varepsilon \, d\varepsilon \qquad (8\text{-}96)$$

where $\sigma(\varepsilon)$ is now the cross section for chemical reaction.   On inserting $\sigma(\varepsilon)$ from Eq. (8-95) and integrating from u^* to ∞, Eq. (8-96) becomes

$$N = 2\kappa n_1 n_2 d_{12}{}^2 (2\pi kT/m^*)^{1/2} e^{-u^*/kT} \qquad (8\text{-}97)$$
$$= Z e^{-u^*/kT} \qquad\qquad\qquad\qquad (8\text{-}98)$$

where $\qquad\quad Z = \kappa n_1 n_2 \pi d_{12}{}^2 (\bar{v}_1{}^2 + \bar{v}_2{}^2)^{1/2} \qquad\qquad (8\text{-}99)$

is the total number of collisions per unit volume per unit time between rigid elastic spheres of diameters d_1 and d_2.   It follows that the number of reactive encounters per cubic centimeter per second N differs from the number of rigid-sphere collisions per cubic centimeter per second Z by the important factor $e^{-u^*/kT}$.   The rate constant of a simple second-order bimolecular reaction, obtained from (8-94) and (8-97) by setting $\partial n_1/\partial t = -N/\kappa = -k^* n_1 n_2$, is

$$k^* = 2d_{12}{}^2 (2\pi kT/m^*)^{1/2} e^{-u^*/kT} \qquad (8\text{-}100)$$

The factor κ is not present in Eq. (8-100) because n_1 decreases by one in a reactive encounter between unlike molecules and by two in a reactive encounter between like molecules.

It is customary to rewrite Eq. (8-100) in terms of molar quantities:

$$k^* = 2d_{12}{}^2 (2\pi RT/M^*)^{1/2} e^{-U^*/RT} \qquad (8\text{-}101)$$

where $M^* = M_1M_2/(M_1 + M_2)$ is the reduced molecular weight and U^* the activation energy per mole. The temperature dependence of the rate constant is correctly predicted by Eq. (8-101); however, the value of U^* must be determined from experiment, e.g., by plotting $\log (k^*/T^{1/2})$ versus T^{-1} and measuring the slope. In the case of the $2HI \rightarrow H_2 + I_2$ reaction, U^* is found to be close to 4.4×10^4 cal/mole, and since $R \simeq 2$ cal/°K/mole, the exponential factor becomes $e^{-22,000/T}$. It is apparent that at ordinary temperatures very few molecules will have thermal energies of the order of u^* or greater and that a reactive encounter is a rare event compared to an ordinary collision. The extreme sensitivity of the reaction rate to the temperature is illustrated by comparing the exponential factor at 300°K and 3000°K. Since the values are 10^{-32} and 10^{-3}, respectively, and the $T^{1/2}$ variation is negligible, it follows that a ten-fold increase in the absolute temperature should lead to a 10^{29}-fold increase in the rate constant. The reaction rate is usually studied over much shorter temperature intervals, and the general result is that the rate increases by a factor of two or three with a 10-degree rise in temperature for reactions of this type. The absolute value of the rate constant predicted by Eq. (8-101) is a severe test of the theory. The comparison between theory and experiment is made by first determining U^* from the measured temperature variation of k^* and then using the observed absolute values of k^* to estimate the reaction diameter d_{12}. The latter is expected to be of the order of molecular dimensions and somewhat smaller than the collision diameter obtained from viscosity or diffusion measurements. The difference between the two diameters can be attributed partly to the more intimate contact between the molecules when they react chemically than when they exchange momentum and partly to the reduction in cross section due to (1) decomposition of the activated complex into the initial reactants and (2) the existence of preferred collisional orientations for reaction. The experimental rate constant for the reaction $2HI \rightarrow H_2 + I_2$ can be represented over a wide temperature range by

$$k^* = 3 \times 10^{-12}T^{1/2}e^{-22,000/T} \qquad cm^3/sec/molecule \qquad (8-102)$$

Comparison with Eq. (8-101) gives $d_{12} \simeq 2.3 \times 10^{-8}$ cm, which is somewhat smaller than the value of 3.5×10^{-8} cm deduced from viscosity measurements. Equally good agreement has been obtained in other instances.* More refined theories of reaction rates† are outside the domain of kinetic theory.

Before concluding this section, we shall touch briefly on a fundamental

* See C. N. Hinshelwood, "The Kinetics of Chemical Change," Oxford University Press, London, 1941.

† S. Glasstone, K. Laidler, and H. Eyring, "The Theory of Rate Processes," McGraw-Hill Book Company, Inc., New York, 1941.

assumption of reaction-rate theory which is implicit in the derivation given above.   It is important to observe that Eq. (8-96) is based on the Maxwell velocity distribution and is strictly valid only for a gas or gas mixture that is in thermal, dynamical, and chemical equilibrium.   The reaction-rate studies of chemical kinetics are made on unbalanced reactions proceeding in one direction primarily.   According to the simple collision theory, one or both of the collision partners must be highly energetic, i.e., in the tail of the Maxwell distribution at ordinary temperatures, in order to surmount the activation barrier and undergo reaction.   The chemical reaction, as it proceeds, tends to deplete the number of very energetic molecules of the reacting gases.   The effect would be to alter the velocity and energy distributions, if the molecules used up were not replaced. However, ordinary nonreactive collisions tend to restore the equilibrium (Maxwellian) distribution and to replenish the number of high-energy molecules.   If the chemical reaction proceeds slowly enough so that the tail of the velocity distribution is replenished by collision as fast as it is depleted by reaction, then the use of the Maxwell distribution function and other equilibrium formulas is a good approximation even though a state of complete equilibrium does not exist.

PROBLEMS

8-1. Obtain Eq. (8-1) for the polar components of acceleration by first transforming the rectangular components and then projecting them in the radial and transverse directions.

8-2. Apply Eq. (8-21) to the scattering of rigid elastic spheres by a fixed sphere and show that $b = d_{12} \cos \frac{1}{2}\chi$.   Obtain this relation directly from Fig. 8-3.

8-3. Consider the small-angle scattering in a field described by the potential $u(r) = c'r^{-q}$ where q is a positive integer and c' may be of either sign.   Show that for small deflections, the polar angle of deflection is given by

$$\chi \simeq q|c'|A_q/Eb^q$$

where

$$A_q = \int_0^{\pi/2} \cos^q \alpha \, d\alpha = \frac{\pi^{1/2}}{2} \frac{\Gamma[(q+1)/2]}{\Gamma[(q/2)+1]}$$

and E is the incident kinetic energy.

Hint: Use the result of Prob. 6-7.

8-4. Show that the angular distribution for the small-angle scattering in Prob. 8-3 is given by

$$S(\chi) \simeq \frac{1}{q} \left(\frac{qA_q|c'|}{E} \right)^{2/q} \frac{1}{\chi^{2+(2/q)}}$$

8-5. Justify Eq. (8-43).

8-6. Derive Eq. (8-53).   *Hint:* Draw the vector triangle showing the final velocity in the laboratory $\mathbf{v}_1'$ as the resultant of the final velocity in the C system $\mathbf{v}_{1c}'$ and the velocity of the center of mass $\mathbf{v}_c$. Show from this diagram that

$$\tan \chi_L = \frac{v_{1c}' \sin \chi_c}{v_{1c}' \cos \chi_c + v_c}$$

8-7. Using Sutherland's model of rigid-elastic-sphere molecules interacting through a weakly attractive inverse power field $[u(r) = -c'r^{-q}]$, show that, to first order in the force constant c', the angles of deflection in contact collisions are given by

$$\chi = 2 \cos^{-1} x_m + \frac{c'}{\varepsilon b^q} \int_0^{x_m} \frac{x^q \, dx}{(1 - x^2)^{3/2}} \qquad x_m \leq 1$$

where $x = b/r$, $x_m = b/d_{12}$, and $\varepsilon = \frac{1}{2}m^* v_r^2$. Show that values of $b > d_{12}$ contribute second-order terms to the transport cross sections.

8-8. Show that in the preceding problem the transport cross section for diffusion is given to first order by

$$\sigma_D = \pi d_{12}^2 + 2\pi c' j_1(q)/\varepsilon d_{12}^{q-2}$$

where $j_1(q) = 2 \int_0^1 dx_m \, x_m^{2-q}(1 - x_m^2)^{1/2} \int_0^{x_m} dx \, x^q(1 - x^2)^{-3/2}$

Note: $j_1(q)$, which is a function of q only, is identical with the quantity $i_1(q + 1)$, which is tabulated on page 184 of Chapman and Cowling's book.

8-9. Through substitution of σ_D from the preceding problem into the formula for Ω_D, show that

$$\Omega_D = \Omega_D^{\text{r.s.}}[1 + (S_{12}/T)]$$
and $$D_{12} = D_{12}^{\text{r.s.}}/[1 + (S_{12}/T)]$$
where $$S_{12} = c' j_1(q)/k d_{12}^q = j_1(q)|u(d_{12})|/k$$

and r.s. denotes the rigid-sphere value.

8-10. Show that the number of collisions between rigid-sphere molecules per unit volume per unit time in which the energy of the component of the relative motion along the line of centers—i.e., the radial kinetic energy—just before impact exceeds a specified value u^* is

$$2\kappa n_1 n_2 d_{12}^2 (2\pi kT/m^*)^{1/2} e^{-u^*/kT}$$

where u^* is interpreted as the activation energy. Explain why this formula is the same as Eq. (8-97).

Hint: Replace $\sigma(v_r)$ in Eq. (8-66) by $d\sigma$ from (8-51). Let $u^* = \frac{1}{2}m^* v^{*2}$. Then the component of $\mathbf{v}_r$ along the line of centers at impact satisfies the condition: $v_r \cos \theta \geq v^*$. The integration over θ is first performed between the limits: $1 \geq \cos \theta \geq v^*/v_r$. The final integration over v_r extends from v^* to ∞.

8-11. The self-diffusion coefficient obtained from the diffusion of parahydrogen in orthohydrogen at 15°C and 1 atm. pressure is 1.40 cm²/sec. The isotopic diffusion coefficient for deuterium in hydrogen at the same temperature and pressure is 1.24 cm²/sec. Compare the ratio of these values with the theoretical prediction.

CHAPTER 9

BROWNIAN MOTION AND DENSITY FLUCTUATIONS

This chapter introduces the fluctuation phenomena and deals with two important examples: the Brownian motion of small particles suspended in a fluid and the fluctuations in density which have important consequences for the scattering of light. In Sec. 9-1 we discuss the nature of the Brownian motions, treat the vertical distribution of the suspended particles under the influence of gravity, and derive the Einstein–von Smoluchowski formula for the mean-square displacement of a particle. The experiments of Perrin and of Millikan and Fletcher are briefly discussed. Section 9-2 deals with the density fluctuations, first in a perfect gas and then in an imperfect gas. The fluctuation formulas of von Smoluchowski and Einstein are derived and applied to imperfect gases well above and also close to the critical point. The remainder of the section is devoted to the scattering of light by gases, treated from the point of view of density fluctuations. The blue color of the sky and the phenomenon of critical opalescence are discussed. In Appendix 9-1 we derive a number of well-known and generally useful formulas describing statistical fluctuations.

9-1. THE BROWNIAN MOTION

The properties of gases treated in earlier chapters have represented averages over enormous numbers of molecules. It has been pointed out in Sec. 1-4 that the smaller the collection, or sample, to which statistical methods are applied, the larger are the percentage deviations from the average, or most probable, behavior. In Appendix 9-1, which deals with statistical fluctuations, it is shown that the root-mean-square relative fluctuation varies inversely with the square root of the size of the collection. The large numbers of molecules involved in all the gaseous phenomena that we have considered ensure that the statistical fluctuations are ordinarily imperceptible. The question arises whether it is possible, either by reducing the number of molecules in the collection or by adopting more sensitive experimental methods, to detect and measure statistical fluctuations and to account theoretically for the observed results. A successful statistical theory would be expected to predict the distribution function for the fluctuations and provide a formula for the mean-square fluctuation. Statistical fluctuations are readily observed in the case of radioactive decay and also in the so-called thermal-noise effects of electronics, e.g., the shot effect. A treatment of these effects, although it falls within the general province of statistical mechanics, is outside the domain of the kinetic theory of gases. Two important gaseous phenomena that owe their very existence to fluctuations are treated in this chapter: the Brownian motion and, in the next section, the fluctuations in density which are responsible for the blue color of the sky and the opalescence of liquid-vapor systems at the critical point.

Particles of microscopic size immersed in a fluid are observed to execute an incessant, irregular, and randomly directed motion, referred to as the *Brownian movement*. Examples are colloidal suspensions in liquids and suspensions of dust particles and fine droplets in the atmosphere. Careful experiments have shown these motions to be without apparent external cause; among the possibilities that have been eliminated are convection currents from unequal heating, mechanical jarring, chemical action, etc. The Brownian movement has been qualitatively and quantitatively explained as a direct manifestation of thermal agitation, the particles in question displaying the expected behavior of macromolecules in equilibrium with the molecules of the fluid. The Brownian particles, which are large enough to be seen through a microscope and small enough to exhibit heat motion, provide a convincing demonstration of the truth of the kinetic-molecular hypothesis. The rapidity of the movement is observed to increase with a decrease in the size of the particles and also with decreasing viscosity of the fluid. The dependence on size would be expected from the greater relative fluctuations in bombardment rate for a smaller particle than for a larger one. When averaged over a sufficiently long time interval, the molecular impacts against the particle from any one direction are balanced by impacts from the opposite direction. In a short time interval, however, fluctuations in the bombardment rate will lead to a small displacement of the particle along the direction in which the greatest impulse is being delivered. In a macroscopic time interval as short as the persistence time of human vision, the displacement of a Brownian particle represents the vector sum, or resultant, of a great number of small deflections.

It is now possible to understand why the mean speed of thermal agitation of a Brownian particle, which can be deduced from the equipartition theorem, is not an observable quantity. The mean kinetic energy of translation of the particle, regarded as a giant molecule in equilibrium with the molecules of the fluid, is equal to $3kT/2$. This leads to a mean speed of the order of 1 cm/sec for a typical particle of dimensions $\sim 10^{-5}$ cm. The observed root-mean-square displacement in a time interval of 30 seconds is $\sim 10^{-3}$ cm in a liquid and $\sim 10^{-2}$ cm in a gas. The apparent velocities that one observes are thus several orders of magnitude smaller than the velocities of thermal agitation.   The difference arises, of course, from the fact that the observed path is a smoothed-out version of the very irregular zigzag path which the particle actually follows and which is too fine to perceive; the total distance traveled by the particle is thus very much greater than it appears to be.   It is clear that the motion of an individual Brownian particle is of the nature of a random walk and that the motion of a group of Brownian particles through a gas or liquid is a special case of mutual diffusion.   The connection between the random-walk problem and diffusion has been established in Sec. 4-4. Equation (4-78) shows that the diffusion coefficient D is approximately the product of the mean thermal speed and the effective step size, or mean free path.   The latter represents the average distance that the Brownian particle travels between two successive significant deflections and would be expected to be $\sim 10^{-8}$ cm in a liquid.   Thus, for a particle of dimensions $\sim 10^{-5}$ cm, one obtains $D \sim 10^{-8}$ cm²/sec.   Equation (4-67) then shows that the root-mean-square displacement in a 30-sec interval is $\sim 10^{-3}$ cm, in agreement with experiment.   These considerations, although they are very rough, indicate the lines along which the theory is to be developed.

We first consider the vertical distribution of Brownian particles suspended in a fluid under the influence of gravity.   Assuming the gravitational field and the temperature to be uniform and the particles to be all of the same mass m (in practice this is achieved by fractional centrifuging), it follows from the Maxwell-Boltzmann distribution law, Eq. (5-2), or from the barometric formula, Eq. (5-51), that the number density of particles at height z is given by

$$n(z) = n(0)e^{-mgz/kT} \tag{9-1}$$

where $n(0)$ is the density at the bottom of the container ($z = 0$).   From the form of the Maxwell-Boltzmann function or from an obvious extension of the barometric formula derivation in Appendix 5-1, it is clear that in a mixture of two perfect gases the partial densities of each will separately obey the barometric equation (9-1).   Thus (9-1) is applicable to a "gas" of Brownian particles suspended in air.   General principles of statistical mechanics show that it can also be applied to the case of particles suspended in a liquid, provided that the mass m is replaced by $m - m'$ where m' is the mass of displaced liquid (buoyancy correction). Equation (9-1) can be directly verified and also used to obtain an approximate value of k.   In a classic series of experiments on the Brownian motion,* J. Perrin prepared colloidal suspensions in which the particles were spherical and of uniform size and measured the mass density and

---

* J. Perrin, "Atoms," Constable & Co., Ltd., London, 1920, and "Brownian Movement and Molecular Reality," Taylor and Francis, London, 1910.

radius a of the particles by several ingenious methods.   Replacing the mass m by $(\frac{4}{3})\pi a^3(\rho_P - \rho_L)$ where ρ_P and ρ_L are the mass densities of the particles and the liquid, Eq. (9-1) becomes

$$kT \log (n_1/n_2) = -(\frac{4}{3})\pi a^3(\rho_P - \rho_L)g(z_1 - z_2) \qquad (9\text{-}2)$$

where n_1 and n_2 are number densities or concentrations of colloidal particles at heights z_1 and z_2.   Though the particles do not all go to the bottom and remain there, for reasons discussed in Appendix 5-1, it is apparent from Eq. (9-1) that the falling off in density with height is extremely rapid for Brownian particles, so that very few particles of radius $\sim 10^{-5}$ cm are to be found at distances from the bottom much greater than 1 mm, since $kT/mg \sim 10^{-2}$ cm.   In Perrin's experiments, photomicrographs were taken at varying heights by adjusting the plane of focus of the microscope.   The distance $z_1 - z_2$ was obtained from the microscope adjustment and the ratio n_1/n_2 from counting particles on the two photographs. The results verified the exponential dependence of density on height given by the barometric formula and, when substituted in Eq. (9-2), determined a value of Boltzmann's constant k and of Avogadro's number $L = R/k$ in fair agreement with modern values.

The Theory of the Brownian Motion.   The theoretical formula for the mean-square displacement of a Brownian particle was developed independently by Einstein* and von Smoluchowski.†   In the abbreviated derivation given here, the effective diffusion coefficient D is found by equating the downward flow caused by gravity to the upward diffusive transport produced by the concentration gradient.   Thus, the net flow of particles per unit area per unit time in the upward $(+z)$ direction is

$$G = -D \, dn/dz - nv = 0 \qquad (9\text{-}3)$$

where v is the terminal velocity of descent of the particles and n is given by the barometric formula.   It is again assumed that all particles are of the same mass m and of the same size and shape.   The terminal velocity is proportional to $(m - m')g$, i.e., to the weight of the particle minus the buoyant force.   This is a special case of the motion of a body through a viscous medium in which the force of resistance, or drag, is proportional to the velocity.   In the steady state, the velocity is then proportional to the applied force causing the motion.   Denoting the viscous drag by Cv, the steady-state descent of a particle of mass m which displaces a mass m' of liquid is characterized by the terminal velocity

$$v = (m - m')g/C \qquad (9\text{-}4)$$

Replacing m by $m - m'$ in (9-1) and substituting in (9-3), one obtains

---

* A. Einstein, *Ann. d. Physik*, vol. 17, p. 549, 1905; vol. 19, p. 371, 1906.
† M. v. Smoluchowski, *Ann. d. Physik*, vol. 21, p. 756, 1906.

$$D \frac{(m - m')g}{kT} n(z) = \frac{(m - m')g}{C} n(z)$$

whence $$D = kT/C \qquad (9\text{-}5)$$

If the particles are spherical and the medium is a liquid, C can be calculated by standard hydrodynamic methods.* The form of the result is easily seen from a dimensional argument. Since the viscous drag f can depend only on the viscosity η, the radius a, and the velocity v, the dimensional equation in terms of force $[F]$, length $[L]$, and time $[T]$ is

$$f\,[F] \propto \eta^m a^n v^p\,[F^m T^m L^{-2m} L^n L^p T^{-p}] \qquad (9\text{-}6)$$

whence $m = n = p = 1$ and
$$f \propto \eta a v$$

which shows that the drag is proportional to the first power of the velocity. The exact result, known as Stokes' law, is

$$f = Cv = 6\pi\eta a v \qquad (9\text{-}7)$$

and, substituting this in (9-5), one gets

$$D = \frac{kT}{6\pi\eta a} \qquad (9\text{-}8)$$

Equations (9-5) and (9-8), although obtained in the special case of a gravitational field, are clearly independent of the type of field producing the forced diffusion. The average square of the x component of the displacement of a particle during a time interval t is given by Eq. (4-67) as†

$$\overline{x^2} = 2Dt = \left(\frac{kT}{3\pi\eta a}\right) t \qquad (9\text{-}9)$$

Equation (9-9), first derived by Einstein, has been tested by Perrin, who followed the motion of single particles over long periods against a background of coordinate lines in the field of view of the microscope. The position of the particle was noted at 30-second intervals and plotted on graph paper. The x components of successive displacements of the same particle for the same time interval, $t = 30$ sec, were used to calculate $\overline{x^2}$. In agreement with Eq. (9-9), the observed values of $\overline{x^2}$ were found to be directly proportional to the time interval t and inversely proportional to the viscosity η of the liquid and the radius a of the particle. An approximate value of k was also obtained. The statistical distribution of the displacements is also of interest. The distribution function for the x

* L. Page, "Introduction to Theoretical Physics," D. Van Nostrand Company, Inc., Princeton, N.J., 1935, p. 273.

† The formulas (4-66) and (4-67) for one-dimensional displacements are readily seen to hold for the x components of three-dimensional displacements.

components of the displacements is given by Eq. (4-66): the probability that a particle receives an x component of displacement between x and $x + dx$ in the time interval t is

$$f(x,t) \ dx = \frac{dx}{(4\pi Dt)^{\frac{1}{2}}} \ e^{-x^2/4Dt} \tag{9-10}$$

Equation (9-10) has also been confirmed experimentally. The interpretation of the Brownian motion as a diffusion process with each particle executing a random walk is thus quantitatively verified.

The Brownian motion is more rapid in a gas than in a liquid, i.e., the same particle will, in the same time interval, undergo greater displacements if suspended in air than if suspended in water. This is obviously accounted for by the smaller viscosity of the gas. The application of the theory to particles suspended in gases, e.g., oil droplets in air, requires examination of the validity of Stokes' law. It has already been pointed out in Secs. 2-5 and 4-3 and in Appendix 3-1 that the laws of viscous flow are applicable to gases only if the molecular mean free path λ is small compared to the relevant dimensions. Stokes' law is valid for a sphere of radius a moving slowly through a gas, provided that $\lambda \ll a$. Since $\lambda \sim 10^{-5}$ cm in air at standard conditions and $a \sim 10^{-4}$ cm for typical suspensions, Stokes' law is inaccurate, and Eqs. (9-8) and (9-9) cannot be used. This difficulty can be circumvented by a method due to L. de Broglie and to Millikan,[*] which not only makes it unnecessary to know the exact law for the viscous drag when $\lambda \sim a$ but also avoids the measurement of a. The well-known Millikan oil-drop apparatus[†] is used, in which charged droplets are formed between two parallel horizontal plates differing in electric potential and the motion of the droplets under the influence of the electric field E is observed with the aid of a horizontal microscope. When the drop descends with velocity v_g under the influence of gravity,

$$mg = Cv_g$$

and when it rises under the influence of the field with velocity v_E

$$veE - mg = Cv_E$$

and, combining these equations,

$$C = \frac{veE}{v_E + v_g} \tag{9-11}$$

The drag coefficient C has already been introduced in Eq. (9-4); it characterizes a drop of given size in a given medium. The charge on the drop,

---

[*] R. A. Millikan, "Electrons, Protons, Photons, Neutrons, Mesotrons, and Cosmic Rays," University of Chicago Press, Chicago, 1947.

[†] *Ibid.*

νe, is an integral multiple of the fundamental charge e of the electron; it can be changed by exposure to a radioactive source.   If the same drop is observed in the same field with varying amounts of charge, the resulting values of $v_E + v_g$ will be proportional to ν according to Eq. (9-11). The greatest common divisor of these values of $v_E + v_g$, which will be denoted by $(v_E + v_g)_1$, must correspond to $\nu = 1$, whence

$$C = \frac{eE}{(v_E + v_g)_1} \qquad (9\text{-}12)$$

Substituting (9-12) in (9-5) and the resulting value of D into (4-67), we obtain for the mean-square x component of the displacement in a time interval t

$$\overline{x^2} = 2Dt = \frac{2kTt(v_E + v_g)_1}{eE} \qquad (9\text{-}13)$$

The procedure in verifying Eq. (9-13) is, first, to measure v_g and v_E for different charges on the selected drop, thus determining $(v_E + v_g)_1/E$. In order to observe the Brownian motion of the same drop, the electric field is adjusted to balance gravity and the horizontal displacements are measured for a chosen time interval.   The velocity and displacement measurements are made with the aid of a ruled scale at the focus of the eyepiece of the microscope.   It is convenient to rewrite Eq. (9-13) as

$$Le = \frac{2RTt(v_E + v_g)_1}{E\overline{x^2}} \qquad (9\text{-}14)$$

All quantities on the right side of (9-14) are measured in the experiment except R, which is known from the gas laws.   The quantity Le on the left side is just the Faraday constant representing the charge transported in the electrolysis of one gram atom of a univalent substance.   Since the values of Le obtained from Eq. (9-14) by Millikan and Fletcher agreed within 2 per cent with the Faraday constant, this method provides the most accurate confirmation of the theory of the Brownian motion.*

9-2. DENSITY FLUCTUATIONS AND THE SCATTERING OF LIGHT

The second problem to be discussed is that of density fluctuations. Consider a small, fixed region in a container of gas.   The number of molecules in the region is continually fluctuating as a result of the molecular chaos.   If the gas is assumed to be perfect or ideal and the effects of

---

* For more recent and advanced developments in this subject, the reader is referred to S. Chandrasekhar, *Rev. Mod. Phys.*, vol. 15, p. 1, 1943, and to M. C. Wang and G. E. Uhlenbeck, *Rev. Mod. Phys.*, vol. 17, p. 323, 1945.

gravity are neglected, the spatial distribution of molecules is governed by the laws of chance, and the formulas of Appendix 9-1 are directly applicable. The molecular density, as defined in Sec. 2-2, refers to the number of molecules in a fixed region or volume element that is very small compared to the size of the container but sufficiently large to contain many molecules. According to Appendix 9-1, these are just the conditions for the applicability of the Laplace-Gauss formula, or normal-distribution law. Since n has been used heretofore to denote the molecular density, we shall preserve this usage and employ ν to denote the number of molecules in the volume element.* Then $\delta = (\nu - \bar{\nu})/\bar{\nu}$ is the *relative fluctuation* in this number. The probability of a fluctuation between δ and $\delta + d\delta$ is given by Eq. (9-56) as

$$W(\delta)\ d\delta = (\bar{\nu}/2\pi)^{1/2} e^{-\bar{\nu}\delta^2/2}\ d\delta \qquad (9\text{-}15)$$

and the root-mean-square relative fluctuation δ^* by (9-49):

$$\delta^* = (\bar{\nu})^{-1/2} \qquad (9\text{-}16)$$

Since the volume is fixed, δ also represents the relative fluctuation in the density, i.e., $\delta = (n - \bar{n})/\bar{n}$. On applying (9-16) to 1 cm³ of gas at standard conditions, we find that $\delta^* = 1.9 \times 10^{-10}$, which clearly represents an imperceptible fluctuation.

The problem becomes more physical, and not simply a problem in the calculus of probabilities, if we turn to the case of an imperfect gas. Considering the molecules to be of finite size, the probability of finding a molecule in a volume element is not independent of the number already present; thus the geometric probabilities of Appendix 9-1 require modification along the lines of Prob. 6-6. The presence of attractive forces between pairs of molecules will also alter these probabilities. As the number of molecules in the volume element increases, the probability of finding an additional molecule in the element is enhanced by attractive intermolecular forces and diminished by repulsions of which the finite size effect is a special case (rigid-sphere repulsion). The calculation of the density fluctuations in an imperfect gas thus apparently requires a detailed knowledge of the intermolecular forces. This laborious investigation can be circumvented by a method due to von Smoluchowski† and Einstein,‡ which enables one to replace unknown molecular properties by macroscopic thermodynamic quantities, e.g., the compressibility of the gas.

It is convenient to treat the simple case of an imperfect gas contained in a vertical cylinder closed at the bottom. The gas is confined from

---

* In Appendix 9-1, the number of molecules in the volume element is denoted by n.
† M. v. Smoluchowski, *Ann. d. Physik*, vol. 25, p. 205, 1908.
‡ A. Einstein, *Ann. d. Physik*, vol. 33, p. 1275, 1910.

above by a heavy, frictionless, leakproof piston of weight w, and above the piston is a vacuum.   We denote the area of the piston by A, its height above the bottom of the cylinder by z, and the corresponding volume of the confined gas by $V = Az$.   The equilibrium values are denoted by z_0 and V_0, respectively, and the equilibrium pressure by $p = p_0 = w/A$. Fluctuations in the momentum imparted to the piston, resulting from the chaotic molecular bombardment of its under surface, cause a minute, irregular bobbing up and down which is ordinarily imperceptible.   This irregular Brownian motion of the piston is correlated with fluctuations in the volume and mean density of the confined gas.   The Maxwell-Boltzmann law has been applied in the preceding section to the Brownian particles, which were treated as giant molecules distributed according to this law, e.g., according to the barometric formula, with results in accord with experiment.   We now extend the range of application of the law still farther by applying it to the Brownian motion of the piston, which is regarded as a giant Brownian particle in equilibrium with the molecules of the gas.*   Then the probability of finding the piston between z and $z + dz$ is given by

$$f(z) \, dz = Ce^{-U(z)/kT} \, dz \tag{9-17}$$

where U denotes the potential energy of the piston referred to its equilibrium or mean position $[U(z_0) = 0]$ and C is a normalization constant. The probability of a volume fluctuation in which the volume of the confined gas is between V and $V + dV$ is then

$$F(V) \, dV = CA^{-1}e^{-U/kT} \, dV \tag{9-18}$$

The potential energy U is partly gravitational potential energy of the piston and partly potential energy stored in the gas, which behaves like a compressed spring.   The gravitational energy is equal to $w(z - z_0)$. The potential energy of the gas when compressed from its equilibrium volume V_0 to a smaller volume V is equal to the work done by the gas on its surroundings in expanding from V to V_0, i.e., to $\int_V^{V_0} p \, dV$.   Thus

$$U = w(z - z_0) + \int_V^{V_0} p \, dV \tag{9-19}$$
$$= (w/A)(Az - Az_0) + \int_V^{V_0} p \, dV$$
$$= p_0(V - V_0) - \int_{V_0}^V p \, dV$$
$$= - \int_{V_0}^V (p - p_0) \, dV \tag{9-20}$$

The potential energy is seen from Eq. (9-20) to increase for any disturbance from equilibrium, whether the volume increases or decreases.   If

* The general principles of statistical mechanics fully justify this use of the Maxwell-Boltzmann formula.

the departures from equilibrium are small, it is easily verified that (see Prob. 9-4)

$$U \simeq -\tfrac{1}{2}(p - p_0)(V - V_0) \tag{9-21}$$

Substituting (9-20) into (9-18), we obtain the volume-fluctuation formula

$$F(V)\, dV = CA^{-1}e^{(1/kT)\int_{V_0}^{V}(p - p_0)\, dV}\, dV \tag{9-22}$$

The relative fluctuation of the density n from its equilibrium value n_0 is given by

$$\delta = \frac{n - n_0}{n_0} = \frac{n}{n_0} - 1 = \frac{V_0}{V} - 1 = \frac{V_0 - V}{V}$$
$$\simeq -\frac{(V - V_0)}{V_0} \tag{9-23}$$

assuming that the fluctuations are small. Equation (9-22) can then be rewritten as

$$W(\delta)\, d\delta = C'e^{(1/kT)\int_{V_0}^{V}(p - p_0)\, dV}\, d\delta \tag{9-24}$$

where C' is a new normalization constant.

Equation (9-24) can be applied to the local density fluctuations in the interior of a gas in equilibrium. In this case the volume V and the density n refer to an element of the fluid of fixed mass comprising a fixed number of molecules, e.g., the ν molecules that are closest to a fixed point P. The local density n in the neighborhood of P is equal to ν/V where V is the fluctuating volume "occupied" by the ν closest molecules, which is clearly somewhat difficult to define. It is preferable to define first the local density n as the number of molecules in a small, fixed sphere of volume V_0 with center at P divided by V_0. The fluctuating volume V can then be defined as ν/n. The confining action of the piston in the example treated is now replaced by the similar confining action of the portion of the fluid contiguous to the element in question, and the gravitational work is replaced by work done by the surrounding gas at pressure p_0. The total potential energy, when the element is compressed from V_0 to V, is then equal to the net work that would be performed during the expansion of the element back to its normal, equilibrium volume V_0, the expansion being opposed throughout by the equilibrium pressure p_0. This leads again to Eq. (9-20).

Since the volume fluctuations are assumed to be small, we expand the pressure p in a Taylor series about the equilibrium pressure p_0

$$p = p_0 + (V - V_0)\left(\frac{\partial p}{\partial V}\right)_0 + \frac{(V - V_0)^2}{2!}\left(\frac{\partial^2 p}{\partial V^2}\right)_0$$
$$+ \frac{(V - V_0)^3}{3!}\left(\frac{\partial^3 p}{\partial V^3}\right)_0 + \cdots \tag{9-25}$$

where the derivatives are to be evaluated for $V = V_0$, i.e., at equilibrium. Hence

$$\int_{V_0}^{V} (p - p_0)\, dV = \left(\frac{\partial p}{\partial V}\right)_0 \int_{V_0}^{V} (V - V_0)\, dV$$

$$+ \frac{1}{2!} \left(\frac{\partial^2 p}{\partial V^2}\right)_0 \int_{V_0}^{V} (V - V_0)^2\, dV$$

$$+ \frac{1}{3!} \left(\frac{\partial^3 p}{\partial V^3}\right)_0 \int_{V_0}^{V} (V - V_0)^3\, dV + \cdots$$

$$= \frac{(V - V_0)^2}{2!} \left(\frac{\partial p}{\partial V}\right)_0 + \frac{(V - V_0)^3}{3!} \left(\frac{\partial^2 p}{\partial V^2}\right)_0 \qquad (9\text{-}26)$$

$$+ \frac{(V - V_0)^4}{4!} \left(\frac{\partial^3 p}{\partial V^3}\right)_0 \cdots$$

$$= \frac{V_0^2 \delta^2}{2} \left(\frac{\partial p}{\partial V}\right)_0 - \frac{V_0^3 \delta^3}{3!} \left(\frac{\partial^2 p}{\partial V^2}\right)_0$$

$$+ \frac{V_0^4 \delta^4}{4!} \left(\frac{\partial^3 p}{\partial V^3}\right)_0 \cdots$$

making use of (9-23).   The partial derivatives can be evaluated with the aid of the equation of state of the fluid; they are to be evaluated with the temperature held constant, since the fluctuations under consideration take place at constant temperature.*   Neglecting all terms beyond the first in Eq. (9-26) and substituting in Eq. (9-24), we obtain

$$W(\delta)\, d\delta = C' e^{(V_0^2 \delta^2 / 2kT)(\partial p/\partial V)_0}\, d\delta \qquad (9\text{-}27)$$

$$= C' e^{-V_0 \delta^2 / 2kT \varkappa_0}\, d\delta$$

where $\varkappa_0$ is the *isothermal compressibility* at volume V_0 and is defined by

$$\varkappa = - \frac{1}{V} \left(\frac{\partial V}{\partial p}\right)_T \qquad (9\text{-}28)$$

If the fluid is a perfect gas, it is easily found that $\varkappa = 1/p$ and, since $p_0 V_0 = \nu kT$ where ν is the number of molecules in the system, i.e., the element of fluid, Eq. (9-27) reduces to

$$W(\delta)\, d\delta = C' e^{-\nu \delta^2 / 2}\, d\delta \qquad (9\text{-}29)$$

Equation (9-29) gives the probability of a relative fluctuation in density between δ and $\delta + d\delta$ in a perfect gas.   The distribution of density fluctuations clearly cannot depend on whether the fluctuations result from a varying number of molecules ν in a fixed element of volume V or from variations in the volume V of a fluid element comprising a fixed number of molecules ν.   Equation (9-29), which was obtained by con-

---

* Volume (or density) fluctuations and temperature fluctuations can be shown to be independent.   See L. D. Landau and E. M. Lifschitz, "Statistical Physics," Oxford University Press, London, 1938, p. 116.

sidering volume variations, can be applied as well to number variations (in this case ν is replaced by $\bar{\nu}$). Comparison of (9-29) with (9-15) then shows that these formulas are completely equivalent. This may be regarded as a confirmation of the fundamental assumptions.

If the fluid is an imperfect gas not too close to the critical point, the more general formula (9-27) is to be used and $\varkappa$ obtained from the equation of state. In normalizing (9-27), one makes the customary approximation of extending the range of δ from $-\infty$ to $+\infty$ (see Appendix 9-1), thus obtaining

$$W(\delta)\,d\delta = \left(\frac{V_0}{2\pi kT\varkappa_0}\right)^{\frac{1}{2}} e^{-V_0\delta^2/2kT\varkappa_0}\,d\delta \tag{9-30}$$

and the corresponding root-mean-square relative fluctuation

$$\delta^* = (kT\varkappa_0/V_0)^{\frac{1}{2}} \tag{9-31}$$

It is apparent from (9-31) that δ^* varies as $\nu^{-\frac{1}{2}}$ or $(\bar{\nu})^{-\frac{1}{2}}$. The mean potential energy associated with the fluctuations is given to first order by

$$\bar{U} = -\frac{V_0^2\overline{\delta^2}}{2}\left(\frac{\partial p}{\partial V}\right)_0 = \frac{V_0\delta^{*2}}{2\varkappa_0} = \frac{kT}{2} \tag{9-32}$$

in agreement with the equipartition theorem. At the critical point $(\partial p/\partial V)_T$ and $(\partial^2 p/\partial V^2)_T$ both vanish (see Sec. 6-1). The development given in Eq. (9-26) then begins with the third term and, if higher-order terms are neglected, we obtain, in the neighborhood of the critical point,

$$W(\delta)\,d\delta = Ce^{-\alpha\delta^4}\,d\delta \tag{9-33}$$

where

$$\alpha = -\frac{V_c^4}{24kT_c}\left(\frac{\partial^3 p}{\partial V^3}\right)_c \tag{9-34}$$

The normalization constant C is given by

$$\begin{aligned} C^{-1} &= \int_{-\infty}^{\infty} e^{-\alpha\delta^4}\,d\delta \\ &= \frac{1}{2\alpha^{\frac{1}{4}}}\int_0^{\infty} e^{-x}x^{-\frac{3}{4}}\,dx \\ &= \frac{\Gamma(\frac{1}{4})}{2\alpha^{\frac{1}{4}}} \end{aligned} \tag{9-35}$$

where the gamma function $\Gamma(\frac{1}{4}) = 3.626$. The mean-square relative fluctuation is then

$$\begin{aligned} \delta^{*2} = \overline{\delta^2} &= C\int_{-\infty}^{\infty} e^{-\alpha\delta^4}\delta^2\,d\delta \\ &= \frac{C}{2\alpha^{\frac{3}{4}}}\int_0^{\infty} e^{-x}x^{-\frac{1}{4}}\,dx \\ &= \frac{C}{2\alpha^{\frac{3}{4}}}\Gamma(\frac{3}{4}) \end{aligned} \tag{9-36}$$

with $\Gamma(\tfrac{3}{4}) = 1.225$.   Hence

$$\delta^* = \left(\frac{\Gamma(\tfrac{3}{4})}{\Gamma(\tfrac{1}{4})}\right)^{\!\!\tfrac{1}{2}} \frac{1}{\alpha^{\tfrac{1}{4}}} = \frac{0.581}{\alpha^{\tfrac{1}{4}}} \qquad (9\text{-}37)$$

It is apparent from the form of (9-34) that α is directly proportional to the number of molecules ν in a fluid element, or to the mean number $\bar{\nu}$ in a fixed element of volume.   Thus δ^* varies as $\bar{\nu}^{-\frac{1}{4}}$ at the critical point instead of $\bar{\nu}^{-\frac{1}{2}}$.   A numerical estimate of α and of δ^* can be obtained from the van der Waals equation of state, which is not very accurate, however, near the critical point.   This gives

$$\alpha = 9\bar{\nu}/64$$
and
$$\delta^* = 0.949\bar{\nu}^{-\frac{1}{4}} \qquad (9\text{-}38)$$

The Scattering of Light as a Fluctuation Phenomenon.   These fluctuation formulas have an important application to the scattering of light by gases.*   The molecular scattering in the visible region of the spectrum is referred to as *Rayleigh scattering*, the theory having been first developed by Lord Rayleigh.   According to the classical theory of this effect, the electrons in the molecules of the scattering medium are set into forced vibration by the electric field of the incident light wave.   The oscillating electric dipole moments that are thus induced radiate the scattered light, which is of the same frequency as the incident light and is emitted in all directions.   Since the wave length of the light is much larger than atomic dimensions, the electrons of any one molecule vibrate and radiate in the same phase; their wave amplitudes (electric fields) are then added before squaring to obtain the intensity of the light scattered by one molecule. For comparison with experiment, the quantity to be calculated is the *differential scattering cross section per unit volume*, which is defined as the energy scattered into the solid angle $d\omega$ per unit time by unit volume of the scattering medium per unit intensity of the incident light.   Because of the random positions of the molecules in a perfect gas, the phases of the wavelets scattered by different molecules are uncorrelated, i.e., the molecular sources are incoherent.   The total intensity is therefore the sum of the separate intensities, and the cross section per unit volume is equal to n times the cross section per molecule where n is the molecular density.

This analysis fails when correlations of the molecular positions and phases exist, as is the case for solids, liquids, and imperfect gases.   Interference effects between the wavelets scattered by different molecules must then be taken into account.   If the scattering medium consists of atoms or molecules in a perfectly regular geometric arrangement, e.g., a crystal

---

* The theory is due to von Smoluchowski, *loc. cit.*, and Einstein, *loc. cit.*

lattice at absolute zero,* and if the wave length is much greater than the interatomic distances, as is the case for visible light,† no scattering to the side can occur because of destructive interference. The total amplitude of the scattered wave at a distant point P is made up of contributions from many identical elements of volume, each of a thickness that is small compared to the wave length but each containing many molecules that scatter in phase at P. Since the composition of these elements is identical, each element can be paired with another element whose contribution to the amplitude at P is 180° out of phase with that of the first. Since all elements can be paired off except those at the surface, it follows that a perfect crystal scatters no light except at the surface. Alternatively, one may consider the electric field at P, which represents the scattered-wave amplitude, to be the product of the field due to one molecule times a phase factor $\Sigma \nu_j e^{i\phi_j}$ where ν_j represents the total number of molecules in the unit volume of scatterer which emit secondary wavelets that arrive at P with the same phase ϕ_j. In any perfectly homogeneous medium, the ν_j are all equal, and the phase factor vanishes, since $\Sigma e^{i\phi_j} = 0$; hence there is no scattering.

The volume scattering from a solid or liquid is then entirely attributable to disordering effects such as thermal agitation. The effects of thermal agitation which are responsible for the scattering of light are (1) the nonuniformities in the spatial distribution of molecules that are associated with density fluctuations and (2) the fluctuations in the orientation of nonspherical anisotropic molecules which cause fluctuations in the molecular dipole moments. We consider only the first of these effects. Let $\nu_j = \bar{\nu}_j + \Delta \nu_j$ where $\bar{\nu}_j$ is the mean value of ν_j and $\Delta \nu_j$ the instantaneous fluctuation. Since the $\bar{\nu}_j$ correspond to a uniform distribution and are therefore all equal, the phase factor reduces to $\Sigma \Delta \nu_j e^{i\phi_j}$. The scattering cross section per unit volume is equal to the product of the cross section per molecule and the absolute square of the phase factor. The latter is given by

$$\left| \sum \Delta \nu_j \, e^{i\phi_j} \right|^2 = \sum_j \sum_k \Delta \nu_j \, \Delta \nu_k \, e^{i(\phi_j - \phi_k)}$$
$$= \sum_j (\Delta \nu_j)^2 + \sum_{j \neq k} \sum \Delta \nu_j \, \Delta \nu_k \, e^{i(\phi_j - \phi_k)} \tag{9-39}$$

In taking the statistical average of (9-39), we obtain terms of the form $\overline{(\Delta \nu_j)^2}$ and $\overline{\Delta \nu_j \, \Delta \nu_k}$. The latter terms take account of correlations between different volume elements. In the case of a perfect gas, the fluctuations

---

* Zero-point motion is neglected as is surface scattering.

† If the wave length is smaller than the interatomic distances, the Bragg conditions can be satisfied as in X-ray scattering.

$\Delta\nu_j$ and $\Delta\nu_k$ are independent, so that $\overline{\Delta\nu_j\,\Delta\nu_k} = \overline{\Delta\nu_j}\cdot\overline{\Delta\nu_k} = 0$; furthermore $\overline{(\Delta\nu_j)^2} = \bar{\nu}_j$ in accordance with Eq. (9-16) or Eq. (9-48). Thus, for a perfect gas,

$$\overline{\left|\Sigma\,\Delta\nu_j\,e^{i\phi_j}\right|^2} = \Sigma\overline{(\Delta\nu_j)^2} = \Sigma\bar{\nu}_j = n \qquad (9\text{-}40)$$

and the cross section per unit volume is equal to the cross section per molecule times the molecular density n. This is the same result as was obtained by assuming incoherence of the scattered wavelets.

In extending the treatment from perfect to imperfect gases far from the critical point, one continues to neglect the correlation terms in Eq. (9-39), but the mean-square fluctuations are now obtained from Eq. (9-31) instead of Eq. (9-16). The scattering cross section is most easily derived by using Rayleigh's formula for the scattering of light by a dielectric particle. The dimensions of the particle are assumed to be small compared to the wave length, and its dielectric constant, or refractive index, is assumed to differ only slightly from that of the surrounding medium. The scattered intensity is proportional to the square of the difference between the indexes of refraction of particle and medium. This formula is applied to the present problem by considering the density fluctuations as producing numerous small regions of condensation and rarefaction in the gas. Each such region has an index of refraction above or below the normal equilibrium value and consequently scatters light like a dielectric particle. On applying Eq. (9-16) to a cube of gas, at standard conditions, whose side is 5×10^{-5} cm and therefore of the order of the wave lengths of visible light, we find that $\delta^* = 5.4 \times 10^{-4}$. The smallness of this value indicates that the significant fluctuations take place in regions with dimensions that are shorter than a wave length. The Rayleigh formula is applicable under these conditions. The density fluctuations are introduced by using the law relating the index of refraction of a gas to its density. On expressing the difference in refractive indexes in terms of the density difference, one finds the scattered intensity to vary as the square of the density fluctuation. If sufficiently far from the critical point, one can neglect the correlations between the many small regions of fluctuating density and treat these regions as incoherent scatterers; then the total intensity is obtained by adding the intensities contributed by all the scatterers. In this way, one finds that the scattering cross section per unit volume is proportional to the mean-square fluctuation in density, i.e., to $(\delta^*)^2$. Substitution of (9-16) gives the original Rayleigh formula for molecular scattering, which is valid for a perfect gas. The appropriate formula for an imperfect gas is obtained by using (9-31).

The molecular scattering is best exemplified by the light from the sky, which is scattered sunlight. The scattering is mainly molecular but is due to a small extent to suspended dust particles and water droplets. In the absence of an atmosphere, the sky would appear to be black. The Rayleigh formula predicts that the scattered intensity should vary as the fourth power of the frequency; the preferential scattering of the shorter wave lengths accounts for the predominant blue color of the scattered light and the predominant red cōlor of the residual transmitted light observed at sunset. The theory can be compared with observations on scattered sunlight. Since the scattering cross section is proportional to $(\delta^*)^2$ and thus to kT (cf. Eq. (9-31)), this provides another method for measuring k or determining Avogadro's number L. The agreement with experiment is very good and the value of k close to values determined by other methods. It is significant that the formulas that have been derived for the Brownian motion and for the molecular scattering of light contain explicitly the molecular, or atomistic, constant k or, equivalently, L. These phenomena are intrinsically molecular and statistical in nature.

We take up, finally, the modifications in the character of the molecular scattering of light in the neighborhood of the critical point. Observations show that as the critical point is approached, the scattered light becomes very intense and its spectral distribution changes from blue toward white. This "critical opalescence" is accounted for in a quantitatively satisfactory way by the theory of light scattering as a fluctuation phenomenon. Since the compressibility becomes very large near the critical point, the fluctuations in density are much greater than in a perfect gas or in an imperfect gas far from the critical point. Equation (9-31) is to be replaced by (9-37) and (9-38). If we use Eq. (9-38) to estimate the fluctuations in a region whose dimensions are of the order of the wave length, we find that δ^* is of the order of 1×10^{-2} instead of 5×10^{-4}. Since the scattering cross section is proportional to $(\delta^*)^2$, it is clear that the large fluctuations in density near the critical point are responsible for the enhanced scattering. From this estimate of δ^* one sees that significant fluctuations take place in regions whose dimensions are comparable to the wave length. The Rayleigh formula is therefore inapplicable. Furthermore, the correlations between the density fluctuations in different volume elements must be taken into account in determining the phase factor; i.e., the regions of inhomogeneity can no longer be treated as incoherent sources of scattered light. The molecular scattering formula for an imperfect gas, which was discussed above, is therefore invalid in the neighborhood of the critical point. The frequency dependence of the scattered intensity is no longer of the Rayleigh form, since the regions of inhomogeneity are not small in comparison with the wave length. As the size of the regions increases, the spectral distribution approaches whiteness if the incident light is white. Detailed treatment of the critical opalescence shows that the frequency dependence is altered from a fourth-power to a second-power law.   Finally, it should be noted that the fluctuations near the critical point are so large that molecular clustering leads to the formation of liquid droplets that contribute to the scattering.*

PROBLEMS

9-1. Show that in a mixture of two perfect gases, the partial densities of each will separately obey the barometric equation.

9-2. What is the effect on the Brownian motion of an increase in temperature?

9-3. In the analysis of observations on the Brownian motion, it is more convenient to compute $(\overline{|x|})^2$ than $\overline{x^2}$. Show that $(\overline{|x|})^2 = (2/\pi)\overline{x^2}$.

9-4. Justify Eq. (9-21) both analytically and graphically.

9-5. Calculate the isothermal compressibilities of a perfect gas and of a van der Waals gas.

9-6. Verify the formulas for α and δ^* given in (9-38).

9-7. Show that α of Eq. (9-34) can be written as

$$\alpha = \frac{\bar{\nu}n_c^2}{24kT_c}\left(\frac{\partial^3 p}{\partial n^3}\right)_c$$

where n_c is the critical density.

9-8. If the volume of a gas specimen is equal to its critical volume and its temperature is slightly above the critical temperature, show that the mean-square density fluctuation, and therefore the intensity of scattered light, vary inversely as $T - T_c$. Show that in the special case of a van der Waals gas

$$\delta^{*2} = \frac{4}{9\nu}\frac{T}{T - T_c}$$

9-9. Why is the sky blue rather than violet?

APPENDIX 9-1

Statistical Fluctuations

Although the formulas to be derived in this appendix have a variety of applications, it is the case of density fluctuations in a gas which is of immediate interest, and the derivations will refer accordingly to this specific case.   With appropriate changes in notation, the results can be adapted to other physical fluctuation phenomena, such as radioactive decay.   We consider a perfect gas of N molecules in a container of volume V and neglect the effects of gravity.   Let n be the number of mole-

---

* For detailed treatments of the scattering of light in gases, the reader is referred to the following books: M. Born, "Optik," Springer-Verlag, Berlin, Vienna, 1933; L. Rosenfeld, "Theory of Electrons," Interscience Publishers, Inc., New York, 1951; S. Bhagavantam, "Scattering of Light and the Raman Effect," Chemical Publishing Company, Inc., New York, 1942; J. O. Hirschfelder, C. F. Curtiss, and R. B. Bird, "Molecular Theory of Gases and Liquids," John Wiley & Sons, Inc., New York, 1954. Some background in electromagnetic theory is essential.

cules present at any instant in a fixed region of the container of volume v. This number will fluctuate about a mean value $\bar{n}$, which is equal to Nv/V. It is assumed that the probability of finding a molecule in the region is independent of the number already present.* The geometric probability of having n specified molecules in the region and $N - n$ outside is given by $g^n(1 - g)^{N-n}$ where $g = v/V$, since the probabilities are independent. The probability P_n of a fluctuation in which n molecules are present in the volume v is obtained by multiplying the geometric probability by the number of ways in which the N molecules can be divided into two groups of n and $N - n$ molecules, i.e., $N!/n!(N - n)!$ Thus†

$$P_n = \frac{N!}{n!(N - n)!}\, g^n(1 - g)^{N-n} \tag{9-41}$$

According to the binomial theorem,

$$(x + y)^N = \sum_{n=0}^{N} \frac{N!}{n!(N - n)!}\, x^n y^{N-n} \tag{9-42}$$

whence
$$\sum_{n=0}^{N} P_n = 1$$

We first verify that $\bar{n} = Ng$ and then calculate $\overline{n(n - 1)}$ in order to obtain $\overline{n^2}$. Since the P_n are normalized,

$$\bar{n} = \sum_{n=0}^{N} nP_n = \sum_{n=1}^{N} nP_n$$

$$= Ng \sum_{n=1}^{N} \frac{(N - 1)!\, g^{n-1}(1 - g)^{(N-1)-(n-1)}}{(n - 1)!\,[(N - 1) - (n - 1)]!} \tag{9-43}$$

$$= Ng \sum_{n'=0}^{N'} \frac{N'!\, g^{n'}(1 - g)^{N'-n'}}{n'!(N' - n')!}$$

where $n' = n - 1$ and $N' = N - 1$. Using (9-42), this becomes

$$\bar{n} = Ng \tag{9-44}$$

* This condition is satisfied by a perfect gas.

† Equation (9-41) is Bernoulli's binomial distribution law.

In a similar way

$$\overline{n(n-1)} = \sum_{n=0}^{N} n(n-1)P_n = \sum_{n=2}^{N} n(n-1)P_n$$

$$= N(N-1)g^2 \sum_{n=2}^{N} \frac{(N-2)!\, g^{n-2}(1-g)^{(N-2)-(n-2)}}{(n-2)!\,[(N-2)-(n-2)]!} \quad (9\text{-}45)$$

$$= N(N-1)g^2 \sum_{n''=0}^{N''} \frac{N''!\, g^{n''}(1-g)^{N''-n''}}{n''!(N''-n'')!}$$

$$= N(N-1)g^2$$

Thus
$$\overline{n^2} = \overline{n(n-1)} + \bar{n}$$
$$= N^2g^2 - Ng^2 + Ng \quad (9\text{-}46)$$

The mean-square fluctuation or deviation is given by

$$\overline{(\Delta n)^2} = \overline{(n-\bar{n})^2} = \overline{n^2} - \overline{2n\bar{n}} + \bar{n}^2$$
$$= \overline{n^2} - \bar{n}^2 = Ng(1-g) \quad (9\text{-}47)$$

using (9-44) and (9-46). The root-mean-square fluctuation is usually referred to as the standard deviation from the mean. If $g \ll 1$, as is usually the case, Eq. (9-47) becomes

$$\overline{(\Delta n)^2} \simeq Ng = \bar{n} \quad (9\text{-}48)$$

The relative fluctuation δ is defined as $\Delta n/\bar{n}$; its root-mean-square value will be denoted by δ^*. Thus, if $g \ll 1$, we obtain the important formula

$$\delta^* = [\overline{(\Delta n)^2}]^{1/2}/\bar{n} \simeq (\bar{n})^{-1/2} \quad (9\text{-}49)$$

which shows that the relative fluctuations decrease as $\bar{n}$ increases.

An important special case of the foregoing arises if $g \ll 1$, $N \gg 1$, and one represents P_n only for $n \ll N$. Then

$$P_n = \frac{N(N-1)\,\cdots\,(N-n+1)}{n!}\, g^n(1-g)^{N-n}$$

$$\simeq \frac{N^n g^n}{n!}\,(1-g)^N$$

$$\simeq \frac{\bar{n}^n}{n!}\left[1 - Ng + \frac{N(N-1)}{2!}\,g^2 - \frac{N(N-1)(N-2)}{3!}\,g^3\,\cdots\right]$$

$$\simeq \frac{\bar{n}^n}{n!}\left[1 - \bar{n} + \frac{\bar{n}^2}{2!} - \frac{\bar{n}^3}{3!}\,\cdots\right]$$

$$\simeq \frac{\bar{n}^n e^{-\bar{n}}}{n!} \quad (9\text{-}50)$$

This is *Poisson's formula;* no condition has been placed on n except that $n \ll N$. If we further assume that $n \gg 1$ and consider only values of

n that are close to the mean, i.e., $|n - \bar{n}| \ll \bar{n}$, Eq. (9-50) reduces to the very useful Laplace-Gauss formula. If we insert Stirling's approximation for $n!$ from Eq. (4-83), Eq. (9-50) becomes

$$P_n \simeq \frac{1}{(2\pi n)^{1/2}} \left(\frac{\bar{n}}{n}\right)^n e^{n-\bar{n}} \tag{9-51}$$

If we take natural logarithms, introduce $\varepsilon \equiv n - \bar{n}$, and retain no terms higher than ε^2 in the expansion of the logarithm, Eq. (9-51) gives

$$\log\left[(2\pi n)^{1/2} P_n\right] \simeq -n \log\left(n/\bar{n}\right) + n - \bar{n}$$
$$\simeq -(\bar{n} + \varepsilon) \log\left[1 + (\varepsilon/\bar{n})\right] + \varepsilon$$
$$\simeq -(\bar{n} + \varepsilon)\left\{\frac{\varepsilon}{\bar{n}} - \frac{\varepsilon^2}{2\bar{n}^2} \cdot \cdot \cdot\right\} + \varepsilon$$
$$\simeq -\varepsilon^2/2\bar{n} \cdot \cdot \cdot$$

Replacing n by $\bar{n}$ on the left side, one obtains the *Laplace-Gauss*, or *normal, distribution*

$$P_n \simeq (2\pi\bar{n})^{-1/2} e^{-(\varepsilon^2/2\bar{n})} = (2\pi\bar{n})^{-1/2} e^{-(n-\bar{n})^2/2\bar{n}} \tag{9-52}$$

which, when written as a continuous function,

$$P(n)\,dn = (2\pi\bar{n})^{-1/2} e^{-(n-\bar{n})^2/2\bar{n}}\,dn \tag{9-53}$$

can be used to estimate the probability of n taking on a value between n_1 and n_2. If P_n as given by (9-52) is plotted against n, the probability of a value between n_1 and n_2 is the sum of the ordinates taken at unit intervals from n_1 to n_2 or, what is the same thing, the sum of the areas of adjacent rectangles of unit base and varying altitudes equal to each of the ordinates. This total area can be approximated by the area under the $P(n)$ curve between $n = n_1$ and $n = n_2$. Thus

$$\sum_{n_1}^{n_2} P_n \rightarrow \int_{n_1}^{n_2} P(n)\,dn \tag{9-54}$$

with increasing accuracy the larger the value of $\bar{n}$; little error is made by treating n as a continuous variable, since an increment of unity represents a small relative change. Although the range of n is from 0 to N, a negligible error is introduced by extending this range from $-\infty$ to $+\infty$ for the purpose of normalization. Since $N \gg \bar{n} \gg 1$ by hypothesis, the exponential will be vanishingly small from $-\infty$ to 0 and from N to ∞. In any case, Eqs. (9-52) and (9-53) are inaccurate unless $|n - \bar{n}| \ll \bar{n}$. Integration of (9-53) gives

$$\int_{-\infty}^{\infty} P(n)\,dn = (2\pi\bar{n})^{-1/2} \int_{-\infty}^{\infty} e^{-(n-\bar{n})^2/2\bar{n}}\,dn$$
$$= (2\pi\bar{n})^{-1/2} \int_{-\infty}^{\infty} e^{-(\varepsilon^2/2\bar{n})}\,d\varepsilon \tag{9-55}$$
$$= 1$$

so that $P(n)\ dn$ is correctly normalized.

It is useful to have the distribution function for the relative fluctuation $\delta = (n - \bar{n})/\bar{n}$. Let $W(\delta)\ d\delta$ be the probability of a fluctuation between δ and $\delta + d\delta$. In the range $d\delta$ there are contained $\bar{n}\ d\delta$ integral values of n for which P_n varies only slightly. Hence

$$
\begin{aligned}
W(\delta)\ d\delta &= P_n \bar{n}\ d\delta \\
&= (\bar{n}/2\pi)^{1/2} e^{-\bar{n}\delta^2/2}\ d\delta
\end{aligned}
\tag{9-56}
$$

which is equivalent to (9-53) and is similarly normalized. Equation (9-49) can also be obtained directly from (9-56).

PROBLEM

A9-1. When the average background of a counter is twelve counts per minute, what is the chance of getting three background counts during a 15-sec interval? Two counts in 15 sec? One count in 15 sec? No counts in 15 sec?

CHAPTER 10

FUNDAMENTAL EXPERIMENTS AND EXPERIMENTAL PROCEDURES

This chapter is devoted to the experimental side of the kinetic theory of gases. In Sec. 10-1 we take up the subject of molecular beams and study the foundations of a technique that has proved to be of great importance in the fields of atomic and nuclear physics. The Estermann-Simpson-Stern experiment on the velocity distribution in a molecular beam is discussed in detail. The remaining sections of the chapter deal with methods of measuring the transport coefficients. No attempt is made to describe all the methods in use now or in the past. Instead, we single out one important, up-to-date method and discuss the experiment in detail, giving the theory of the method and the precautions and corrections needed in applying it. We take up the rotating-cylinder method of measuring viscosity, the hot-wire potential-lead cell for measuring thermal conductivity and the accommodation coefficient, the determination of the mutual-diffusion coefficient by a recent modification of the Loschmidt-tube method, and the use of stable and radioactive isotopes in measuring the coefficient of self-diffusion. It will be seen that in the case of heat conduction and diffusion measurements, very careful experimentation is required in order to achieve accuracy of the order of 1 per cent. Important advances in experimental techniques have been made within recent years.

10-1. MOLECULAR BEAMS AND THE VERIFICATION OF THE MAXWELL DISTRIBUTION LAW

A molecular beam is produced by the effusion of a gas or vapor through a narrow slit from a source, or oven, into a highly evacuated region. The distance traversed by the beam in the evacuated region is much less than the mean free path in the region; thus the molecules pass through this region without undergoing molecular encounters, and their paths approximate straight lines to the extent that gravity can be neglected. The great importance of the molecular-beam technique for atomic physics rests on the fact that, as the beam traverses the evacuated apparatus, the individual molecules are isolated and follow out their trajectories in externally applied force fields without interacting with other molecules. The small deflections of the beam which are observed in such experiments then represent the effects of the external fields acting on single molecules, just as if one molecule at a time were to pass through the apparatus. Molecular-beam methods were first developed in a practical form and applied to problems of atomic physics by O. Stern and his school; these methods received their fullest development at the hands of I. I. Rabi and his collaborators, who converted the technique into a powerful precision tool for the investigation of the electromagnetic properties of atoms and atomic nuclei.

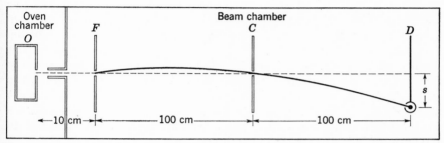

FIG. 10-1. Schematic diagram of apparatus for the deflection of a molecular beam by gravity: O is the oven, F the foreslit, C the collimating slit, and D the detector.

The essential parts of a molecular-beam apparatus are (1) the source or oven chamber containing the oven in which the beam material, usually an alkali metal or one of its salts, is vaporized, and (2) the observation or beam chamber in which the beam, defined by a foreslit and a collimating slit, passes through deflecting fields to the detector that measures the position and intensity of the deflected beam. The type of source, or oven, and the type of detector depend on the beam material chosen, and the apparatus for deflecting the beam depends, of course, on the purpose of the experiment. Although the principal applications of the molecular-beam techniques are in the fields of atomic and nuclear physics,* we shall consider here only the application of the method to the direct verification of the Maxwell velocity distribution. The most precise experiment of this sort is the free-fall experiment of Estermann, Simpson, and Stern,† in which a narrow, horizontal beam of cesium atoms is deflected by the earth's gravitational field. A schematic diagram of the apparatus is shown in Fig. 10-1. The oven containing vaporized cesium at pressures

* For a good introduction to molecular-beam methods in atomic and nuclear physics, the reader is referred to the review article by D. R. Hamilton, *Amer. Jour. Phys.*, vol. 9, p. 319, 1941. A more comprehensive account is to be found in K. F. Smith, "Molecular Beams," Methuen & Co., Ltd., London, 1955.

† I. Estermann, O. C. Simpson, and O. Stern, *Phys. Rev.*, vol. 71, p. 238, 1947; I. Estermann, *Rev. Mod. Phys.*, vol. 18, p. 300, 1946.

from 0.019 to 0.096 mm Hg has a horizontal slit 0.05 mm in width.   The mean free path of cesium atoms at the lowest oven pressure is 0.07 mm and is only slightly greater than the slit width.   The condition for effusive flow (cf. Sec. 2-5) is thus satisfied only approximately.*

It is of some interest to consider the limitations imposed on the intensity of the beam by the effusive-flow requirement.   The rate of effusion from the oven into the low-pressure region outside is proportional to both the oven pressure and the area of the oven slit and thus varies linearly with a/λ where a is the slit width and λ the mean free path of the gas inside the oven.*   The effusion condition $(\lambda \gg a)$ must be compromised with the need for intensity, with the result that the best working beam is obtained in practice for λ slightly larger than a.   Since the beam intensity depends on oven pressure and slit width only through the factor a/λ, and since this ratio must be kept near unity for an optimum beam, it follows that the intensity of the optimum beam is effectively independent of the width of the oven slit.   To facilitate alignment, the oven slit is made slightly wider than the foreslit and collimating slit which define the beam.   These two slits are made as narrow as possible in order to achieve the best resolution at the detector.   Both slits were 0.02 mm wide in the free-fall experiment.

There are several advantages to the use of a foreslit.   If the beam is defined by the oven slit and collimating slit, the alignment of slits is difficult to maintain as the temperature of the oven is raised.   When a foreslit is used to define the beam, the foreslit and collimating slit both remain at room temperature and can be rigidly connected through plate-glass supports.   The alignment of slits and detector is the most difficult part of the experiment.   Another important advantage of using a fore-slit is that the beam chamber and oven chamber can be isolated and separately pumped; a separately pumped intermediate chamber located between the oven chamber and the foreslit can also be used.   This permits a higher vacuum to be maintained in the beam chamber.   The use of a foreslit is also desirable when $\lambda \approx a$ at the oven slit, since a small tendency toward collective motion or "cloud formation" then exists which increases the effective width of the oven slit by an uncertain amount.

According to Prob. 2-2, the number of molecules effusing per unit time per unit area of an ideal orifice into the solid angle $d\omega$ is $n\bar{v} \cos \theta \, d\omega/4\pi$. The angle θ, representing the angle between the direction of effusion and the normal to the plane of the orifice, is effectively zero ($\sim 10^{-5}$ radian) for the molecules that constitute the long, narrow beam.   Thus most of the molecules leaving the oven do not go into the beam.   The formula

---

* The slit length is not involved in the effusive-flow condition and may be taken as large as is convenient (~ 3 mm).

above is valid only if the wall thickness is much smaller than the dimensions of the aperture. In practice, the wall thickness is several times greater than the slit width, so that the slits are essentially short canals rather than ideal orifices. The rate of effusion is then less than for an ideal orifice (cf. Prob. 10-1), and the cosine law no longer holds for the angular distribution. If λ is greater than the wall thickness, however, the intensity in the forward direction ($\theta = 0$) is the same for the canal as for an orifice of the same area. The substitution of a canal for an ideal orifice thus leaves the beam intensity practically unaffected but reduces the number of stray molecules that have to be pumped out to maintain a good vacuum. In the free-fall experiment, the complete collimating system consisted of the oven slit, a long canal through the partition separating the oven chamber and the beam chamber, the foreslit, and the collimating slit, the latter two defining the beam.

The distances from foreslit to collimating slit and from collimating slit to detector were both 100 cm in the free-fall experiment. A beam of this length is required in order that the weak gravitational field will produce sufficiently large deflections. The pressure in the beam chamber must be kept low enough so that the beam molecules have only a small chance of being scattered by the residual gas. This means that λ must be several times larger than the length L of the beam (if $\lambda = L$, the fraction $1/e$ reach the detector). The pressure in the beam chamber was maintained between 10^{-8} and 10^{-7} mm Hg. The beam atoms were detected by means of the Langmuir-Taylor surface-ionization method, in which nearly every Cs atom striking a hot tungsten wire is re-evaporated as an ion and then collected on a negatively charged plate. The plate current gives the number of beam atoms striking the detector wire per unit time. This method can be used only when the ionization potential of the beam substance is less than the work function of the wire collector. The tungsten wire used in the experiment was 0.02 mm in diameter, i.e., of the same width as the slits.

Denoting the distance from foreslit to detector by $2l$ (collimating slit in the middle), one readily sees that a molecule of velocity v will fall a distance $s = gl^2/v^2$ before reaching the detector. For an oven temperature of 450°K and for $l = 100$ cm, a Cs atom of the most probable velocity $[v_m = (2RT/M)^{1/2}]$ falls a distance of only 0.174 mm. However, since the slit widths and detector-wire diameter are only 0.02 mm, it is possible to measure fairly accurately the vertical variation in intensity as the detector is moved up or down through the gravity-deflected beam. The vertical intensity distribution in the beam represents the velocity distribution of the beam molecules. The distribution in speeds of the molecules effusing from the oven is proportional to $vf(v)\,dv$ where $f(v)$ is the Maxwell speed distribution function given by Eq. (5-14). The fraction of beam atoms with speeds in the interval v to $v + dv$ is then

$$dN/N = 2(v/v_m)^3 e^{-(v/v_m)^2} d(v/v_m) \tag{10-1}$$

where $v_m = (2RT/M)^{1/2}$ and T is the oven temperature. If the slits were infinitely narrow and the detector wire infinitely thin, the expected vertical intensity distribution would be obtained directly from Eq. (10-1) on substituting $v^2 = gl^2/s$. However, account must be taken of the finite width of the slits, which causes an intensity distribution across an undeflected beam, e.g., a beam defined by vertical instead of horizontal slits.

FIG. 10-2. Intensity profile of undeflected beam.

Since the molecules travel in straight lines like rays of light, the two slits lead to a trapezoidal intensity pattern consisting of a central region of constant intensity (*umbra*) and a region to either side (*penumbra*) where the intensity drops linearly to zero (cf. Fig. 10-2). The theoretical vertical intensity distribution is then obtained by integrating the infinitesimal slit distribution over the trapezoidal pattern or profile.* The result is shown in Fig. 10-3, along with experimental points for the case of a Cs beam (oven temperature $\sim$450°K).

The agreement between the experimental points and the calculated curve is very close except for the slowest molecules, for which the measured intensity falls below the calculated intensity. This deficiency is found to increase with increasing deflection s (or decreasing velocity v) and also to increase, for a given value of s or v, with increasing oven pressure. At the lowest oven pressures, the deviations begin to set in for deflections exceeding s_m where $s_m = gl^2/v_m^2$. In Table 10-1 are listed values of the ratio of observed to calculated intensities (I_{obs}/I_{cal}) for $s = s_m$ and $s = 2s_m$ over the complete range of oven pressures. In the best case (lowest oven pressure) the Maxwell law is accurately verified for speeds exceeding the most probable speed v_m. The existence of a discrepancy at lower speeds is obviously connected with the fact that the effusive-flow condition is not satisfied with a sufficient margin of

---

* One integrates the product of the two distribution functions to obtain the final distribution. The mathematical expression, of the form $h(x) = \int f(y)g(x - y)\, dy$, is referred to as a *convolution*.

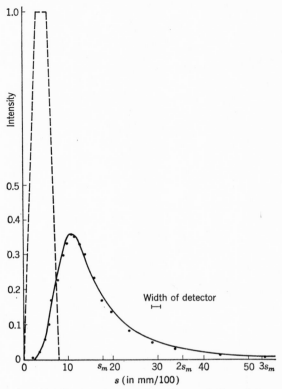

Fig. 10-3. Intensity distribution in a cesium beam deflected by gravity. (After Estermann, Simpson, and Stern.)

TABLE 10-1. RATIO OF MEASURED TO CALCULATED INTENSITIES IN THE FREE-FALL EXPERIMENT

Oven pressure (mm Hg)	$\dfrac{I_{\text{obs}}(s_m)}{I_{\text{cal}}(s_m)}$	$\dfrac{I_{\text{obs}}(2s_m)}{I_{\text{cal}}(2s_m)}$
1.90×10^{-2}	1.01	0.87
2.27	0.90	0.79
2.95	0.93	0.75
3.52	0.92	0.75
3.99	0.93	0.77
4.17	0.94	0.70
8.87	0.79	0.51
9.23	0.86	0.52
9.59	0.82	0.52

safety. It has already been mentioned that the mean free path in the oven barely exceeds the oven-slit width at the lowest pressure. The existence of an incipient tendency toward hydrodynamic flow with "cloud formation" in front of the slit must alter the velocity distribution away from the Maxwellian $vf(v)\, dv$ distribution. As a consequence of the extreme narrowness and great length of the beam, any encounter in which a molecule is deflected by as little as 10^{-5} radians removes it from the beam. Even the very few encounters that occur near the oven slit when $\lambda \approx a$ may be expected to have an effect on the velocity distribution of

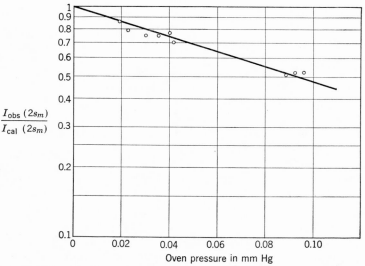

FIG. 10-4. Semilogarithmic plot of the intensity ratio $I_{\mathrm{obs}}(2s_m)/I_{\mathrm{cal}}(2s_m)$ versus the oven pressure.

the beam. Since the chance of an encounter near the orifice is greatest for the slowest of the emerging molecules, one has a qualitative explanation of the low-velocity deficiency. Estermann, Simpson, and Stern have derived a rough theoretical formula for the distortion of the velocity distribution, according to which $I_{\mathrm{obs}}/I_{\mathrm{cal}}$ should fall off exponentially with increasing oven pressure. It is instructive to extrapolate the experimental results to zero oven pressure. In Fig. 10-4 we have made a semilogarithmic plot of the intensity ratio $I_{\mathrm{obs}}/I_{\mathrm{cal}}$ versus the oven pressure, using the data given in Table 10-1 for the case in which $s = 2s_m$. It is seen that the points fall reasonably well about a straight line that passes through an intensity ratio of unity at zero oven pressure. Thus it appears likely that the direct verification of the Maxwell law could be extended to lower speeds if the ratio λ/a could be increased in the experiments.

10-2. MEASUREMENT OF THE COEFFICIENT OF VISCOSITY

The coefficient of viscosity of a gas can be determined by measuring the viscous flow through a long capillary tube and also by observing the amplitudes of the damped oscillations of a disk suspended between two fixed horizontal disks and oscillating parallel to them in the gas. The most accurate absolute determinations have been carried out by the *rotating-cylinder method,* in which the gas is confined between two vertical coaxial cylinders, one of which is kept in uniform rotation and the other suspended by a torsion wire. The motor-driven, rotating cylinder communicates its motion to the gas, which transmits a shearing stress to the suspended cylinder. The torque on the latter turns it until equilibrium is reached between the viscous torque exerted by the gas and the restoring torque of the wire suspension. In most cases, the rotating cylinder is on the outside. The suspended inner cylinder, which is shorter than the rotating cylinder, is separated by narrow gaps from fixed guard cylinders, above and below it, of the same external diameter as the suspended cylinder. The use of the guard cylinders greatly reduces the end effects, but it is still necessary to apply a small end correction, which makes the effective length of the suspended cylinder slightly greater (by approximately half the total gap width) than its actual length.*

It is necessary to measure the viscous torque on the suspended cylinder with great accuracy. Before considering this and other experimental details, we shall develop the simple theory underlying the experiment. The spacing between the inner and outer cylinders is usually so large that it would be a poor approximation to treat the viscous flow as rectilinear (as was suggested in Prob. 3-1). Equation (3-19), although it is not directly applicable to curvilinear flow, can be adapted to the present problem if care is exercised. Let r, ϕ, and z be cylindrical coordinates with r representing the distance from the common axis of the cylinders, ϕ the azimuth about the axis, and z the vertical distance along the axis. The shearing stress, which is in the ϕ direction (tangent to the circles of flow) and acts over the cylindrical surface with normal in the r direction, will be denoted by $P_{r\phi}$. The velocity gradient between the inner and outer cylinders is du/dr where $u(r)$ represents the linear velocity of a rotating element of fluid at distance r from the axis. We set $u(r) = r\omega(r)$ where the angular velocity ω must depend on r if there are nonvanishing shearing stresses. An angular velocity independent of r corresponds to a rigid rotation of the fluid in which the fluid elements are not deformed and both the shearing strains and stresses vanish. Thus

$$du/dr = \omega + r\,d\omega/dr \qquad (10\text{-}2)$$

* This correction takes account of the small torque exerted on the ends of the suspended cylinder by the gas in the gaps and also of the small torque on the inner surface.

The first term, which represents the velocity gradient in a rigid rotation, contributes nothing to the viscous shearing stress. The second term, representing the rate of shearing strain, alone determines the viscous stress $P_{r\phi}$. Hence

$$P_{r\phi} = \eta r \, d\omega/dr \qquad (10\text{-}3)$$

Consider the motion of the fluid in a unit length of the cylinders, e.g., between $z = 0$ and $z = 1$. The shearing force acting over the surface of an imaginary cylinder of radius r and unit length is $2\pi r P_{r\phi}$, and the moment of this force about the axis is given by

$$\tau_1 = 2\pi r^2 P_{r\phi} \qquad (10\text{-}4)$$

The rotation of a cylindrical shell of fluid of thickness Δr is accelerated by the torque $\tau_1(r + \Delta r)$ exerted over its outer surface and decelerated by the reaction torque $-\tau_1(r)$ over its inner surface. Assuming that a steady state has been reached, the angular acceleration vanishes and $\tau_1(r + \Delta r) = \tau_1(r)$. Hence the torque τ_1 is independent of r in the steady state. Substitution of (10-3) in (10-4) gives

$$\tau_1 = 2\pi\eta r^3 \, d\omega/dr \qquad (10\text{-}5)$$

If the inner cylinder of radius a is at rest and the outer cylinder of radius b rotates uniformly with angular velocity ω_0, the integration of (10-5) gives

$$\tau_1 \int_a^b dr/r^3 = 2\pi\eta \int_0^{\omega_0} d\omega$$

$$\therefore \eta = \frac{\tau_1}{4\pi\omega_0} \left(\frac{1}{a^2} - \frac{1}{b^2} \right) \qquad (10\text{-}6)$$

Denoting by τ the total viscous shearing torque acting on the suspended cylinder of effective length l, this becomes

$$\eta = \frac{\tau}{4\pi\omega_0 l} \frac{b^2 - a^2}{a^2 b^2} \qquad (10\text{-}7)$$

Equation (10-7) applies as well to the case in which the outer cylinder is at rest and the inner cylinder rotates with angular velocity ω_0.

When a steady state has been reached, the suspended cylinder is at rest and the viscous torque τ is balanced by the restoring torque exerted by the twisted wire. Thus $\tau = F\phi$ where F is the torsion constant of the suspension and ϕ the angular deflection of the cylinder. The angle ϕ is measured with the aid of a small mirror, attached to the suspension, which reflects a light beam onto a graduated scale. The torsion constant F is found by measuring the period of oscillation T when objects of known or calculable moments of inertia I are suspended from the wire. The elementary relation $T = 2\pi(I/F)^{1/2}$ can be used if the effect of damping on the period is negligible and if the amplitude of oscillation is small enough that deviations from Hooke's law (*anharmonicity*) can be neglected. In very precise work, account must be taken of the anharmonicity, which has the effect of making T depend slightly on the amplitude. The observed increase of T with amplitude implies that F decreases slightly with increasing deflection ϕ. This slight dependence of F on ϕ can be determined from the graph of T versus amplitude and is taken into account in the restoring torque $F(\phi)\phi$, which is substituted for τ in Eq. (10-7). A small correction to Eq. (10-7) arises from the effect of "slip" (cf. Sec. 4-3). It is important that the speed of the rotating cylinder be low enough that the flow of gas is laminar and not turbulent.

A very precise determination of the viscosity of air was made by Bearden* in 1939 in order to resolve a discrepancy between Millikan's oil-drop value of the charge on the electron and the X-ray value. The rotating-cylinder method was used, with the outer cylinder suspended and the inner cylinder in rotation. This arrangement made possible a more accurate alignment of the cylinders and a more precise measurement of their dimensions than in the conventional arrangement with the rotating cylinder on the outside. The outer surface of the rotating cylinder and the inner surfaces of the suspended cylinder and guard cylinders were machined to be accurately cylindrical, and the alignment ensured that the surfaces were coaxial to within about 0.005 mm (a correction for non-coaxiality was calculated by Inglis). The error in the apparatus constant $(b^2 - a^2)/la^2b^2$ was 2×10^{-3} per cent. All measurements were made at a temperature of 20.00°C. The apparatus was contained in a bell jar and the inner cylinder was rotated by a magnetic drive; this made it possible to evacuate the apparatus and fill it with the gas to be studied without disturbing the driving mechanism. It was necessary that this mechanism maintain a constant, known speed over long periods of time; this was accomplished by synchronizing a d-c motor with an electrically driven tuning fork by means of a Thyratron circuit. In this way the angular velocity ω_0 was kept constant to within one part in 10^6. The tuning-fork–controlled motor, with reduction gears, was also used as a timing device (recording clock) in conjunction with a movie camera to record the positions of divided dials illuminated by flashes of light. This clock was used to measure the oscillation periods T needed in the determination of the torsion constant F.

The angular deflection ϕ of the suspended cylinder was measured with the aid of a telescope, a comparator calibrated to within 0.001 mm, and a light source mounted on the comparator, consisting of a vertical wire with a neon lamp behind it. The instrumental error in ϕ was about 2×10^{-3} per cent. A variety of precautions must be taken in the selec-

* J. A. Bearden, *Phys. Rev.*, vol. 56, p. 1023, 1939.

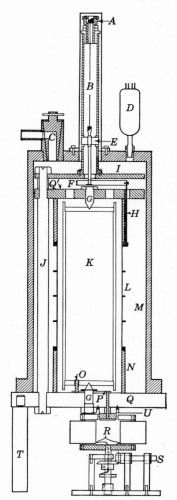

tion and use of the torsion wire. A fine wire of high tensile strength is required, and it is important that there be no zero drift in either the normal or the deflected position and that the torsion constant be the same for static and dynamic conditions, i.e., independent of the period of oscillation. A method of heat treatment under tension in the presence of dry hydrogen was found to improve the characteristics of tungsten wires. Another precaution is the use of proper clamps. Since the torsion constant F of a given wire depends on the load, the objects of known moments of inertia which were used in the determination of F were chosen to have the same weight as the suspended cylinder and its supports. The error in the torsion constant was 0.6×10^{-3} per cent. Runs were made for six different angular velocities, all well below the onset of turbulence. The final result for the viscosity of air at 20.00°C is $(1819.20 \pm 0.06) \times 10^{-7}$ cgs units. Figure 10-5 shows Bearden's apparatus.

10-3. THE MEASUREMENT OF THERMAL CONDUCTIVITY AND THE ACCOMMODATION COEFFICIENT

The conduction of heat in a gas can be measured by filling the space between two coaxial cylinders with the gas to be studied and suddenly cooling the outer cylinder in a constant-temperature bath. The thermal conductivity K can then be determined from the rate of cooling of the inner cylinder, the temperature difference decreasing exponentially with the time. Another method uses two large, parallel, horizontal plates placed close together with the gas between them.

Fig. 10-5. Cross section of Bearden's apparatus: A, adjustable torsion-wire support; B, torsion wire; C, stopcock; D, ionization gauge; E, mirror; F, "three-legged" spider; G, centers; H, supporting strips; I, shelf; J, supporting rods; K, inner cylinder rotating on centers (G); L, suspended cylinder; M, bell jar; N, guard cylinders; O, driving pin; P, spur gear; Q, steel base; Q', secondary base; R, electromagnet; S, shaft; T, support; U, vacuumtight housing. (After J. A. Bearden.)

The upper plate is electrically heated and the lower cooled by flowing water. When a steady state is reached, the temperatures of the plates are measured and the electrical-power input determined. Convection currents are absent in this method.

Nearly all precise measurements of K have been made by the *hot-wire method*. The apparatus consists of a cylindrical tube which is kept at constant temperature in a thermostatically controlled bath and which contains the gas to be studied. A fine wire, stretched along the axis of the tube, is heated electrically, and the Joulean power dissipated in the wire is determined. The temperature of the wire is found by measuring its resistance. When a steady state is reached, these measurements, together with the dimensions of the wire and tube, permit calculation of the conductivity K. The very simple theory of the hot-wire cell will now be given. We calculate the heat flow between two coaxial cylinders of sufficient length that end effects can be neglected. Let Q_1 be the heat conducted through the gas per unit time per unit length of the cylinders; this unit length is taken far enough from the ends so that the temperature gradient and the heat flow are radial. Let a and b denote the radii of the inner and outer cylinders and T_a and T_b their respective temperatures. The heat-flow vector at a distance r from the axis $q(r)$ is related to the temperature gradient dT/dr by

$$q(r) = -K \, dT/dr$$

Assume $T_a > T_b$, then $dT/dr < 0$, and $q(r) > 0$. We note that $Q_1 = 2\pi r q(r)$ and that Q_1 is independent of r in the steady state. Then

$$Q_1 = -2\pi K r \, dT/dr \qquad (10\text{-}8)$$

and

$$\frac{2\pi K}{Q_1} \int_{T_a}^{T_b} dT + \int_a^b \frac{dr}{r} = 0 \qquad (10\text{-}9)$$

giving, for the conductivity,

$$K = \frac{Q_1}{2\pi} \frac{\log \ (b/a)}{T_a - T_b} \qquad (10\text{-}10)$$

Equation (10-10) requires a small correction, to be described below.

Corrections to the method are necessitated by heat conducted away through the ends of the wire, by radiative heat transfer, by possible convection currents, and by the "temperature-jump" effect. Three principal modifications of the hot-wire cell have been devised in order to minimize errors resulting from the first of these effects, i.e., the end conduction. In the "compensating-cell" method, two cells differing only in length are operated under identical conditions. The difference between the measured heat flows is divided by the difference in lengths to give a value of Q_1 in which the effects of end conduction are approximately

canceled out.   In the "thick-wire cell," the ends of the cell are designed
so that a precise theoretical correction can be made for the conduction of
heat through the ends.   In the "potential-lead cell," which has been used
in the most accurate work, very fine wires are attached to the axial wire
in order to determine the potential drop over a central segment.   The
power dissipated in the segment and its temperature are obtained from
the resistance measurement.   The effective length of the cell is that of
the segment between the potential leads.   A small correction must be
applied for the heat conducted away from the central segment through
the wire itself.

The radiative transfer of heat can be calculated or measured with the
cell evacuated.   Convection currents must be avoided in accurate work.
They are minimized by having the tube narrow and in a horizontal position, and they can be effectively eliminated by reducing the pressure of
the gas sufficiently (below about 100 mm Hg in practice).   Although
the thermal conductivity, like the viscosity, is independent of pressure
at ordinary pressures, the values of K found by the hot-wire method will
show a slight dependence on pressure unless corrected for the "temperature-jump" effect.   This effect increases with decreasing pressure and
must be taken into account at the pressures needed to ensure a convection-
free measurement.

The Temperature-jump Effect and the Accommodation Coefficient.
The temperature-jump is an apparent discontinuity in temperature
occurring at a gas-solid interface when heat is flowing across the boundary.   Consider a gas conducting heat between two parallel plates at
different temperatures, and let the mean free path be much shorter than
the plate separation.   As predicted by the law of heat conduction, the
temperature in the body of the gas will be found to increase linearly with
distance from the cooler plate, but the observed temperature gradient in
the gas is less than the gradient obtained by dividing the temperature
difference between the plates by the plate separation.   In general, the
hotter wall is at a higher temperature and the cooler wall at a lower temperature than would be predicted by extrapolating the temperature variation found in the body of the gas.

In order to understand this effect, we consider the collisions of molecules
with the cooler wall and assume initially that the reflected or reemitted
molecules have come into thermal equilibrium with the surface and have
a mean energy corresponding to the surface temperature T_s.   Before colliding with the wall, these molecules had a mean energy corresponding to
the temperature T_λ in the gas at the average site of their last collisions,
i.e., at a distance $2\lambda/3$ from the wall (cf. Prob. 3-3).   Since heat is being
transported to the cooler wall by molecular impact, the reflected molecules
must take away less energy than they bring.   Hence $T_s < T_\lambda$, and the
temperature of the wall is different from that in the adjacent layers of

gas a few mean free paths away.   In order to estimate the temperature difference $T_\lambda - T_s$, we equate the net transport of heat to the wall to the transport in the gas close to the wall.   The former is given, per unit area per unit time, by $(n\bar{v}/4)mc_v(T_\lambda - T_s)$ and the latter by $K\, dT/dz$ where the z axis is normal to the surface.   On substituting Eq. (3-28), we obtain

$$\frac{n\bar{v}}{4}\, mc_v(T_\lambda - T_s) = \frac{1}{3}\, nm\bar{v}\lambda c_v\, \frac{dT}{dz} \tag{10-11}$$

where we are neglecting a slight variation of n, $\bar{v}$, and c_v within a few free paths of the wall.   The derivative dT/dz represents the temperature gradient in the body of the gas extrapolated to the wall.   From Eq. (10-11), it follows that $T_\lambda - T_s = (4\lambda/3)\, dT/dz$.   Since the average distance from the wall of the last collision site is $2\lambda/3$, the temperature drop $T_\lambda - T_s$ is twice the drop in T obtained from the gradient.

The effective thermal conductivity of the gas within a few free paths of the wall cannot be the same as in the interior of the gas because of the effect of the wall collisions.   Instead of taking explicit account of the more rapid temperature variation within several free paths of the surface, it is customary to use the mathematical artifice of the temperature jump.   One assumes that the heat conduction follows the same law, with the same value of K as in the interior of the gas, from surface to surface, but that at the surfaces the temperature changes discontinuously.   The *temperature jump*, or discontinuity at the wall, is defined as the difference between the actual surface temperature and the temperature predicted by extrapolating the law of temperature variation in the body of the gas. If T_e denotes the extrapolated temperature at the surface, it follows from the discussion in the preceding paragraph that

$$T_\lambda - T_e = (2\lambda/3)\, dT/dz = \tfrac{1}{2}(T_\lambda - T_s) \tag{10-12}$$

The temperature jump δT is then given by

$$\delta T = T_e - T_s = (2\lambda/3)\, dT/dz \tag{10-13}$$

The relations (10-11) through (10-13) are approximate; they are subject to the usual uncertainties in numerical factors characterizing elementary free-path considerations.   A more important limitation is the initial assumption that the molecules leaving the wall have come into thermal equilibrium with it, as might be the case if they were temporarily trapped in surface pockets or adsorbed.   This assumption is not usually justified, and it is necessary to introduce a fractional quantity known as the "accommodation coefficient" to represent the extent to which the colliding molecules adjust their mean energy or temperature to that of the wall.*   Without going into further detail on this point, we write the gen-

---

* The *accommodation coefficient* is defined as the ratio of the actual mean-energy change of molecules colliding with a wall to the mean-energy change if the molecules came into equilibrium with the wall.

eral formula for the temperature jump as

$$\delta T = g \, dT/dz \tag{10-14}$$

where dT/dz again represents the temperature gradient in the body of the gas extrapolated to the surface (normal in the z direction). The temperature-jump distance g depends on the value of the accommodation coefficient and may be many times larger than λ if the accommodation coefficient is small (values of g as large as 20λ are found occasionally). In general, the lighter the gas, the higher the temperature, and the smoother and cleaner the surface, the smaller is the value of the accommodation coefficient.* Although no rigorous theory of the temperature jump exists, an approximate evaluation of g in terms of the accommodation coefficient can be worked out in analogy to the theory of slip.†

The temperature-jump correction to the hot-wire method is readily obtained from the foregoing discussion. Let T_a and T_b be the actual temperatures of the wire and tube, respectively, and T_a' and T_b' the corresponding temperatures as extrapolated from the gas. The temperature jumps are given according to Eqs. (10-14) and (10-8) by

$$
\begin{aligned}
T_a - T_a' &= -g_a \left(\frac{dT}{dr} \right)_a = \frac{g_a Q_1}{2\pi a K_a} \\
T_b' - T_b &= -g_b \left(\frac{dT}{dr} \right)_b = \frac{g_b Q_1}{2\pi b K_b}
\end{aligned}
\tag{10-15}
$$

whence
$$T_a' - T_b' = (T_a - T_b) - \frac{Q_1}{2\pi} \left(\frac{g_a}{a K_a} + \frac{g_b}{b K_b} \right) \tag{10-16}$$

The temperature-jump distances g_a and g_b are unequal in general; the use of K_a and K_b takes account of the slight temperature variation of the conductivity. In place of Eq. (10-10) we now have two equations, one for the apparent conductivity K_{ap}, in which the temperature jump is neglected, and the other for the true conductivity K_{tr}, in which the unmeasured temperatures T_a' and T_b' appear:

$$K_{\mathrm{ap}} = \frac{Q_1}{2\pi} \frac{\log{(b/a)}}{T_a - T_b} \qquad K_{\mathrm{tr}} = \frac{Q_1}{2\pi} \frac{\log{(b/a)}}{T_a' - T_b'} \tag{10-17}$$

Substitution of (10-17) in (10-16) then gives

$$\frac{1}{K_{\mathrm{ap}}} = \frac{1}{K_{\mathrm{tr}}} + \frac{1}{\log{(b/a)}} \left(\frac{g_a}{a K_a} + \frac{g_b}{b K_b} \right) \tag{10-18}$$

* M. Knudsen, "Kinetic Theory of Gases," Methuen & Co., Ltd., London, 1950; L. B. Loeb, "Kinetic Theory of Gases," McGraw-Hill Book Company, Inc., New York, 1934.

† E. H. Kennard, "Kinetic Theory of Gases," McGraw-Hill Book Company, Inc., New York, 1938.

The jump length g is proportional to the mean free path and therefore varies inversely with the pressure p. We set $g_a = g_a^*/p$ and $g_b = g_b^*/p$ and obtain finally

$$K_{\mathrm{ap}}^{-1} = K_{\mathrm{tr}}^{-1} + A p^{-1} \tag{10-19}$$

$$A = \frac{1}{\log (b/a)} \left(\frac{g_a^*}{a K_a} + \frac{g_b^*}{b K_b} \right) \tag{10-20}$$

where A is independent of pressure.

The terms in g_a and g_b in Eq. (10-18) represent temperature-jump corrections; they are of order λ/a and λ/b, respectively, and are thus small at ordinary pressures. Since $b \gg a$ in the hot-wire apparatus, the term in g_b is ordinarily negligible. The term in g_a would also become negligible at sufficiently high pressures, but these cannot be used in practice because of the convection effects. The true average conductivity of the gas over the temperature range T_b to T_a has been designated by K_{tr}. The measured conductivity, corrected for end losses, radiation, etc., but not for temperature-jump, is what we have referred to as the apparent conductivity K_{ap}. It follows from Eq. (10-19) that a graph of the measured values of K_{ap}^{-1} versus p^{-1} for fixed T_a and T_b should be a straight line of slope A and ordinate intercept K_{tr}^{-1}. Knowing the conductivity and its approximate temperature-dependence, the value of A can be used to obtain the temperature-jump distance g_a. Since the jump distance is theoretically related to the accommodation coefficient, the coefficient can be obtained for the particular combination of gas and cell-wire surface at the temperature used in the experiment. Some recent measurements by this method, using the potential-lead type of hot-wire cell, have yielded values for the thermal conductivities of several gases accurate to within about 0.5 per cent over a wide temperature range, as well as accommodation coefficients for the same gases on a bright platinum wire.*

In conclusion, it may be mentioned that thermal-conductivity methods have proved useful in gas analysis and that measurements of the accommodation coefficient are helpful in providing information about the state of a solid surface, e.g., in studies of contact catalysis.

10-4. MEASUREMENT OF THE COEFFICIENTS OF MUTUAL AND SELF-DIFFUSION

Most measurements of the gaseous mutual-diffusion coefficient D_{12} have been based on a method due to Loschmidt.† In its simplest form, the apparatus consists of a long, closed, vertical tube that can be divided into two equal sections by a removable partition at its center. The

---

* W. J. Taylor, H. L. Johnston, and E. R. Grilly, *Jour. Chem. Phys.*, vol. 14, pp. 219, 233, and 435, 1946.

† J. Loschmidt, *Wien. Ber.*, vol. 61, p. 367; vol. 62, p. 468, 1870.

upper half is filled with the lighter gas and the lower half with the heavier gas, both at the same temperature and pressure. The partition is removed and diffusion takes place for a measured time τ, after which the partition is reinserted and the contents of the two sections are analyzed to determine the change in composition. The theory of the Loschmidt method involves the solution of the one-dimensional diffusion equation (4-58) for the given boundary conditions and initial conditions. Let $c_1(z,t)$ be the fractional molecular concentration or mole fraction of gas 1, which initially fills the lower half of the tube. Then the diffusion equation

$$\partial c_1/\partial t = D\partial^2 c_1/\partial z^2 \tag{10-21}$$

is to be solved to determine $c_1(z,t)$. The tube extends from $z = 0$ to $z = l$, and at the two ends the diffusive transport vanishes at all times. The boundary conditions

$$(\partial c_1/\partial z)_{z=0} = (\partial c_1/\partial z)_{z=l} = 0 \qquad \text{for all } t \tag{10-22}$$

correspond to the vanishing of the concentration gradient at the ends of the tube. If the lower half of the tube is initially filled with pure gas 1 and the upper half with pure gas 2, the initial condition is

$$c_1(z,0) = \begin{cases} 1 & 0 \le z < l/2 \\ 0 & l/2 < z \le l \end{cases} \tag{10-23}$$

A particular solution of (10-21) is obtained by inserting

$$c_1(z,t) = e^{-\alpha t}(A \sin \beta z + B \cos \beta z)$$

which is seen to satisfy (10-21) if $\alpha = \beta^2 D$. Thus

$$\partial c_1/\partial z = e^{-\beta^2 Dt}(\beta A \cos \beta z - \beta B \sin \beta z)$$
$$(\partial c_1/\partial z)_{z=0} = \beta A e^{-\beta^2 Dt} = 0$$

whence $A = 0$. The other boundary condition

$$(\partial c_1/\partial z)_{z=l} = -\beta B e^{-\beta^2 Dt} \sin \beta l = 0$$

is satisfied if $\beta l = n\pi$ where $n = 0, 1, 2, 3, \ldots$. The general solution satisfying the boundary conditions (10-22) is then

$$c_1(z,t) = \sum_{n=0}^{\infty} B_n e^{-(n\pi/l)^2 Dt} \cos (n\pi z/l) \tag{10-24}$$

and initially

$$c_1(z,0) = \sum_{n=0}^{\infty} B_n \cos (n\pi z/l) \tag{10-25}$$

Equation (10-25) is a Fourier series expansion, and the coefficients B_n

can be determined for any given piecewise-continuous function $c_1(z,0)$ by standard methods.* Integration of (10-25) from $z = 0$ to $z = l$ gives

$$B_0 = \frac{1}{l} \int_0^l c_1(z,0)\ dz \tag{10-26a}$$

The other coefficients are obtained by multiplying both sides of (10-25) by $\cos(m\pi z/l)$ where $m = 1, 2, 3, \ldots$ and integrating from $z = 0$ to $z = l$. This gives

$$\underset{n>0}{B_n} = \frac{2}{l} \int_0^l c_1(z,0)\ \cos(n\pi z/l)\ dz \tag{10-26b}$$

Inserting the initial condition (10-23) for pure gases in equal volumes, one obtains

$$B_0 = \frac{1}{2} \qquad \underset{n>0}{B_n} = \frac{2}{n\pi} \sin \frac{n\pi}{2} \tag{10-27}$$

Thus B_n vanishes for even n if $n > 0$ and is equal for odd n to $(-1)^{(n-1)/2}$ $\cdot (2/n\pi)$. The solution to the diffusion problem is given by

$$c_1(z,t) = \frac{1}{2} + \frac{2}{\pi} \sum_{\text{odd } n} \frac{(-1)^{(n-1)/2}}{n} e^{-(n\pi/l)^2 Dt} \cos \frac{n\pi z}{l} \tag{10-28}$$

If the diffusion is terminated at time τ and the gas in the bottom section is analyzed, the mole fraction of gas 1 will be given by

$$\begin{aligned}
\bar{c}_{1b}(\tau) &= \frac{2}{l} \int_0^{l/2} c_1(z,\tau)\ dz \\
&= \frac{2}{l} \sum_{n=0}^{\infty} B_n e^{-(n\pi/l)^2 D\tau} \int_0^{l/2} \cos \frac{n\pi z}{l}\ dz \\
&= B_0 + \sum_{n=1}^{\infty} B_n^2 e^{-(n\pi/l)^2 D\tau} \\
&= \frac{1}{2} + \frac{4}{\pi^2} \sum_{\text{odd } n} \frac{1}{n^2} e^{-(n\pi/l)^2 D\tau} \tag{10-29}
\end{aligned}$$

The diffusion time τ is chosen long enough so that the terms in the series drop off rapidly and can be neglected beyond $n = 5$. Equation (10-29) gives the desired relation between the diffusion coefficient D and the observed quantities l, τ, and $\bar{c}_{1b}(\tau)$ from which D can be calculated by successive approximations or obtained by interpolation from prepared tables of solutions to (10-29).

---

* Cf. any book on advanced calculus, e.g., R. Courant, "Differential and Integral Calculus," vol. 1, Interscience Publishers, Inc., New York, 1937.

It has been implicitly assumed in the foregoing that D is independent of the mole fraction, or composition, of the mixture. In order to test this assumption experimentally, without making the complicated revision of the preceding analysis needed to take into account various possible forms for the dependence of D on composition, the observations can be carried out with gas mixtures instead of pure gases. If the two sections are filled with gas mixtures of slightly different proportions, the possible variation of D with composition can be neglected, and the preceding method of treatment for a constant D can be used provided that the initial condition (10-23) is replaced by the one appropriate to the initial mixtures. One thus obtains a value of D corresponding to the mean composition of the initial mixtures. Experiments of this sort have shown D_{12} to vary only slightly with composition.[*]

An interesting new interferometric method of measuring D_{12}, based on the Loschmidt geometry and Eq. (10-28), will now be described briefly.[†] In this method the change in composition of the gas at a fixed position in the diffusion cell is determined by measuring the change in refractive index with an interferometer. Windows in the walls provide an optical path across the cell for one beam of the interferometer. As the diffusion run proceeds, a shift takes place in the interference fringes. The observed fringe shift is directly proportional to the change in refractive index. Since the refractive index of a gas mixture is a known function of its composition, it is possible to determine the composition at the position in the cell traversed by the light beam from the measured fringe shift. The diffusion cell, which is of uniform rectangular cross section, consists of two equal sections, or half cells, with sliding plates attached to the bottom of the upper half cell and to the top of the lower, as shown in Fig. 10-6. The half cells are slid together at the beginning of a run. The rectangular cross section makes it possible to have a long optical path.

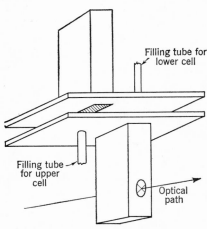

Filling tube for lower cell

Filling tube for upper cell

Optical path

FIG. 10-6. Schematic diagram of the diffusion cell. (After Boyd, Stein, Steingrimsson, and Rumpel.)

Since the geometry is essentially the same as in Loschmidt's apparatus and since the half cells of length $l/2$ were filled with pure gases, the previous analysis applies without any modification, and Eq. (10-28) gives

[*] A. Lonius, *Ann. d. Physik*, vol. 29, p. 664, 1909.

[†] Boyd, Stein, Steingrimsson, and Rumpel, *Jour. Chem. Phys.*, vol. 19, p. 548, 1951.

the concentration at time t at a height z above the bottom of the lower half cell. If the optical path crosses the cell at a height $z = l/6$, it is seen from (10-28) that in the series for $c_1(l/6,t)$ the term with $n = 3$ vanishes. By choosing the times t long enough so that the $n = 5$ term is inappreciable, the series can be replaced by the single term with $n = 1$, and the diffusion coefficient is then given by

$$D = \frac{l^2}{\pi^2 t} \log \left[\frac{\sqrt{3}/\pi}{c_1(l/6,t) - \frac{1}{2}} \right] \qquad (10\text{-}30)$$

The diffusion cell is mounted in a thermostat in order to eliminate errors associated with temperature gradients, e.g., thermal-diffusive transport and convection. During the course of a run, integral fringe shifts are counted visually with the aid of a telescope while simultaneous photographs of the fringes and a timer permit an accurate measurement of the fringe shift at a known time t. Several determinations of D can be made in the course of one run. Values of D_{12} accurate to within 0.5 per cent have been obtained by this method.

Self-diffusion Measurements with Isotopes. The closest approximation to self-diffusion is realized through the use of isotopic molecules.[*] The intermolecular forces and effective cross sections for the interaction between two type-1 molecules, two type-2 molecules, and a type-1 with a type-2 molecule are all virtually identical in this case. However, the isotopic diffusion coefficient is slightly different from the idealized self-diffusion coefficient because the reduced mass, which appears in the diffusion-coefficient formulas (4-23) and (8-84), is $m_1 m_2/(m_1 + m_2)$ for isotopic diffusion and $m_1/2$ or $m_2/2$ for self-diffusion. The first isotopic diffusion measurements were made by Groth and Harteck,[†] who determined the coefficients of krypton and xenon by the Loschmidt method. The experimental gases of altered isotopic content were obtained from Clusius-Dickel thermal-diffusion columns, and isotopic analyses were performed by thermal-conductivity methods. A more accurate method of making isotopic-diffusion measurements was developed in 1943 by Ney and Armistead[‡] for the purpose of determining the self-diffusion coefficient of uranium hexafluoride vapor. Since nearly all subsequent measurements of self-diffusion have utilized the Ney-Armistead technique, this method will be described in some detail.

The Ney-Armistead apparatus differs from that of Loschmidt in that two large chambers are used with a straight tube or pipe connecting them. In the original apparatus the connecting tube consisted of two equal-sized

[*] In the case of hydrogen, the interdiffusion of the ortho and para forms can be measured. P. Harteck and H. Schmidt, *Z. Phys. Chem.*, vol. 21B, p. 447, 1933.

[†] W. Groth and P. Harteck, *Z. Elektrochem.*, vol. 47, p. 167, 1941.

[‡] E. Ney and F. Armistead, *Phys. Rev.*, vol. 71, p. 14, 1947.

copper pipes with a section of neoprene tubing between them; by pinching the rubber with a clamp, the two chambers could be isolated. One chamber was filled with a sample enriched in $U^{235}F_6$ and the other with a sample enriched in $U^{238}F_6$. With both chambers at the same pressure and temperature, the diffusion process was started by unpinching the neoprene. Samples from one chamber were slowly bled through an adjustable capillary leak into the ion source of a mass spectrometer in order to follow the concentration changes. The measured "relaxation time" (see below) together with the geometric constants of the apparatus give the diffusion coefficient. The method can also be used with radioactive isotopes in tracer quantities; the radioactive gas is released in one chamber and the concentration changes are followed by means of end-window counters attached to the sides of the two chambers.* The continuous withdrawal of material to the mass spectrometer in the first case and the measurement of concentration with counters in the second case both require that portions of the gas in the diffusion cell be uniform in composition. This is true of the gas in both chambers of the Ney-Armistead apparatus but not of the gas in the Loschmidt tube, where the composition is everywhere nonuniform. Besides making possible continuous concentration measurements, the newer geometry has the advantage of greater compactness, thus reducing the errors associated with temperature gradients.

The theory of the Ney-Armistead method is based on three assumptions: (1) that the composition of the gas in the chambers is uniform, the concentration gradient being confined to the connecting tube, (2) that the concentration in the connecting tube varies linearly with distance along the tube, and (3) that the volume of the connecting tube is negligible compared with the volume of the chambers. The validity of these assumptions will be examined after the simple theory has been developed. Let $n_a(t)$ and $n_b(t)$ denote the number density of tracer molecules at time t in chambers a and b, respectively. If l represents the length and A the area of cross section of the connecting tube, and if D is the diffusion coefficient, we can write for the net rate of transport of tracer molecules through the tube at time t

$$\begin{aligned} \Gamma(t) &= -AD\, dn/dz \\ &= (DA/l)[n_a(t) - n_b(t)] \\ &= k[n_a(t) - n_b(t)] > 0 \end{aligned} \qquad (10\text{-}31)$$

Let V_a and V_b be the volumes of the two chambers and $V = V_a + V_b$ the total volume. Then, since Γ is equal to the rate of increase of tracer molecules in chamber b and to the rate of decrease in a, it follows that

* S. Visner, *Phys. Rev.*, vol. 82, p. 297, 1951; Report K-688, 1951, Carbide and Carbon Chemicals Corporation, Oak Ridge, Tennessee.

$$\Gamma(t) = \frac{d}{dt}(V_b n_b) = -\frac{d}{dt}(V_a n_a) \qquad (10\text{-}32)$$

and
$$V_b \, dn_b/dt = k n_a(t) - k n_b(t) \qquad (10\text{-}33)$$

Conservation of tracer molecules gives

$$V_a n_a(t) + V_b n_b(t) = V n(\infty) \qquad (10\text{-}34)$$

where $n(\infty)$ is the ultimate number density of tracer molecules in either chamber after complete mixing has taken place $(t = \infty)$. Substituting (10-34) in (10-33), one finds that

$$dn_b/dt = -\alpha n_b(t) + \beta \qquad (10\text{-}35)$$

with $\alpha = kV/V_a V_b$ and $\beta = \alpha n(\infty)$. The integration constant for (10-35) is obtained from the initial condition: $n_b = n_b(0)$ at $t = 0$ when the diffusion begins. Since α and β are constants, Eq. (10-35) is readily integrated and the solution is

$$n_b(t) = n(\infty) - [n(\infty) - n_b(0)]e^{-\alpha t} \qquad (10\text{-}36)$$

It is convenient to take natural logarithms, thus obtaining

$$\log\,[n(\infty) - n_b(t)] = \log\,[n(\infty) - n_b(0)] - \alpha t \qquad (10\text{-}37)$$

When the experimental data for $n_b(t)$ are used to make a plot of $\log\,[n(\infty) - n_b(t)]$ versus t, a straight line should be obtained, according to (10-37), of slope equal to $-\alpha$. Knowing V_a, V_b, A, and l, one can derive the value of D from the measured value of α. The relaxation time for the diffusion run, defined as the time in which the difference between the instantaneous and ultimate concentrations becomes equal to $1/e$ times the difference between the initial and ultimate concentrations, is equal to $1/\alpha$. The diffusion run is terminated at the end of one or two relaxation times, since little extra precision is gained by a longer run. The value of $n(\infty)$ can be obtained from Eq. (10-34) if $n_a(0)$ and $n_b(0)$ are known; it can also be measured directly by waiting for several relaxation times to elapse or by pumping out and analyzing the contents of the two chambers at the end of a run. It is obvious from Eq. (10-36) that the number densities can be replaced by any quantities proportional to them, e.g., concentrations obtained from the isotopic ratios measured by the mass spectrometer or counting rates measured by the counter attached to chamber b.

The three assumptions of the method will now be considered. If the volume of the connecting tube cannot be neglected, a simple correction can be made to take it into account. Assuming the tube to be initially clamped at its center, the mean concentration in the tube is equal to the average of the end concentrations. Equation (10-34) is then replaced by

$$V_a n_a(t) + V_b n_b(t) + lA \frac{n_a(t) + n_b(t)}{2} = n(\infty)(V_a + V_b + lA)$$

or
$$V'_a n_a(t) + V'_b n_b(t) = V' n(\infty) \tag{10-38}$$

where $V'_a = V_a + \tfrac{1}{2}lA$, $V'_b = V_b + \tfrac{1}{2}lA$ and $V' = V + lA$. Thus $\alpha = kV'/V'_a V'_b$. We have assumed that at any instant there is a linear variation of the concentration in the connecting tube along the axis, i.e., a uniform concentration gradient. In order to justify this assumption, one must solve the diffusion equation (10-21) for appropriate boundary conditions. As a first approximation, one assumes that the composition of the gas at the ends of the tube remains constant. The solution, which is obtained by the same methods used to derive Eq. (10-28), consists of a linear term in z which represents a constant, uniform concentration gradient plus a transient sine series with the same exponential time factors as in (10-28). The relaxation time of the transient, defined as the time required for the first and leading term to drop to $1/e$ of its initial value, is equal to $l^2/D\pi^2$. In practice, this time is usually less than a second and is thus very much shorter than the relaxation time for the diffusion run, α^{-1}, which may be several hours. The rapid disappearance of the transient and the slow change in concentration in the chambers ensure a uniform gradient in the connecting tube at all times. As a second approximation, one may assume time-dependent boundary conditions in which the concentrations at the ends of the tube are given by (10-36) and a similar equation for $n_a(t)$. The solution of the diffusion equation can be obtained by standard methods, and the result is a linear term in z depending on the instantaneous concentrations in the chambers plus a transient series. The latter becomes negligible after a few seconds and the solution then represents a uniform concentration gradient in the tube which changes slowly with the changing composition of the gas in the chambers.

If the connecting tube consists of two or more sections of different diameters, as in the original apparatus of Ney and Armistead, it follows from the existence of a uniform concentration gradient in each section that the effective value of l/A is to be taken equal to $\Sigma(l_i/A_i)$. Thus $k = D/\Sigma(l_i/A_i)$ instead of DA/l. The analogy to electrical resistances in series is apparent. Since the values of l/A appropriate to the chambers are entirely negligible compared to the value of l/A for the connecting tube, the assumption that the concentration gradient is all in the connecting tube is justified providing a small end correction is made. Actually, the concentration gradient extends slightly beyond the ends of the tube, and the correction is made by replacing the measured length of the tube by a slightly greater effective length. In calculating this correction, we assume the connecting tube to be of uniform diameter and the chambers to be of infinite volume. The variation of the system with time is so slow, after the transient dies out, that negligible error arises from assuming a steady-state diffusion ($\partial n/\partial t = 0$). In the one-dimensional case, we then have $\partial^2 n/\partial z^2 = 0$ and thus obtain again the linear variation of concentration along the axis of the tube which was discussed above. The three-dimensional equation for steady-state diffusion is obtained from Eq. (4-60) by putting $\partial n/\partial t = 0$. The resulting partial differential equation

$$\partial^2 n/\partial x^2 + \partial^2 n/\partial y^2 + \partial^2 n/\partial z^2 = 0 \qquad (10\text{-}39)$$

is the famous equation of Laplace, which has ubiquitous applications. The end-correction problem involves solving Eq. (10-39) for the given boundary conditions at the ends of the tube. This problem has an exact mathematical analogue in electric-current flow and in the propagation of sound at long wave lengths. The result of the analysis, giving the so-called Maxwell-Rayleigh end correction,* is that the length l of the tube should be replaced by an effective length l' (corrected at both ends) given by

$$l' = l + 2\kappa a \qquad (10\text{-}40)$$

where a is the radius of the tube and κ is a monotonic function of the ratio a/l. In the case of interest, $l \gg a$, the value of κ is found by successive approximations† to be 0.821. The effective increase in the length at each end by 0.821 times the radius is taken into account in computing $\Sigma(l_i/A_i)$. Values of the self-diffusion coefficient, obtained by this method, are accurate to within a few per cent.

PROBLEMS

10-1. Compare the free-molecule flow through a long tube of radius a and length l with the effusive flow through an ideal orifice of the same area.

10-2. Show that in the free-fall experiment, a molecule of velocity v will fall a distance $s = gl^2/v^2$ before reaching the detector.

10-3. Rework Prob. 3-1 by the method of Sec. 10-2, i.e., without making the approximation of rectilinear flow.

10-4. Discuss the analogy between electrical resistances in series and diffusion through tubes in series when the concentration gradient is uniform in each tube. Why is the effective value of l/A equal to $\Sigma(l_i/A_i)$ in the Ney-Armistead apparatus? Why is the concentration gradient in the chambers negligible?

10-5. Assuming the connecting tube of the self-diffusion apparatus to be of uniform diameter throughout, solve the diffusion equation (10-21) for the case of a fixed or constant composition at the ends of the tube. Let the boundary

---

* J. C. Maxwell, "Electricity and Magnetism," Dover Publications, New York, 1954, p. 434; Lord Rayleigh, "Theory of Sound," Dover Publications, New York, 1945, vol. 2, p. 291.

† L. V. King, *Phil. Mag.*, vol. 21, p. 128, 1936.

conditions for $c_1(z,t)$ be $c_1(0,t) = 0$, $c_1(l,t) = C$, and let the initial condition be $c_1(z,0) = 0$.

10-6. Suggest reasons for the qualitative dependence of the accommodation coefficient on the temperature, the molecular weight of the gas, and the condition of the surface.

10-7. Calculate the theoretical vertical intensity distribution in a gravity-deflected molecular beam, using Eq. (10-1) and assuming the intensity distribution of the undeflected beam to be given by an isosceles trapezoid corresponding to defining slits of equal width b. If I_0 is the maximum intensity of the undeflected beam and $I(s)$ the intensity of the deflected beam at a distance s from the upper edge of the undeflected beam, show that

$$\frac{I(s)}{I_0} = \frac{s}{b} e^{-s_m/s} - \frac{s-b}{b} e^{-s_m/(s-b)} - \frac{s-2b}{b} e^{-s_m/(s-2b)} + \frac{s-3b}{b} e^{-s_m/(s-3b)}$$

CHAPTER 11

INTRODUCTION TO ADVANCED TRANSPORT THEORY

This chapter treats the most fundamental problems of the kinetic theory of gases. The first two sections are based on the methods of Maxwell and on developments that have grown out of his pioneering work. The first part of Sec. 11-1 takes up the derivation of Maxwell's equation of change for dynamical quantities associated with the individual molecules. The fundamental assumptions underlying all advanced transport theory are presented in this section. The equation of change for the molecular mass is shown to be identical with the hydrodynamical equation of continuity, and the equation of change for linear momentum is found to reduce to the hydrodynamical equation of motion of a continuous fluid. Section 11-2 deals with the Maxwell-Chapman transport theory. It is shown that in all three transport phenomena, the distribution of molecular velocities is non-Maxwellian. The distribution function is expanded in a power series in the velocity components, and a first-approximation function is obtained for the case of viscous flow. Following Chapman, we select the appropriate equation of change and show in detail that it reduces to the standard viscosity equation. All the steps are worked through which lead to the general formula for the viscosity coefficient in the first approximation of advanced transport theory. The formula is applied to rigid, spherical molecules and to molecules having an inverse fifth-power repulsion.

Section 11-3 is devoted to the derivation of Boltzmann's integro-differential equation for the general distribution function when the gas is in a nonuniform, nonsteady, nonequilibrium state. The collision term is discussed in detail and evaluated for the case of spherically symmetric intermolecular forces. The equation of change is then obtained directly from Boltzmann's equation. In Sec. 11-4 the Boltzmann equation is used to give a rigorous derivation of the Maxwell-Boltzmann distribution law for a gas in equilibrium. The detailed balancing of each encounter by its inverse, which is a sufficient condition for equilibrium, is shown also to be a necessary condition; the proof is provided by Boltzmann's H theorem. The Maxwell distribution law is derived from the detailed balancing condition. The Maxwell-Boltzmann function is seen to satisfy Boltzmann's equation when an external field is present. The H theorem is generalized to the case of nonuniform states, and it is shown that the H function, which decreases with the time, attains a minimum value at equilibrium. The relationship of this proof to the statistical-mechanical derivation of the Maxwell-Boltzmann law (cf. Appendix 5-2) leads to an important connection between the H function and the probability of a macrostate. The "reversibility paradox" of Loschmidt is taken up, and we consider at length how the reversibility of classical dynamics is to be reconciled with the irreversibility predicted by the H theorem and found in nature. Finally, we show that the entropy of a monatomic perfect gas is simply related to the H function and to the probability of a macrostate. These last two sections are based mainly on the work of Boltzmann.

11-1. MAXWELL'S EQUATION OF CHANGE AND THE HYDRODYNAMICAL EQUATIONS

The advanced theory of transport phenomena has been developed along two different lines of approach which are closely related and which yield identical results. The first, or Boltzmann-Enskog, method is based on Boltzmann's integrodifferential equation for the velocity distribution function and involves the solution of this equation by a method of successive approximations, which was first carried through in detail by Enskog.* The second, or Maxwell-Chapman, method is based on Maxwell's equation of transfer or change for dynamical quantities and also proceeds by successive approximations according to a procedure first developed and applied by Chapman.† The Boltzmann equation, which plays a fundamental role in all transport theory, will be taken up in Sec. 11-3. However, the first approximation formulas for the transport coefficients can be derived more simply by the Maxwell-Chapman method, which will be followed here in preference to the more abstract method of Enskog.

The first step is the derivation of Maxwell's equation of change. Although this equation can be deduced from Boltzmann's equation, it is simpler to obtain it directly with the aid of the collision formulas developed in Chap. 8. The conditions for the validity of Maxwell's equation are the same as for Boltzmann's; these will be taken up in this section and again briefly in Sec. 11-3, when Boltzmann's equation is discussed. A very fundamental assumption is that the density of the gas must be low

---

* L. Boltzmann, *Wien. Ber.*, vol. 66, p. 275, 1872; D. Enskog, dissertation, Upsala, 1917, and *Svensk. Vet. Akad., Arkiv. f. Mat., Ast. och Fys.*, vol. 16, p. 1, 1921.

† J. C. Maxwell, *Phil. Trans. Royal Soc.*, vol. 157, p. 49, 1867, or "Collected Works," vol. 2, p. 26; S. Chapman, *Phil. Trans. Royal Soc.*, vol. A211, p. 433, 1912, vol. A216, p. 279, 1916, and vol. A217, p. 115, 1917.

enough to ensure that the mean free path is large compared to the effective range of the intermolecular forces. This condition makes it possible to neglect ternary and higher-order encounters and to apply the principle of molecular chaos in the treatment of binary encounters, as explained below. Since the range of intermolecular forces is between 10^{-8} and 10^{-7} cm, the condition is satisfied at ordinary densities for which $\lambda \sim 10^{-5}$ cm. At the same time, we require that the mean free path be short compared to the dimensions of the container; this eliminates consideration of the effects of wall collisions except in a thin surface layer. Other assumptions of the method will be introduced at appropriate places in the development.

Let $n(\mathbf{r},t)$ denote the number density in the neighborhood of the point $\mathbf{r}$, or x, y, z, at time t. Let $F(\mathbf{v},\mathbf{r},t)$ be the normalized velocity distribution function such that $F(\mathbf{v},\mathbf{r},t)\, dv_x\, dv_y\, dv_z$ represents the probability that a molecule, which is near the point $\mathbf{r}$ at time t, has a velocity between $\mathbf{v}$ and $\mathbf{v} + d\mathbf{v}$, i.e., an x component of velocity between v_x and $v_x + dv_x$, etc. Then $n(\mathbf{r},t)F(\mathbf{v},\mathbf{r},t)\, d\tau\, dv_x\, dv_y\, dv_z$ denotes the number of molecules in the volume element $d\tau$ which have velocities between $\mathbf{v}$ and $\mathbf{v} + d\mathbf{v}$ at time t. The dependence of F on $\mathbf{r}$ may arise from a gradient in temperature, in composition, or in the velocity of mass flow. In the latter case, if the flow is in the y direction and the velocity gradient in the z direction, F will depend implicitly on z through $\bar{v}_y(z)$. Let $Q(\mathbf{v})$ denote a dynamical quantity, associated with each molecule, which we shall assume to depend only on $\mathbf{v}$ and not on $\mathbf{r}$ and t. We seek a differential equation to describe the rate of change of the aggregate amount of Q contained in a fixed element of volume $d\tau$, assuming that there is no external field of force acting on the molecules. The changes in Q can then be of two sorts only: (1) the influx and efflux of Q arising from molecular transport of Q through the bounding surfaces of the element, and (2) the changes in Q produced by molecular collisions inside the element. The first of these will now be calculated. We assume a pure gas.

Consider an element of volume in cartesian coordinates bounded by planes at x, $x + dx$, y, $y + dy$, z, and $z + dz$. The number of molecules with velocities between $\mathbf{v}$ and $\mathbf{v} + d\mathbf{v}$ which enter the element through the x face in unit time is equal to $v_x\, dy\, dz \cdot nF\, dv_x\, dv_y\, dv_z$ where the first factor is the volume of the oblique cylinder of slant length v and base $dy\, dz$ and the second factor is the density of the selected velocity group. The amount of Q transported by this group of molecules in unit time is $Qv_x\, dy\, dz \cdot nF\, dv_x\, dv_y\, dv_z$, and the total flux of Q through the x face in unit time is

$$n(\mathbf{r},t)\, dy\, dz \int\!\!\!\int\!\!\!\int_{-\infty}^{\infty} v_x Q(\mathbf{v})F(\mathbf{v},\mathbf{r},t)\, dv_x\, dv_y\, dv_z \tag{11-1}$$

where the integral is positive for a net influx and negative for a net efflux. We shall henceforth employ the symbol $\langle \quad \rangle$ to denote an average value computed with the general velocity distribution function $F(\mathbf{v},\mathbf{r},t)$ and reserve the bar for an average value computed with the Maxwell function (5-11). Then (11-1) can be rewritten as $n\langle v_x Q\rangle\, dy\, dz$ where $\langle v_x Q\rangle$ is a function of x, y, z, and t in general. The transport of Q through the opposite face at $x + dx$ is obtained by evaluating $n\langle v_x Q\rangle$ at $x + dx$. Thus, the total flux of Q through the $x + dx$ face in unit time is

$$(n\langle v_x Q\rangle)_{x+dx}\, dy\, dz = [n\langle v_x Q\rangle + \partial/\partial x\, (n\langle v_x Q\rangle)\, dx]\, dy\, dz \qquad (11\text{-}2)$$

and is positive for a net efflux and negative for a net influx. The net flux of Q through these two opposite faces is then given by

$$\partial/\partial x\, (n\langle v_x Q\rangle)\, dx\, dy\, dz$$

and is positive for a net efflux. The net flux of Q through the two faces at y and $y + dy$ is similarly given by $\partial/\partial y\, (n\langle v_y Q\rangle)\, dx\, dy\, dz$, and a corresponding result is obtained for the z, $z + dz$ faces. Consequently, the net rate of efflux of Q through all sides of the element $d\tau$ is

$$\left[\frac{\partial}{\partial x}\, (n\langle v_x Q\rangle) + \frac{\partial}{\partial y}\, (n\langle v_y Q\rangle) + \frac{\partial}{\partial z}\, (n\langle v_z Q\rangle) \right] d\tau \qquad (11\text{-}3)$$

The total amount of Q contained in $d\tau$ at time t is obviously given by

$$n(\mathbf{r},t)\, d\tau \iiint\limits_{-\infty}^{\infty} Q(\mathbf{v})F(\mathbf{v},\mathbf{r},t)\, dv_x\, dv_y\, dv_z = n\langle Q\rangle\, d\tau \qquad (11\text{-}4)$$

where $\langle Q\rangle$ is a function of x, y, z, and t in general. The rate of change of the aggregate amount of Q in $d\tau$ is $\partial/\partial t\, (n\langle Q\rangle)\, d\tau$. We represent the total change in Q in unit time resulting from collisions occurring in $d\tau$ by $\Delta Q\, d\tau$ where ΔQ denotes the collisional change in Q per unit volume per unit time. Equating the rate of change of the total Q in $d\tau$ to the rate at which Q is transported in through the sides of the element, plus the rate at which collisional changes in Q take place within the element, we obtain

$$\frac{\partial}{\partial t}\, (n\langle Q\rangle)\, d\tau$$

$$= -\left[\frac{\partial}{\partial x}\, (n\langle v_x Q\rangle) + \frac{\partial}{\partial y}\, (n\langle v_y Q\rangle) + \frac{\partial}{\partial z}\, (n\langle v_z Q\rangle) \right] d\tau + \Delta Q\, d\tau \quad (11\text{-}5)$$

The negative sign in front of the bracket in (11-5) is introduced because a positive value for the bracketed expression corresponds to a net flux of Q *out* of the element and the contribution to $\partial(n\langle Q\rangle)/\partial t$ is accordingly negative.

The calculation of ΔQ is based on the assumption that only binary

encounters need be taken into account.   It has already been pointed out
that ternary and higher-order encounters can be neglected if the density
is sufficiently low.   We further stipulate that the molecules and their
intermolecular fields must be spherically symmetrical.   The applicability
of classical mechanics is, of course, assumed (cf. Sec. 1-3).   We consider
encounters taking place in the element $d\tau$ between two groups of mole-
cules, one having initial velocities in the range $\mathbf{v}_1$ to $\mathbf{v}_1 + d\mathbf{v}_1$ and the
other between $\mathbf{v}_2$ and $\mathbf{v}_2 + d\mathbf{v}_2$.   The number of encounters that take
place in unit time between the two groups has already been determined
in Sec. 8-2.   If dn_1 and dn_2 are the number densities of the two groups,
then the number of encounters between them taking place in $d\tau$ per unit
time for impact parameters in the range b to $b + db$ is given, according
to Eqs. (8-59) and (8-61), by

$$\kappa 2\pi b \; db \; v_r \; dn_1 \; dn_2 \; d\tau \tag{11-6}$$

where $\kappa = \frac{1}{2}$ for like-molecule encounters, as in the case of a pure gas.
We set

$$dn_i = n(\mathbf{r},t)F(\mathbf{v}_i,\mathbf{r},t) \; dv_{ix} \; dv_{iy} \; dv_{iz} \qquad i = 1, 2 \tag{11-7}$$

where $F(\mathbf{v}_i,\mathbf{r},t)$ is the velocity distribution function in the neighborhood
of the point $\mathbf{r}$ at the center of the element $d\tau$.   The use of (11-7) for the
two number densities appearing in (11-6) involves a further important
assumption.   This is the assumption that one can neglect in the distribution function a possible correlation between the initial velocities of the
two approaching collision partners even though forces exist between them.
This assumption enables one to use independent distribution functions
$F(\mathbf{v}_i,\mathbf{r},t)$ for the two colliding molecules, as in (11-7).   The assumption
is an example of the principle of molecular chaos.   If the density is low
enough to ensure that the mean free path is much greater than the range
of the intermolecular forces, the two molecules at the beginning of the
free paths that terminate in their collision are so far apart that a correlation between their initial velocities is improbable.   A further assumption
is involved in referring dn_1 and dn_2 to the same values of $\mathbf{r}$ and t.   This
is equivalent to assuming that the distribution function does not vary
appreciably over a distance of the order of the range of intermolecular
forces or in a time interval comparable to the duration of an encounter.

On substituting (11-7) into (11-6), we obtain for the number of encounters between the two velocity groups per unit volume per unit time, with
impact parameters between b and $b + db$,

$$\tfrac{1}{2}2\pi b \; db \; v_r n^2(\mathbf{r},t)F(\mathbf{v}_1,\mathbf{r},t)F(\mathbf{v}_2,\mathbf{r},t) \; dv_{1x} \cdot \; \cdot \; \cdot \; \cdot \; dv_{2z} \tag{11-8}$$

Let δQ denote the change in the dynamical quantity Q for both molecules
participating in the encounter.   Then

$$\delta Q = Q(\mathbf{v}_1') + Q(\mathbf{v}_2') - Q(\mathbf{v}_1) - Q(\mathbf{v}_2) \tag{11-9}$$

where $\mathbf{v}_1'$ and $\mathbf{v}_2'$ are the velocities of the two molecules after the encounter. Since the molecules and their fields are assumed to be spherically symmetrical, the deflection pattern in the center-of-mass system has an axis of symmetry along the line of head-on approach, i.e., parallel to the initial relative velocity $\mathbf{v}_r$. In obtaining (11-8) we have already integrated over azimuths about the symmetry axis. The change in Q to be used in conjunction with (11-8) is not δQ itself but its value averaged over directions perpendicular to the symmetry axis, which will be denoted by $\overline{\overline{\delta Q}}$. We thus obtain for the collisional change in Q per unit volume per unit time

$$\Delta Q = \pi n^2(\mathbf{r},t) \int_{-\infty}^{\infty} dv_{1x} \cdots \int_{-\infty}^{\infty} dv_{2z}$$
$$\cdot \int_0^{\infty} db\, b\, \overline{\overline{\delta Q}}\, v_r F(\mathbf{v}_1,\mathbf{r},t) F(\mathbf{v}_2,\mathbf{r},t) \quad (11\text{-}10)$$

Insertion of (11-10) in (11-5) gives the *Maxwell equation of change or transfer for the dynamical quantity* Q:

$$\frac{\partial(n\langle Q\rangle)}{\partial t} + \frac{\partial(n\langle v_x Q\rangle)}{\partial x} + \frac{\partial(n\langle v_y Q\rangle)}{\partial y} + \frac{\partial(n\langle v_z Q\rangle)}{\partial z}$$
$$= \pi n^2 \int_{-\infty}^{\infty} dv_{1x} \cdots \int_{-\infty}^{\infty} dv_{2z} \int_0^{\infty} db\, b\, \overline{\overline{\delta Q}}\, v_r F(\mathbf{v}_1,\mathbf{r},t) F(\mathbf{v}_2,\mathbf{r},t) \quad (11\text{-}11)$$

Equation (11-11), which holds for a pure gas, is readily generalized to the case of a gas mixture.

Derivation of the Hydrodynamical Equations and the Stress Formulas. The equation of change becomes particularly simple when Q represents a dynamical quantity that is conserved in an encounter; i.e., the sum of Q over the collision partners is unchanged by the collision. Such a quantity is referred to as a *collisional or summational invariant:* if Q is a collisional invariant, then $\delta Q = 0$ and $\Delta Q = 0$; thus the right side of (11-11) vanishes. The equation of change of a collisional invariant has very great generality, since the special assumptions introduced in order to derive Eq. (11-10) are no longer required. We consider binary encounters of structureless molecules possessing no internal degrees of freedom. The four and only four velocity-dependent quantities $Q(\mathbf{v})$ which are collisional invariants are the three components of linear momentum and the kinetic energy.* The conservation laws for energy and momentum, together with the specified values of the impact parameter and the impact azimuth,† completely determine the six velocity components after collision when the six velocity components before collision are given. If

---

* If the molecules have internal degrees of freedom, the total thermal energy per molecule is a collisional invariant; in this case, other collisional invariants are possible.

† The *impact azimuth* is the azimuth of the plane of the relative orbit measured about an axis along the direction of head-on approach. In the case of rigid elastic spheres, the geometry of the encounter is specified by giving the two angles that determine the direction of the line of centers at impact.

there existed any further invariant function of velocity which was linearly independent of these four, there would be an additional conservation equation that would overdetermine the dynamical problem.   An important collisional invariant, which is independent of velocity, is the molecular mass, and we shall first write the equation of change for the case in which $Q = m$.   Introducing the mass density $\rho(\mathbf{r},t) = mn(\mathbf{r},t)$, we obtain

$$\frac{\partial \rho}{\partial t} + \frac{\partial(\rho\langle v_x\rangle)}{\partial x} + \frac{\partial(\rho\langle v_y\rangle)}{\partial y} + \frac{\partial(\rho\langle v_z\rangle)}{\partial z} = 0 \tag{11-12}$$

where $\langle v_x\rangle$, $\langle v_y\rangle$, and $\langle v_z\rangle$ are components of the velocity of mass motion of the gas.   This differential equation, which expresses the conservation of mass, is identical with the *hydrodynamical equation of continuity* of a continuous fluid if one identifies the components of the velocity field of the fluid with the components of the velocity of mass motion of the gas. Equation (11-12) can be rewritten as

$$\frac{\partial \rho}{\partial t} + \frac{\partial \rho}{\partial x}\langle v_x\rangle + \frac{\partial \rho}{\partial y}\langle v_y\rangle + \frac{\partial \rho}{\partial z}\langle v_z\rangle + \rho\left(\frac{\partial\langle v_x\rangle}{\partial x} + \frac{\partial\langle v_y\rangle}{\partial y} + \frac{\partial\langle v_z\rangle}{\partial z}\right) = 0 \tag{11-13}$$

It is important to distinguish between the partial time derivative $\partial\rho/\partial t$, which gives the rate of change of ρ in the neighborhood of a fixed point in space (x,y,z held fixed), and the total time derivative, $d\rho/dt$, which is given by

$$\frac{d\rho}{dt} = \frac{\partial \rho}{\partial t} + \frac{\partial \rho}{\partial x}\frac{dx}{dt} + \frac{\partial \rho}{\partial y}\frac{dy}{dt} + \frac{\partial \rho}{\partial z}\frac{dz}{dt}$$

and which is interpreted to be the rate of change of ρ in the neighborhood of a fluid particle moving with velocity components dx/dt, dy/dt, and dz/dt.   We introduce the derivative

$$\frac{D\rho}{Dt} \equiv \left\langle\frac{d\rho}{dt}\right\rangle = \frac{\partial \rho}{\partial t} + \frac{\partial \rho}{\partial x}\langle v_x\rangle + \frac{\partial \rho}{\partial y}\langle v_y\rangle + \frac{\partial \rho}{\partial z}\langle v_z\rangle \tag{11-14}$$

to represent the rate of change of ρ in a moving element following the mass motion of the gas.   The differential operator D/Dt is called the "mobile operator."   Substitution of (11-14) in (11-13) gives

$$\frac{D\rho}{Dt} + \rho\left(\frac{\partial\langle v_x\rangle}{\partial x} + \frac{\partial\langle v_y\rangle}{\partial y} + \frac{\partial\langle v_z\rangle}{\partial z}\right) = 0 \tag{11-15}$$

which is an alternative form of the equation of continuity.

The equation of change for linear momentum will next be obtained. Since $Q = mv_x$ is a collisional invariant, we obtain from Eq. (11-11)

$$\frac{\partial}{\partial t}(\rho\langle v_x\rangle) + \frac{\partial}{\partial x}(\rho\langle v_x{}^2\rangle) + \frac{\partial}{\partial y}(\rho\langle v_x v_y\rangle) + \frac{\partial}{\partial z}(\rho\langle v_x v_z\rangle) = 0 \tag{11-16}$$

In order to interpret this equation, we introduce the *thermal* (or *peculiar*) *velocity* $\mathbf{V} = \mathbf{v} - \langle \mathbf{v} \rangle$, whose components are given by

$$v_x = \langle v_x \rangle + V_x \qquad v_y = \langle v_y \rangle + V_y \qquad v_z = \langle v_z \rangle + V_z \qquad (11\text{-}17)$$

Obviously $\langle V_x \rangle = \langle V_y \rangle = \langle V_z \rangle = 0$. The thermal, or peculiar, velocity $\mathbf{V}$ is the velocity of the random individual motion of thermal agitation in contrast to $\langle \mathbf{v} \rangle$, which is the velocity of the collective mass motion associated with a streaming of the gas. Since the temperature measures the mean kinetic energy of thermal agitation, the *kinetic theory definition of temperature* for a gas in mass motion is embodied in the basic relation

$$m\langle V^2 \rangle / 2 = 3kT/2 \qquad (11\text{-}18)$$

The Maxwell distribution function for a uniformly streaming gas is given by $F(v_x - \bar{v}_x, v_y - \bar{v}_y, v_z - \bar{v}_z)$ or $F(V_x, V_y, V_z)$. The averages appearing in Eq. (11-16) can be rewritten with the aid of (11-17) as

$$\begin{aligned}
\langle v_x{}^2 \rangle &= \langle v_x \rangle^2 + \langle V_x{}^2 \rangle \\
\langle v_x v_y \rangle &= \langle v_x \rangle \langle v_y \rangle + \langle V_x V_y \rangle \\
\langle v_x v_z \rangle &= \langle v_x \rangle \langle v_z \rangle + \langle V_x V_z \rangle
\end{aligned} \qquad (11\text{-}19)$$

and, on substituting these relations in (11-16) and differentiating products, one obtains

$$\langle v_x \rangle \left[\frac{\partial \rho}{\partial t} + \frac{\partial(\rho\langle v_x \rangle)}{\partial x} + \frac{\partial(\rho\langle v_y \rangle)}{\partial y} + \frac{\partial(\rho\langle v_z \rangle)}{\partial z} \right]$$

$$+ \rho \left[\frac{\partial\langle v_x \rangle}{\partial t} + \langle v_x \rangle \frac{\partial\langle v_x \rangle}{\partial x} + \langle v_y \rangle \frac{\partial\langle v_x \rangle}{\partial y} + \langle v_z \rangle \frac{\partial\langle v_x \rangle}{\partial z} \right]$$

$$+ \frac{\partial(\rho\langle V_x{}^2 \rangle)}{\partial x} + \frac{\partial(\rho\langle V_x V_y \rangle)}{\partial y} + \frac{\partial(\rho\langle V_x V_z \rangle)}{\partial z} = 0 \qquad (11\text{-}20)$$

The first bracket in (11-20) vanishes according to Eq. (11-12). The second bracket is seen from Eq. (11-14) to be equal to $D\langle v_x \rangle / Dt$ and represents the x component of the acceleration of a moving element following the mass motion of the gas. Thus Eq. (11-20) reduces to

$$\rho \frac{D\langle v_x \rangle}{Dt} = -\frac{\partial}{\partial x}(\rho\langle V_x{}^2 \rangle) - \frac{\partial}{\partial y}(\rho\langle V_x V_y \rangle) - \frac{\partial}{\partial z}(\rho\langle V_x V_z \rangle) \qquad (11\text{-}21)$$

It will now be shown that the *hydrodynamical equation of motion* of a continuous fluid is of the same form as (11-21). Considering a moving fluid element of volume $d\tau$, the product $\rho \, d\tau \, D\langle v_x \rangle / Dt$ is the mass of the element times its x component of acceleration and is equal, in the absence of external fields, to the resultant x component of force acting on the element due to the stresses exerted over its surface. Let the element be bounded by planes at x, $x + dx$, y, $y + dy$, z, and $z + dz$ in a coordinate system moving with the element. Let P_{xx} be the normal component of stress exerted over the x face *by* the fluid on the $-x$ side *on* the fluid on the $+x$ side.   Then $P_{xx} + (\partial P_{xx}/\partial x)\, dx$ will represent the normal stress over the $x + dx$ face.   The x component of force acting on the element over the x face is $P_{xx}\, dy\, dz$, and the x component of the reaction on the element over the $x + dx$ face is $-[P_{xx} + (\partial P_{xx}/\partial x)\, dx]\, dy\, dz$.   The resultant of these two forces is $-(\partial P_{xx}/\partial x)\, d\tau$.   Forces in the x direction also result from shearing stresses on the other surfaces.*   Let P_{yx} be the shearing stress in the x direction exerted over the y face by the fluid on the $-y$ side on the fluid on the $+y$ side.   Then $P_{yx} + (\partial P_{yx}/\partial y)\, dy$ will represent the shearing stress over the $y + dy$ face.   The x component of force acting on the element over the y face is $P_{yx}\, dx\, dz$, and the x compo-nent of the reaction on the element over the $y + dy$ face is $-[P_{yx} + (\partial P_{yx}/\partial y)\, dy]\, dx\, dz$.   The resultant of these two forces is $-(\partial P_{yx}/\partial y)\, d\tau$. In a similar way, the shearing stresses over the z and $z + dz$ faces give rise to a resultant x component of force equal to $-(\partial P_{zx}/\partial z)\, d\tau$.   Com-bining these results, we obtain for the unbalanced x component of force acting on the element of fluid

$$-\left(\frac{\partial P_{xx}}{\partial x} + \frac{\partial P_{yx}}{\partial y} + \frac{\partial P_{zx}}{\partial z}\right) d\tau$$

and, equating this to the product of the mass and the x component of acceleration of the element, we have finally

$$\rho\, \frac{D\langle v_x\rangle}{Dt} = -\frac{\partial P_{xx}}{\partial x} - \frac{\partial P_{yx}}{\partial y} - \frac{\partial P_{zx}}{\partial z} \qquad (11\text{-}22)$$

This is the hydrodynamical equation for the x component of the motion of a continuous fluid.

Comparison of Eq. (11-21) with (11-22) shows that they are of the same form and enables one to write explicit formulas for the stress components in a streaming gas:

$$P_{xx} = \rho\langle V_x{}^2\rangle \qquad P_{yx} = \rho\langle V_x V_y\rangle = P_{xy}$$
and
$$P_{zx} = \rho\langle V_x V_z\rangle = P_{xz} \qquad (11\text{-}23)$$

with corresponding formulas for other components.   These stresses refer to a reference system moving with the local mass velocity of the gas, as is apparent from the fact that they are exerted over the faces of a moving element and are consequently functions of the thermal velocities of the molecules rather than their total velocities.   Writing Eqs. (11-23) out

---

* The convention for the shearing stresses is the same as that used previously: the first subscript designates the normal to the surface and the second subscript the direc-tion of the force.

explicitly, we obtain

$$P_{xx} = mn(\mathbf{r},t) \iiint_{-\infty}^{\infty} V_x^2 F(\mathbf{v},\mathbf{r},t) \, dv_x \, dv_y \, dv_z$$

$$= mn(\mathbf{r},t) \iiint_{-\infty}^{\infty} V_x^2 F^*(\mathbf{V},\mathbf{r},t) \, dV_x \, dV_y \, dV_z \tag{11-24}$$

and

$$P_{yx} = P_{xy} = mn(\mathbf{r},t) \iiint_{-\infty}^{\infty} V_x V_y F(\mathbf{v},\mathbf{r},t) \, dv_x \, dv_y \, dv_z$$

$$= mn(\mathbf{r},t) \iiint_{-\infty}^{\infty} V_x V_y F^*(\mathbf{V},\mathbf{r},t) \, dV_x \, dV_y \, dV_z \tag{11-25}$$

where $F^*(\mathbf{V},\mathbf{r},t)$ is the distribution function for the components of the thermal velocity. On comparing these formulas with Eqs. (6-10) and (6-12), which define the stresses in a perfect gas at rest, we see that the stresses in a flowing gas are calculated with respect to a surface moving with the local velocity of mass motion; i.e., the molecular flux and the momentum are both reckoned with respect to the moving surface. The stresses of Eqs. (11-23) are kinetic in origin (they arise from the transport of momentum by moving molecules), and the static stresses have not been taken into account. The latter, which are due to intermolecular forces between molecules on opposite sides of the surface, have been taken into consideration in the theory of the equation of state as given in Sec. 6-2. In the theory of transport phenomena, on the other hand, these stresses can be neglected at ordinary densities.

The derivation of the hydrodynamical equations of motion and of continuity from the equations of change provides justification for the treatment of problems in gas dynamics at ordinary pressures by standard hydrodynamical methods. As an example, the propagation of sound waves in a gas can be treated directly from the equations of motion and of continuity without reference to the kinetic-molecular properties of the gas.*

The equation of change for the molecular kinetic energy is obtained by setting $Q = mv^2/2$. Since this is a collisional invariant for a monatomic gas, $\Delta Q = 0$, and the right side of Eq. (11-11) vanishes. If the molecules have internal degrees of freedom, the total thermal energy of a molecule ε replaces the translational energy $mv^2/2$ as a collisional invariant. The equation of change for $Q = \varepsilon$, in which $\Delta Q = 0$, is known as the *equation of thermal-energy balance*. The derivation of these equations may be

---

* However, if the wave length is so short as to be comparable with the mean free path, the hydrodynamical equations can no longer be correctly applied.

found elsewhere.* The equation of change can be generalized to take account of external fields and to include the case in which Q depends on r and t as well as on v.†

11-2. THE MAXWELL-CHAPMAN TRANSPORT THEORY; CALCULATION OF THE VISCOSITY COEFFICIENT

The transport theory is used to treat nonuniform states of gases not in thermodynamic equilibrium.   A gas is said to be in thermodynamic equilibrium if it is in thermal equilibrium, mechanical equilibrium, and chemical equilibrium.   A gas in thermal equilibrium is at uniform temperature throughout and at the same temperature as its surroundings.   A gas in mechanical equilibrium in the absence of an external force field is at uniform pressure throughout.   A gas in chemical equilibrium is of uniform composition throughout.   In the case of steady heat flow, the temperature is nonuniform, and thermal equilibrium does not exist.   In steady viscous flow, the shearing stresses associated with the velocity gradient lead to pressure differentials, and an equilibrium state in the mechanical sense does not exist.   A diffusing gas is not in equilibrium in the chemical sense. *An equilibrium state in the sense of kinetic theory is one in which the distribution of molecular velocities is independent of position and of time and is thus necessarily unaffected by molecular encounters.*   It will be shown in Sec. 11-4 that the Maxwell distribution law holds for an equilibrium state.   In all three transport phenomena, the distribution of molecular velocities is non-Maxwellian.   This has already been shown for the case of mutual diffusion in Sec. 8-3, where the Maxwell law was seen to give zero momentum transfer.   In heat conduction, the net rate of transport of translational kinetic energy across unit area of the xy plane in the interior of the gas is given by

$$q = \iiint\limits_{-\infty}^{\infty} (mv^2/2)v_z nF(v_x,v_y,v_z)\ dv_x\ dv_y\ dv_z$$

and this is equal to zero when the Maxwell function (5-11) is substituted for $F(v_x,v_y,v_z)$, since the integrand is then an odd function of v_z.   Finally, the shearing stresses in a flowing gas would vanish if the thermal velocities were distributed according to Maxwell's law.   Equation (6-12) shows that the stress P_{zy} is zero for a gas at rest.   If the gas is in mass motion in the y direction with velocity $\langle v_y \rangle = u(z)$, the stress P_{zy} must be cal-

* See S. Chapman and T. G. Cowling, "The Mathematical Theory of Nonuniform Gases," Cambridge University Press, London, 1939, chap. 3.
    † *Ibid.*

culated with respect to a reference system moving with the gas, and the Maxwell distribution refers to this same frame of reference. Accordingly, the thermal velocity $V_y = v_y - u(z)$ appears in place of v_y in the integrand of (6-12), and the result for P_{zy} is again zero. *Thus, if the velocity distribution were Maxwellian, the gas could not support a shearing stress, i.e., would be nonviscous; it could not conduct heat, and the diffusive transport would be zero.*

Although the transport properties depend for their very existence on departures from the Maxwell law, it is a basic assumption of the advanced transport theory that these departures are small. The gas is assumed to be very nearly in equilibrium, and the nonuniformities corresponding to the gradients of flow velocity, temperature, and composition are required to be small. The quantitative criterion is that the fractional change in flow velocity, temperature, or composition in one mean free path shall be much less than unity; e.g., in heat conduction this means that $\lambda \, dT/dz \ll T$. At ordinary pressures and for ordinary gradients, these assumptions are justified.* Although a nonuniform gas is not in thermodynamic equilibrium, it is convenient to define a temperature that will reduce to the usual Kelvin temperature when the gas approaches the equilibrium state. The temperature is defined in the same way as for a uniform gas; the only difference is that the mean kinetic energy of thermal agitation is calculated with the non-Maxwellian instead of the Maxwellian distribution function. Equation (11-18) continues to be the kinetic-theory definition of temperature in a flowing gas in a nonuniform state.

When a gas is in mass motion, the velocity distribution function refers to a frame of reference moving with the local mass velocity and is a function only of the thermal velocities V_x, V_y, and V_z. We denote the distribution function by $F^*(\mathbf{V})$. The Maxwell-Chapman approximation method starts with the Maxwell function and applies successive corrections in the form of a power series in the velocity components V_x, V_y, and V_z. Thus

$$F^*(\mathbf{V}) = Ae^{-mV^2/2kT}\left(1 + \sum_\lambda a_\lambda V_\lambda + \sum_\lambda \sum_\mu a_{\lambda\mu}V_\lambda V_\mu \right.$$
$$\left. + \sum_\lambda \sum_\mu \sum_\nu a_{\lambda\mu\nu}V_\lambda V_\mu V_\nu \cdots\right) \quad (11\text{-}26)$$

where the subscripts λ, μ, and ν each stand for x, y, and z. Since the order in which the velocity components are written in the sums is immaterial, we set $a_{\mu\lambda} = a_{\lambda\mu}$ and $a_{\lambda\mu\nu} = a_{\mu\nu\lambda} = a_{\nu\lambda\mu}$, etc.; e.g., $a_{yx} = a_{xy}$ and $a_{xxy} = a_{xyx} = a_{yxx}$. The temperature T appearing in the exponent will

* They do not hold for the extraordinary gradients occurring in shock waves.

be seen to correspond to Eq. (11-18). It is not necessary to go beyond cubic terms in the expansion in order to obtain the first approximations to the three transport coefficients. We shall take up the case of the viscosity coefficient in detail. The correct first approximation for the mutual-diffusion coefficient was obtained in Sec. 8-3 (cf. also Prob. 11-9). The thermal conductivity will not be taken up; the treatment is similar to that to be given for the viscosity coefficient but somewhat longer.   Furthermore, the contribution to the energy transport from the internal degrees of freedom cannot be properly treated by classical methods.

We shall assume the gas to be flowing in the y direction with velocity gradient in the z direction.   Then, substituting (11-26) into (11-25), we obtain for the shearing stress

$$P_{zy} = nm \int\!\!\!\int\!\!\!\int_{-\infty}^{\infty} V_y V_z F^*(\mathbf{V})\, dV_x\, dV_y\, dV_z$$

$$= nmA \int\!\!\!\int\!\!\!\int_{-\infty}^{\infty} V_y V_z\, e^{-mV^2/2kT} \left(1 + \sum_\lambda a_\lambda V_\lambda + \sum_\lambda \sum_\mu a_{\lambda\mu} V_\lambda V_\mu \right. \tag{11-27}$$

$$\left. + \sum_\lambda \sum_\mu \sum_\nu a_{\lambda\mu\nu} V_\lambda V_\mu V_\nu \right) dV_x\, dV_y\, dV_z$$

We denote an average over the Maxwellian distribution $Ae^{-mV^2/2kT}$ by a bar; thus

$$\overline{V_x^{\,l} V_y^{\,m} V_z^{\,n}} \equiv A \int\!\!\!\int\!\!\!\int_{-\infty}^{\infty} V_x^{\,l} V_y^{\,m} V_z^{\,n} e^{-mV^2/2kT}\, dV_x\, dV_y\, dV_z \tag{11-28}$$

The integral vanishes when l, m, or n are odd.   Equation (11-27) becomes

$$(nm)^{-1} P_{zy} = \overline{V_y V_z} + a_x \overline{V_x V_y V_z} + a_y \overline{V_y^{\,2} V_z} + a_z \overline{V_y V_z^{\,2}} + a_{xx} \overline{V_x^{\,2} V_y V_z}$$
$$+ a_{yy} \overline{V_y^{\,3} V_z} + a_{zz} \overline{V_y V_z^{\,3}} + 2a_{xy} \overline{V_x V_y^{\,2} V_z} + 2a_{yz} \overline{V_y^{\,2} V_z^{\,2}} \tag{11-29}$$
$$+ 2a_{zx} \overline{V_x V_y V_z^{\,2}} + a_{xxx} \overline{V_x^{\,3} V_y V_z} + \cdots$$

Inspection of (11-29) shows that all terms obtained by including linear, quadratic, and cubic terms in the expansion of (11-26) will vanish with one exception.   Equation (11-29) thus reduces to

$$(nm)^{-1} P_{zy} = 2a_{yz} \overline{V_y^{\,2} V_z^{\,2}} \tag{11-30}$$

On dropping those terms in (11-26) which do not contribute to the shearing stress P_{zy}, we obtain for the first-approximation distribution function

$$F^*(\mathbf{V}) = Ae^{-mV^2/2kT}(1 + aV_y V_z) \tag{11-31}$$

where a, which replaces $2a_{yz}$, is assumed to be small so that terms in a^2

can be neglected. Normalization of (11-31) gives

$$\iiint_{-\infty}^{\infty} F^*(\mathbf{V}) \, dV_x \, dV_y \, dV_z = 1 + a\overline{V_y V_z} = 1 \qquad (11\text{-}32)$$

with $A = (m/2\pi kT)^{3/2}$ as before. The average values of the thermal velocity components are given by

$$\langle V_\lambda \rangle = \iiint_{-\infty}^{\infty} V_\lambda F^*(\mathbf{V}) \, dV_x \, dV_y \, dV_z$$

whence

$$\begin{align}
\langle V_x \rangle &= \overline{V_x} + a\overline{V_x V_y V_z} = 0 \\
\langle V_y \rangle &= \overline{V_y} + a\overline{V_y^2 V_z} = 0 \\
\langle V_z \rangle &= \overline{V_z} + a\overline{V_y V_z^2} = 0
\end{align} \qquad (11\text{-}33)$$

in agreement with Eq. (11-17). The mean-square thermal velocity is

$$\langle V^2 \rangle = \overline{V^2} + a\overline{V^2 V_y V_z} = \overline{V^2} = 3kT/m \qquad (11\text{-}34)$$

in agreement with (11-18). The shearing stress is given by

$$P_{zy} = nm\langle V_y V_z \rangle = nm(\overline{V_y V_z} + a\overline{V_y^2 V_z^2}) = nma\overline{V_y}^2 \cdot \overline{V_z}^2 \qquad (11\text{-}35)$$

and, since $\overline{V_x^2} = \overline{V_y^2} = \overline{V_z^2} = \overline{V^2}/3 = kT/m$, we find that

$$a = \left(\frac{m}{kT}\right)^2 \frac{P_{zy}}{nm} \qquad (11\text{-}36)$$

The correction to Maxwell's law is directly proportional to the shearing stress and, accordingly, to the velocity gradient. In first approximation, we retain only linear terms in P_{zy} and $d\langle v_y \rangle/dz$.

Chapman's Method of Selecting Q and the Evaluation of $\overline{\delta Q}$. The Chapman method is based on Maxwell's general equation of change (11-11). Assuming a steady-state viscous flow, i.e., one independent of time, the term in $\partial/\partial t$ on the left side of (11-11) vanishes. Since the gradient has been chosen in the z direction, the terms in $\partial/\partial x$ and $\partial/\partial y$ are also equal to zero. Furthermore, the number density n is independent of z as are p and T. Thus Eq. (11-11) reduces to

$$n \, d/dz \, \langle v_z Q \rangle = \Delta Q \qquad (11\text{-}37)$$

We shall retain only first-order terms on both sides of this equation.* The left side is automatically small because it involves a gradient; to first order we can replace the non-Maxwellian average $\langle v_z Q \rangle$ by the Maxwellian average $\overline{v_z Q}$, since the gradient of their difference is second order.

---

* If the first-order terms vanished, it would be necessary to go to second order. This is not the case.

Then

$$n \, d/dz \, (\overline{v_z Q}) = \Delta Q \tag{11-38}$$

Chapman's method consists of selecting the function $Q(\mathbf{v})$ in such a way as to yield an equation of the desired form. Since we wish (11-38) to reduce to the standard viscosity equation $(P_{zy} = -\eta \, d\bar{v}_y/dz)$, we select $Q(\mathbf{v})$ with the object of having $d\bar{v}_y/dz$ appear on the left side of (11-38). The choice $Q = v_y$ reduces both sides of the equation to zero (Q is proportional to the y component of momentum). The simplest choice for Q, which yields a result of the desired form, is obviously

$$Q(\mathbf{v}) = v_y v_z \tag{11-39}$$

which gives

$$\frac{d}{dz} (\overline{v_z Q}) = \frac{d}{dz} (\overline{v_z^2 v_y}) = \overline{V_z^2} \frac{d\bar{v}_y}{dz} = \frac{\overline{V^2}}{3} \frac{d\bar{v}_y}{dz} = \frac{kT}{m} \frac{du}{dz} \tag{11-40}$$

where $u(z)$ is the velocity of mass motion. Equation (11-38) then becomes

$$(nkT/m) \, du/dz = \Delta(v_y v_z) \tag{11-41}$$

Although the left side of Eq. (11-41) has been obtained without explicit use of the distribution function, it is easily seen that the same result follows from a direct evaluation of the left side of Eq. (11-37), i.e., of $n \, d/dz \, \langle v_z^2 v_y \rangle$, with the first-approximation function (11-31).

The distribution function (11-31), with a given by (11-36), is used to calculate $\Delta(v_y v_z)$. Neglecting second-order terms, it is expected that the result will be proportional to a and therefore to P_{zy}. This will be shown in detail below. The equation of change for $Q = v_y v_z$ then takes the form of the standard viscosity equation, and a formula for the viscosity coefficient is thus obtained. We proceed to evaluate $\Delta(v_y v_z)$. The first step is the calculation of $\overline{\delta Q} = \overline{\delta(v_y v_z)}$. From the definition of δQ, we have

$$\delta(v_y v_z) = v'_{1y} v'_{1z} + v'_{2y} v'_{2z} - v_{1y} v_{1z} - v_{2y} v_{2z} \tag{11-42}$$

in accordance with Eq. (11-9). Rewriting (11-42) in terms of the center-of-mass and relative velocities defined in Eqs. (5-19), this becomes

$$\begin{aligned}
\delta(v_y v_z) &= (v_{cy} + \tfrac{1}{2} v'_{ry})(v_{cz} + \tfrac{1}{2} v'_{rz}) + (v_{cy} - \tfrac{1}{2} v'_{ry})(v_{cz} - \tfrac{1}{2} v'_{rz}) \\
&\quad - (v_{cy} + \tfrac{1}{2} v_{ry})(v_{cz} + \tfrac{1}{2} v_{rz}) - (v_{cy} - \tfrac{1}{2} v_{ry})(v_{cz} - \tfrac{1}{2} v_{rz}) \\
&= \tfrac{1}{2}(v'_{ry} v'_{rz} - v_{ry} v_{rz})
\end{aligned} \tag{11-43}$$

We resolve the final relative velocity $\mathbf{v}'_r$ into a component $v'_{r\parallel}$, which is parallel to the initial relative velocity $\mathbf{v}_r$, and a component $v'_{r\perp}$, which is perpendicular to $\mathbf{v}_r$. In terms of the deflection angle χ between the directions of $\mathbf{v}_r$ and $\mathbf{v}'_r$, these become

$$v'_{r\parallel} = v_r \cos \chi \quad \text{and} \quad v'_{r\perp} = v_r \sin \chi \tag{11-44}$$

since $\mathbf{v}'_r$ and $\mathbf{v}_r$ are equal in magnitude (cf. Eq. (8-34)).   It is convenient to treat $v'_{r\parallel}$ and $v'_{r\perp}$ as vector quantities denoted by $\mathbf{w}_\parallel$ and $\mathbf{w}_\perp$ respectively. Thus

$$\mathbf{v}'_r = \mathbf{w}_\parallel + \mathbf{w}_\perp \qquad \text{where } \mathbf{w}_\parallel = \mathbf{v}_r \cos \chi \qquad (11\text{-}45)$$

and $\mathbf{w}_\perp$ is perpendicular to $\mathbf{v}_r$ and of magnitude $v_r \sin \chi$.   Then the first term on the right side of Eq. (11-43) becomes

$$v'_{ry}v'_{rz} = (w_{\parallel y} + w_{\perp y})(w_{\parallel z} + w_{\perp z}) \qquad (11\text{-}46)$$

where $w_{\parallel y}$ is the y component of $\mathbf{w}_\parallel$, etc.   We now average (11-46) over directions perpendicular to $\mathbf{v}_r$; in performing this average, the velocity vector $\mathbf{v}_r$ and the angle of deflection χ are held fixed and the average is taken with respect to the impact azimuth measured about the line of head-on approach.   Denoting this average by a double bar, we have

$$\overline{\overline{v'_{ry}v'_{rz}}} = w_{\parallel y}w_{\parallel z} + w_{\parallel y}\overline{\overline{w_{\perp z}}} + \overline{\overline{w_{\perp y}}}w_{\parallel z} + \overline{\overline{w_{\perp y}w_{\perp z}}} \qquad (11\text{-}47)$$

In deriving formula (11-10) for ΔQ, it was assumed that the molecules and their force fields possessed spherical symmetry.   The deflection pattern for the relative motion after collision then has an axis of symmetry along the line of head-on approach which is parallel to $\mathbf{v}_r$.   On averaging over directions perpendicular to the symmetry axis, the vector $\mathbf{w}_\perp$ and its components will average to zero, since any given orientation of $\mathbf{w}_\perp$ and the reverse orientation are equally likely.   Therefore

$$\overline{\overline{v'_{ry}v'_{rz}}} = w_{\parallel y}w_{\parallel z} + \overline{\overline{w_{\perp y}w_{\perp z}}} \qquad (11\text{-}48)$$

The term $\overline{\overline{w_{\perp y}w_{\perp z}}}$, which is quadratic in the components of $\mathbf{w}_\perp$, will not vanish in general.   To evaluate this term in a simple fashion, we resolve $\mathbf{w}_\perp$ into two rectangular component vectors $\mathbf{w}_\xi$ and $\mathbf{w}_\eta$.   Thus $\mathbf{w}_\perp = \mathbf{w}_\xi + \mathbf{w}_\eta$, and the three vectors $\mathbf{w}_\parallel$, $\mathbf{w}_\xi$, and $\mathbf{w}_\eta$ represent the components of $\mathbf{v}'_r$ along three mutually perpendicular axes.   Evidently, $\mathbf{w}_\xi$ and its components and $\mathbf{w}_\eta$ and its components will independently average to zero.*   Thus

$$\overline{\overline{w_{\perp y}w_{\perp z}}} = \overline{\overline{(w_{\xi y} + w_{\eta y})(w_{\xi z} + w_{\eta z})}} \qquad (11\text{-}49)$$
$$= \overline{\overline{w_{\xi y}w_{\xi z}}} + \overline{\overline{w_{\eta y}w_{\eta z}}}$$

since
$$\overline{\overline{w_{\xi y}w_{\eta z}}} = \overline{\overline{w_{\xi y}}} \cdot \overline{\overline{w_{\eta z}}} = 0$$
$$\overline{\overline{w_{\eta y}w_{\xi z}}} = \overline{\overline{w_{\eta y}}} \cdot \overline{\overline{w_{\xi z}}} = 0$$

Furthermore,

$$\overline{\overline{w_{\xi y}w_{\xi z}}} = \overline{\overline{w_\xi^2}} \cos (\xi,y) \cos (\xi,z) \qquad (11\text{-}50)$$
$$\overline{\overline{w_{\eta y}w_{\eta z}}} = \overline{\overline{w_\eta^2}} \cos (\eta,y) \cos (\eta,z)$$

where $\cos (\xi,y)$ is the direction cosine between the ξ and y axes.   Also

* If $\mathbf{w}_\xi$ is held fixed, $\mathbf{w}_\eta$ is as likely from symmetry to be in the $+\eta$ or $-\eta$ directions.

$$w_\xi^2 + w_\eta^2 = w_\perp^2 = v_r^2 \sin^2 \chi$$

and
$$\overline{w_\xi^2} = \overline{w_\eta^2} = \tfrac{1}{2}\overline{w_\perp^2} = \tfrac{1}{2}v_r^2 \sin^2 \chi \qquad (11\text{-}51)$$

Substitution of (11-50) and (11-51) in (11-49) then gives

$$
\begin{aligned}
\overline{w_{\perp y}w_{\perp z}} &= \tfrac{1}{2}v_r^2 \sin^2 \chi \,[\cos\,(\xi,y)\,\cos\,(\xi,z) + \cos\,(\eta,y)\,\cos\,(\eta,z)] \\
&= -\tfrac{1}{2}v_r^2 \sin^2 \chi \,\cos\,(v_r,y)\,\cos\,(v_r,z) \qquad (11\text{-}52) \\
&= -\tfrac{1}{2}v_{ry}v_{rz} \sin^2 \chi
\end{aligned}
$$

We can now rewrite Eq. (11-48) with the aid of (11-45) and (11-52):

$$\overline{v'_{ry}v'_{rz}} = v_{ry}v_{rz} \cos^2 \chi - \tfrac{1}{2}v_{ry}v_{rz} \sin^2 \chi \qquad (11\text{-}53)$$

Thus the averaging of (11-43) gives

$$
\begin{aligned}
\overline{\delta(v_y v_z)} &= \tfrac{1}{2}(\overline{v'_{ry}v'_{rz}} - v_{ry}v_{rz}) \\
&= -\tfrac{3}{4}v_{ry}v_{rz} \sin^2 \chi
\end{aligned}
\qquad (11\text{-}54)
$$

with the aid of (11-53). This is the value of $\overline{\delta Q}$ which is to be inserted in the integrand of Eq. (11-10) for $\Delta(v_y v_z)$.

Evaluation of the Collision Integral ΔQ. We now obtain

$$
\begin{aligned}
\Delta(v_y v_z) &= \tfrac{1}{2}n^2 \int_{-\infty}^{\infty} dv_{1x} \cdots \int_{-\infty}^{\infty} dv_{2z} \\
&\qquad \cdot \int_0^{\infty} 2\pi b\,db(-\tfrac{3}{4}v_{ry}v_{rz} \sin^2 \chi)v_r F(\mathbf{v}_1)F(\mathbf{v}_2) \qquad (11\text{-}55) \\
&= -\frac{3n^2}{8} \int_{-\infty}^{\infty} dv_{1x} \cdots \int_{-\infty}^{\infty} dv_{2z}\, v_r \sigma_\eta(v_r) v_{ry}v_{rz} F(\mathbf{v}_1)F(\mathbf{v}_2)
\end{aligned}
$$

on inserting the transport cross section for viscosity, $\sigma_\eta(v_r)$, which has been defined in Eq. (8-49). Since the distribution function (11-31) is expressed in terms of the thermal velocity $\mathbf{V}$, we shall rewrite the rest of the integrand in terms of $\mathbf{V}$ instead of $\mathbf{v}$; i.e., we go over to a reference frame moving with the local mass velocity $\mathbf{u}$. Then $\mathbf{V}_1 = \mathbf{v}_1 - \mathbf{u}$ and $\mathbf{V}_2 = \mathbf{v}_2 - \mathbf{u}$, and the relative velocity $\mathbf{V}_r = \mathbf{V}_1 - \mathbf{V}_2 = \mathbf{v}_1 - \mathbf{v}_2 = \mathbf{v}_r$ since both collision partners have the same mass velocity. Equation (11-55) becomes

$$
\begin{aligned}
\Delta(v_y v_z) &= -\frac{3n^2}{8} \int_{-\infty}^{\infty} dV_{1x} \cdots \\
&\qquad \cdot \int_{-\infty}^{\infty} dV_{2z} V_r \sigma_\eta(V_r) V_{ry} V_{rz} F^*(\mathbf{V}_1)F^*(\mathbf{V}_2) \\
&= -\frac{3n^2 A^2}{8} \int_{-\infty}^{\infty} dV_{1x} \cdots \qquad (11\text{-}56) \\
&\qquad \cdot \int_{-\infty}^{\infty} dV_{2z} V_r \sigma_\eta(V_r) V_{ry} V_{rz} e^{-(m/2kT)(V_1^2 + V_2^2)} \\
&\qquad\qquad \cdot [(1 + aV_{1y}V_{1z})(1 + aV_{2y}V_{2z})]
\end{aligned}
$$

using the distribution function (11-31). We again transform from $\mathbf{V}_1$

and $\mathbf{V}_2$ to the relative velocity $\mathbf{V}_r$ of the two molecules and the velocity $\mathbf{V}_c$ of their center of mass in the moving reference frame. Using Eqs. (5-19) through (5-22), Eq. (11-56) becomes

$$
\begin{aligned}
\Delta(v_y v_z) = {}& -\frac{3n^2 A^2}{8} \int_{-\infty}^{\infty} dV_{cx} \cdot \cdots \\
& \cdot \int_{-\infty}^{\infty} dV_{rz} V_r \sigma_\eta(V_r) V_{ry} V_{rz} e^{-(1/2kT)(2mV_c^2 + m^* V_r^2)} \\
& \cdot [1 + a(2V_{cy}V_{cz} + \tfrac{1}{2} V_{ry}V_{rz}) + a^2(V_{cy}^2 V_{cz}^2 \\
& \qquad - \tfrac{1}{4} V_{cy}^2 V_{rz}^2 - \tfrac{1}{4} V_{cz}^2 V_{ry}^2 + \tfrac{1}{16} V_{ry}^2 V_{rz}^2)] \\
= {}& -\frac{3n^2 A^2}{8} \int_{-\infty}^{\infty} dV_{cx} \cdot \cdots \\
& \cdot \int_{-\infty}^{\infty} dV_{rz} V_r \sigma_\eta(V_r) e^{-(1/2kT)(2mV_c^2 + m^* V_r^2)} \left[V_{ry} V_{rz} \right. \\
& + 2a V_{ry}V_{rz}V_{cy}V_{cz} + \frac{a}{2} V_{ry}^2 V_{rz}^2 + a^2 (V_{ry}V_{rz}V_{cy}^2 V_{cz}^2 \\
& \left. - \tfrac{1}{4} V_{ry} V_{rz}^3 V_{cy}^2 - \tfrac{1}{4} V_{ry}^3 V_{rz} V_{cz}^2 + \tfrac{1}{16} V_{ry}^3 V_{rz}^3) \right]
\end{aligned}
\tag{11-57}
$$

The part of the integrand preceding the bracket in (11-57) is an even function of all velocity components. The first term inside the bracket is an odd function of V_{ry} and V_{rz} and therefore vanishes upon integration. The uncorrected Maxwell function, which gives rise to this term, therefore makes no contribution to $\Delta(v_y v_z)$. Since all terms within the brackets except the third are odd functions of one or more velocity components, Eq. (11-57) reduces to

$$
\begin{aligned}
\Delta(v_y v_z) = {}& -\frac{3n^2 A^2 a}{16} \iiint_{-\infty}^{\infty} e^{-2mV_c^2/2kT}\, dV_{cx}\, dV_{cy}\, dV_{cz} \\
& \cdot \iiint_{-\infty}^{\infty} e^{-m^* V_r^2/2kT} V_r \sigma_\eta(V_r) V_{ry}^2 V_{rz}^2\, dV_{rx}\, dV_{ry}\, dV_{rz}
\end{aligned}
\tag{11-58}
$$

The first triple integral is equal to $(\pi kT/m)^{3/2}$. We insert this value, substitute for A^2, and transform the second triple integral to spherical coordinates, thus obtaining

$$
\begin{aligned}
\Delta(v_y v_z) = {}& -\frac{3n^2 a}{16} \left(\frac{m}{2\pi kT}\right)^3 \left(\frac{\pi kT}{m}\right)^{3/2} \iiint e^{-m^* V_r^2/2kT}\sigma_\eta(V_r) \\
& \qquad \cdot V_r^5 \sin^2\theta_r \cos^2\theta_r \sin^2\phi_r\; V_r^2\, dV_r\, \sin\theta_r\, d\theta_r\, d\phi_r \\
= {}& -\frac{3n^2 a}{128} \left(\frac{m}{\pi kT}\right)^{3/2} \int_0^{2\pi} \sin^2\phi_r\, d\phi_r \\
& \cdot \int_0^{\pi} \sin^2\theta_r \cos^2\theta_r \sin\theta_r\, d\theta_r \int_0^{\infty} e^{-m^* V_r^2/2kT}\sigma_\eta(V_r) V_r^7\, dV_r
\end{aligned}
\tag{11-59}
$$

The ϕ_r integral is equal to π, and the θ_r integral gives $\frac{4}{15}$. Thus

$$\Delta(v_y v_z) = -\frac{\pi n^2 a}{160}\left(\frac{m}{\pi kT}\right)^{3/2}\int_0^\infty e^{-m^* V_r{}^2/2kT}\sigma_\eta(V_r)V_r{}^7\,dV_r \quad (11\text{-}60)$$

It is customary to express the integral appearing in Eq. (11-60) in terms of the standard Ω integral of the Chapman-Enskog theory:*

$$\Omega_\eta = \left(\frac{kT}{\pi m}\right)^{1/2}\int_0^\infty e^{-g^2}\sigma_\eta(V_r)g^7\,dg \quad (11\text{-}61)$$

where $g^2 = m^* V_r{}^2/2kT = mV_r{}^2/4kT$. Then

$$\Delta(v_y v_z) = -\frac{\pi n^2 a}{160}\left(\frac{m}{\pi kT}\right)^{3/2}\left(\frac{4kT}{m}\right)^4\left(\frac{\pi m}{kT}\right)^{1/2}\Omega_\eta$$

We insert the value of a from (11-36) obtaining

$$\Delta(v_y v_z) = -\frac{\pi n^2}{160}\frac{P_{zy}}{nm}\left(\frac{m}{kT}\right)^2\left(\frac{m}{\pi kT}\right)^{3/2}\left(\frac{4kT}{m}\right)^4\left(\frac{\pi m}{kT}\right)^{1/2}\Omega_\eta \quad (11\text{-}62)$$

$$= -(8n\Omega_\eta/5m)P_{zy}$$

This result is of the expected form; on substituting it in Eq. (11-41), we find

$$P_{zy} = -\frac{5kT}{8\Omega_\eta}\frac{du}{dz} \quad (11\text{-}63)$$

whence†

$$\eta = 5kT/8\Omega_\eta \quad (11\text{-}64)$$

This is the general formula for the viscosity coefficient in the first approximation of the Chapman-Enskog transport theory. It was first obtained by Maxwell for the special case of the inverse fifth-power repulsion, which will be discussed below. It is remarkable that the higher approximations of the theory lead to only very small corrections.‡ We observe that the general expression for η does not contain the number density n, thus confirming the elementary result that the viscosity of a gas at ordinary pressures is independent of its density. The temperature dependence of η can be obtained from an explicit evaluation of σ_η and Ω_η in terms of a special molecular model.

Calculation of η for Two Molecular Models. It is very simple to calculate σ_η, Ω_η, and η for the rigid-elastic-sphere model. According to

---

* Chapman and Cowling, op. cit., p. 157; J. O. Hirschfelder, C. F. Curtiss, and R. B. Bird, "Molecular Theory of Gases and Liquids," John Wiley & Sons, Inc., New York, 1954, pp. 484, 525.

† The sign in (11-63) agrees with that in Eq. (3-23) and differs from the sign convention of Eq. (3-19).

‡ Chapman and Cowling, op. cit., p. 169.

Eqs. (8-49) and (8-52),

$$\sigma_\eta = 2\pi(d/2)^2 \int_0^\pi \sin^3 \chi \, d\chi = 2\pi d^2/3 \tag{11-65}$$

Thus σ_η, while differing from σ_D, is also independent of velocity.   Then

$$\Omega_\eta = \frac{2\pi d^2}{3}\left(\frac{kT}{\pi m}\right)^{1/2} \int_0^\infty e^{-g^2}g^7 \, dg = 2\pi d^2 (kT/\pi m)^{1/2} \tag{11-66}$$

since the integral is equal to 3.   Hence

$$\eta = \frac{5}{16d^2}\left(\frac{mkT}{\pi}\right)^{1/2} \tag{11-67}$$

We obtain a value for the dimensionless group $\rho D_{11}/\eta$ by combining (11-67) with the rigid-sphere formula (8-87) for D_{12} (replacing d_{12} by d and m^* by $m/2$):

$$\rho D_{11}/\eta = \tfrac{6}{5} \tag{11-68}$$

It is interesting to compare Eqs. (11-67) and (11-68) with the corresponding formulas of the elementary free-path theory.   Combining Eqs. (3-24), (3-9), and (5-16), we obtain

$$\eta = \frac{2}{3\pi d^2}\left(\frac{mkT}{\pi}\right)^{1/2} \tag{11-69}$$

which is smaller than (11-67) by a factor of $32/15\pi$.   The elementary value of $\rho D_{11}/\eta$ is unity according to Eq. (3-29).   The higher approximations to the viscosity coefficient for rigid, spherical molecules have been worked out;[*] they lead to the same result (11-67) as in the first approximation except that the numerical factor is increased by 1.6 per cent. Taking account of this small correction, we find in place of Eq. (3-24) the more exact relation $\eta = 0.499\rho\bar{v}\lambda$, which has already been quoted in Prob. 3-6.

The calculation of η from Eq. (11-64) is somewhat lengthy when other assumptions are made about the intermolecular forces.   These calculations have been carried out for the special models introduced in Sec. 6-3; details may be found in Chap. 10 of Chapman and Cowling's book. The procedure is first to obtain χ in terms of b and v_r from Eqs. (8-21) and (8-15), then to evaluate σ_η with the aid of (8-46) and (8-49), and finally to compute Ω_η from (11-61).   Except in the case of rigid spheres, it is usually necessary to perform some of the integrations numerically. One of the simpler cases is the van der Waals–Sutherland model of rigid spheres with a weak inverse power attraction, for which terms of the first degree in the force constant are retained and higher-order terms neglected.

[*] Chapman and Cowling, *loc. cit.*

It is left as an exercise for the reader (see Probs. 11-2 and 11-3) to work out the details for this model and to verify Eq. (6-39).

The case in which the molecules are treated as point centers of an inverse fifth-power repulsion is again of interest (cf. Sec. 8-3). When the law of force $F = cr^{-s}$ is assumed, it is easily seen by the method of dimensions that (cf. Eqs. (7-3) and (8-88))

$$V_r \sigma_\eta(V_r) \propto V_r^{(s-5)/(s-1)} \tag{11-70}$$

When $s = 5$, the product $V_r \sigma_\eta(V_r)$ is independent of V_r. The general formula for $\Delta(v_y v_z)$, as given by Eq. (11-56), becomes in this special case

$$
\begin{aligned}
\Delta(v_y v_z) &= -\frac{3n^2}{8} \int_{-\infty}^{\infty} dV_{1x} \cdots \\
&\qquad \cdot \int_{-\infty}^{\infty} dV_{2z}\, V_r \sigma_\eta(V_r) V_{ry} V_{rz} F^*(\mathbf{V}_1) F^*(\mathbf{V}_2) \\
&= -\frac{3n^2}{8} V_r \sigma_\eta(V_r) \int_{-\infty}^{\infty} dV_{1x} \cdots \\
&\qquad \cdot \int_{-\infty}^{\infty} dV_{2z}\, (V_{1y} - V_{2y})(V_{1z} - V_{2z}) F^*(\mathbf{V}_1) F^*(\mathbf{V}_2) \\
&= -\frac{3n^2}{8} V_r \sigma_\eta(V_r)(\langle V_{1y} V_{1z}\rangle + \langle V_{2y} V_{2z}\rangle \\
&\qquad\qquad\qquad - \langle V_{1y}\rangle\langle V_{2z}\rangle - \langle V_{1z}\rangle\langle V_{2y}\rangle) \\
&= -\frac{3n^2}{4} V_r \sigma_\eta(V_r)\langle V_y V_z\rangle
\end{aligned}
\tag{11-71}
$$

since $\langle V_{1y} V_{1z}\rangle = \langle V_{2y} V_{2z}\rangle = \langle V_y V_z\rangle$ and

$$\langle V_{1y}\rangle = \langle V_{1z}\rangle = \langle V_{2y}\rangle = \langle V_{2z}\rangle = 0$$

Then, using (11-23),

$$\Delta(v_y v_z) = -(3n/4m) V_r \sigma_\eta(V_r) P_{zy} \tag{11-72}$$

and, inserting (11-72) in (11-41), we obtain the standard viscosity formula with

$$\eta = \frac{4kT}{3 V_r \sigma_\eta(V_r)} \tag{11-73}$$

Since both Eqs. (11-41) and (11-72) have been derived without making any explicit assumption about the form of the distribution function, the resulting formula for η is more exact than Eq. (11-64), which is based on the assumption that terms of higher order than cubic in the expansion (11-26) can be dropped. Equation (11-73) was first obtained by Maxwell,[*] who showed that the three transport coefficients η, K, and D_{12}

---

[*] J. C. Maxwell, *Phil. Trans. Royal Soc.*, vol. 157, p. 49, 1867, or "Collected Works," vol. 2, p. 26.

could be calculated without knowing the form of the distribution function in the special case of the inverse fifth-power law.* Maxwell evaluated $V_r\sigma_\eta(V_r)$ by expressing (8-21) in terms of the complete elliptic integral of the first kind and then integrating (8-49) numerically. The result is

$$V_r\sigma_\eta(V_r) = 3.87(c/m)^{1/2} \tag{11-74}$$

and the viscosity coefficient for the inverse fifth-power repulsion $F = cr^{-5}$ is given explicitly by

$$\eta = 0.344kT(m/c)^{1/2} \tag{11-75}$$

The value of $\rho D_{11}/\eta$ is obtained by combining Eq. (11-75) with Eq. (8-93) with $m^* = m/2$. Thus

$$\rho D_{11}/\eta = 1.54 \tag{11-76}$$

The inverse fifth-power repulsion is unusually "soft" for actual molecules. It is to be expected that the observed values of $\rho D_{11}/\eta$ will be intermediate between 1.54 and the rigid-sphere value of 1.20 given by Eq. (11-68). Measured values generally lie between 1.3 and 1.5.

The thermal conductivity of a monatomic gas can be calculated by the same methods used here to obtain the viscosity coefficient. Some of the details can be found in other books, in which the treatment is based on Chapman's method and differs only in small respects from the form in which that method has been developed and presented here.† The result in the first approximation is that $K = (5/2)\eta c_v$ for monatomic gases regardless of the law of interaction.

11-3. THE BOLTZMANN INTEGRODIFFERENTIAL EQUATION

The state of a gas or gas mixture at a particular instant is completely specified for the purposes of kinetic theory if the distribution function for the molecular velocities and positions is known throughout the gas. Observable properties of the gas are obtained from suitable averages over the distribution, which can be calculated when the distribution function is known. In this section we treat the fundamental problem of determining the distribution function in a very general situation, and in the next section we obtain the solution for the equilibrium case. We allow for the possibility that the gas may be in a nonuniform state characterized by nonvanishing gradients (e.g., of mass velocity or temperature) and also that the state may be a nonsteady one so that the distribution

---

* An additional property of the inverse fifth-power law which was pointed out in Sec. 7-1 is the vanishing of the thermal-diffusion effect.

† Cf. E. H. Kennard, "Kinetic Theory of Gases," McGraw-Hill Book Company, Inc., New York, 1938, pp. 165–180; G. N. Patterson, "Molecular Flow of Gases," John Wiley & Sons, Inc., New York, 1956, chap. 3.

function depends explicitly on the time.   An external field of force may be present (e.g., gravity), which we shall assume to depend on position and time but not on velocity.   Let $\mathbf{a}(\mathbf{r},t)$ be the field-produced acceleration of a molecule that happens to be at the point $\mathbf{r}$ at the time t; this is a known function when the external field has been specified.

Consider first the case of a pure gas.   The distribution was specified in Sec. 11-1 by the molecular number density $n(\mathbf{r},t)$ and the normalized velocity distribution function $F(\mathbf{v},\mathbf{r},t)$.   It is convenient to introduce a single distribution function: $f(\mathbf{v},\mathbf{r},t) = n(\mathbf{r},t)F(\mathbf{v},\mathbf{r},t)$ such that

$$dN = f(\mathbf{v},\mathbf{r},t) \; dv_x \, dv_y \, dv_z \, dx \, dy \, dz$$

represents the number of molecules that have velocities between $\mathbf{v}$ and $\mathbf{v} + d\mathbf{v}$ (i.e., components between v_x and $v_x + dv_x$, etc.) and positions between $\mathbf{r}$ and $\mathbf{r} + d\mathbf{r}$ (i.e., coordinates between x and $x + dx$, etc.) at the time t.   For brevity we let $d\tau_r = dx \, dy \, dz$ and $d\tau_v = dv_x \, dv_y \, dv_z$.   If no collisions occur, the molecules that at time t are located in the element $d\tau_r$ near $\mathbf{r}$ with velocities in the range $d\tau_v$ about $\mathbf{v}$ will at a later time $t + dt$ be found in the element $d\tau_r'$ near $\mathbf{r}'$ with velocities in the range $d\tau_v'$ about $\mathbf{v}'$, where evidently $\mathbf{r}' = \mathbf{r} + \mathbf{v} \, dt$ and $\mathbf{v}' = \mathbf{v} + \mathbf{a} \, dt$.   The number of molecules which at time $t + dt$ are located in $d\tau_r'$ with velocities in the range $d\tau_v'$ is given by $f(\mathbf{v}', \mathbf{r}', t + dt) \, d\tau_v' \, d\tau_r'$ and, since $d\mathbf{r}' = d\mathbf{r}$ and $d\mathbf{v}' = d\mathbf{v}$, this can be rewritten as

$$dN' = f(\mathbf{v} + \mathbf{a} \, dt, \mathbf{r} + \mathbf{v} \, dt, t + dt) \, d\tau_v \, d\tau_r$$

If there were no intermolecular collisions, all the molecules contained in the unprimed set of number dN would be included in the primed set of number dN', and there would be no others; hence $dN' = dN$ in this special case.

The effects of molecular encounters are two-fold: some molecules of the unprimed set will be intercepted during the time dt and hence will not be included in dN', whereas other molecules, not included in dN, will be deflected into the primed set and will contribute to dN'.   Since the two effects do not in general cancel, we represent the net change from collisions by dN_{coll} so that $dN' - dN = dN_{coll}$ in the general case.   However,

$$dN' - dN = [f(\mathbf{v} + \mathbf{a} \, dt, \mathbf{r} + \mathbf{v} \, dt, t + dt) - f(\mathbf{v},\mathbf{r},t)] \, d\tau_v \, d\tau_r$$
$$= \left[\frac{\partial f}{\partial v_x} a_x + \frac{\partial f}{\partial v_y} a_y + \frac{\partial f}{\partial v_z} a_z + \frac{\partial f}{\partial x} v_x + \frac{\partial f}{\partial y} v_y + \frac{\partial f}{\partial z} v_z + \frac{\partial f}{\partial t} \right]$$
$$\cdot dt \, d\tau_v \, d\tau_r \quad (11\text{-}77)$$

where we have taken dt to be infinitesimal and represented the total change in f resulting from changes in the seven variables on which f depends explicitly by means of the first partial derivatives.   The expression in brackets is equal to the total time derivative df/dt. We set $dN_{coll} = (\partial f/\partial t)_{coll} \, dt \, d\tau_v \, d\tau_r$ where $(\partial f/\partial t)_{coll}$ represents the rate of change of the distribution function $f(\mathbf{v},\mathbf{r},t)$ due to collisions. Evidently $(\partial f/\partial t)_{coll} \, d\tau_v$ is equal to the number of molecules per unit volume per unit time which are deflected into the velocity range $\mathbf{v}$ to $\mathbf{v} + d\mathbf{v}$ by encounters minus the number which are deflected out of this range. Combining the expression for dN_{coll} with the formula (11-77) for $dN' - dN$, we obtain the equation for $f(\mathbf{v},\mathbf{r},t)$:

$$\frac{\partial f}{\partial t} + v_x \frac{\partial f}{\partial x} + v_y \frac{\partial f}{\partial y} + v_z \frac{\partial f}{\partial z} + a_x \frac{\partial f}{\partial v_x} + a_y \frac{\partial f}{\partial v_y} + a_z \frac{\partial f}{\partial v_z} = \left(\frac{\partial f}{\partial t}\right)_{coll} \quad (11\text{-}78)$$

This is Boltzmann's equation; it is not yet in final form, since the right-hand member is purely schematic and an explicit expression must be developed for it. It will be shown below that $(\partial f/\partial t)_{coll}$ is given by a multiple integral with the unknown function f appearing in the integrand. Thus Boltzmann's equation is both a partial differential equation and an integral equation.

We proceed to the evaluation of $(\partial f/\partial t)_{coll}$. Up to this point, our considerations have been kinematical, and the essential statistical hypothesis has not yet been introduced. This hypothesis enters in the evaluation of the collision term. We assume molecular chaos, spherical symmetry of the molecules and their force fields, and binary encounters only. The statistical assumption of molecular chaos enables one to neglect possible correlations between the velocity of a molecule and its position or between the initial velocities of two colliding molecules before their encounter. These assumptions will be passed over briefly since they have already been discussed in connection with the evaluation of ΔQ in Sec. 11-1. We set

$$(\partial f/\partial t)_{coll} = (\partial f/\partial t)^+_{coll} - (\partial f/\partial t)^-_{coll}$$

where $(\partial f/\partial t)^-_{coll} \, d\tau_v$ is the number of molecules deflected out of, and $(\partial f/\partial t)^+_{coll} \, d\tau_v$ the number deflected into, the velocity range $\mathbf{v}$ to $\mathbf{v} + d\mathbf{v}$ per unit volume per unit time. In order to evaluate $(\partial f/\partial t)^-_{coll}$, we consider the encounters taking place in the volume element $d\tau_r$ between the molecules in this velocity range and molecules of all velocities; each such encounter leads in general to the loss of one molecule from the specified velocity range.* For convenience in notation, we shall henceforth employ the subscript 1 for the specific velocity range referred to in Eq. (11-78) and the subscript 2 for the velocity of the collision partner. The number of encounters between the two groups of number densities dn_1 and dn_2 taking place in $d\tau_r$ in time dt with impact parameters between

---

* Since the range is infinitesimal, we can neglect encounters between two molecules in the specified velocity range for which the relative velocity is infinitesimal.

b and $b + db$ and impact azimuths between ϵ and $\epsilon + d\epsilon$ is given by*

$$b \, db \, d\epsilon \, v_r \, dn_1 \, dn_2 \, d\tau_r \, dt = b \, db \, d\epsilon \, v_r f(\mathbf{v}_1,\mathbf{r},t) f(\mathbf{v}_2,\mathbf{r},t) \, d\tau_{v1} \, d\tau_{v2} \, d\tau_r \, dt \quad (11\text{-}79)$$

The total number of encounters between members of the dn_1 group and all other molecules per unit volume per unit time is

$$f(\mathbf{v}_1,\mathbf{r},t) \, d\tau_{v1} \int_{-\infty}^{\infty} d\tau_{v2} \int_0^{2\pi} d\epsilon \int_0^{\infty} db \, b v_r f(\mathbf{v}_2,\mathbf{r},t)$$

and, since this is equal to the number of molecules deflected out of the range $\mathbf{v}_1$ to $\mathbf{v}_1 + d\mathbf{v}_1$ per cubic centimeter per second, we obtain

$$\left(\frac{\partial f(\mathbf{v}_1,\mathbf{r},t)}{\partial t}\right)_{\text{coll}}^{-} = \int_{-\infty}^{\infty} d\tau_{v2} \int_0^{2\pi} d\epsilon \int_0^{\infty} db \, b v_r f(\mathbf{v}_1,\mathbf{r},t) f(\mathbf{v}_2,\mathbf{r},t) \quad (11\text{-}80)$$

The "type number" κ, which appears in Eqs. (8-61) and (11-6), has not been introduced in (11-80) and will not appear in subsequent formulas because the integration is carried out over one collision partner only. Each collision is then counted only once, whether the encounter is between like or unlike molecules.

The Inverse Encounters.   The evaluation of $(\partial f/\partial t)_{\text{coll}}^{+}$ requires knowing how many encounters terminate with one molecule in the specified small range of velocities about $\mathbf{v}_1$. A simple relation exists between the collisions that deplete this $\mathbf{v}_1$ group and the encounters that replenish it. In a depleting collision the initial velocities are $\mathbf{v}_1$ and $\mathbf{v}_2$, and the final velocities will be denoted by $\mathbf{v}_1'$ and $\mathbf{v}_2'$ as usual. It has already been pointed out on page 208 that the conservation laws for energy and momentum, together with specified values of the impact parameter and azimuth, completely determine the final velocities $\mathbf{v}_1'$ and $\mathbf{v}_2'$ when the initial velocities $\mathbf{v}_1$ and $\mathbf{v}_2$ are given. The impact parameter b of the relative orbit of molecule 1 about molecule 2 is the perpendicular distance from the center of 2 to the initial asymptote of the relative orbit. Let b' be the perpendicular distance from the center of 2 to the final asymptote. It follows from the conservation of relative angular momentum and the equality of v_r and v_r' that $b' = b$; this can also be seen from the symmetry of the relative orbit about the apse line, which is illustrated in Fig. 8-1. Let us now consider an encounter between two molecules of initial velocities $\mathbf{v}_1'$ and $\mathbf{v}_2'$ which are approaching each other with the same impact parameter b and the same impact azimuth ϵ as in the depleting collision just discussed. Since the conservation equations are invariant to an interchange of initial and final velocities (the left- and right-hand mem-

---

* For additional generality we have decomposed the impact-parameter ring, or annulus, of area $2\pi b \, db$ into elements $b \, db \, d\epsilon$, where the impact azimuth ϵ is the azimuth of the plane of the relative orbit about an axis along the line of head-on approach. Evidently b and ϵ are polar coordinates in a plane perpendicular to this axis.

bers are simply interchanged), the final velocities will be $\mathbf{v}_1$ and $\mathbf{v}_2$. The second encounter is said to be the *inverse* of the first;[*] evidently the inverse of a depleting collision is a replenishing collision, and vice versa. It can be shown that if the molecules are not spherically symmetrical,

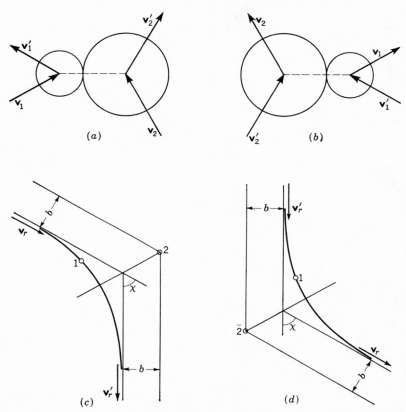

FIG. 11-1. Inverse encounters: (*a*) collision of rigid elastic spheres; (*b*) collision that is the inverse of (*a*); (*c*) relative orbit in an encounter between point-center-of-force molecules; (*d*) relative orbit in an encounter that is the inverse of (*c*).

an arbitrarily chosen collision will not in general possess an inverse; however, an inverse always exists if there is spherical symmetry, as we have assumed.[†] Figure 11-1 depicts a collision and its inverse for the case of rigid elastic spheres and also for the case of point centers of force.

[*] An inverse encounter is to be distinguished from a *reverse* encounter in which the final velocities of the original encounter are reversed and the molecules retrace their original paths. The initial velocities of a reverse encounter are $-\mathbf{v}_1'$ and $-\mathbf{v}_2'$, and the final velocities are $-\mathbf{v}_1$ and $-\mathbf{v}_2$.

[†] Cf. R. C. Tolman, "The Principles of Statistical Mechanics," Oxford University Press, London, 1938, p. 117.

For every depleting collision $(\mathbf{v}_1,\mathbf{v}_2 \rightarrow \mathbf{v}_1',\mathbf{v}_2')$ there will be an inverse, replenishing collision $(\mathbf{v}_1',\mathbf{v}_2' \rightarrow \mathbf{v}_1,\mathbf{v}_2)$; and for every replenishing collision there will be an inverse, depleting collision. Thus all* collisions that replenish the velocity range close to $\mathbf{v}_1$ are obtained from encounters between molecules of initial velocities close to $\mathbf{v}_1'$ and $\mathbf{v}_2'$. The number of such encounters taking place in time dt in the element $d\tau_r$ with impact parameters between b' and $b' + db'$ and azimuths between ϵ' and $\epsilon' + d\epsilon'$ is

$$b'\,db'\,d\epsilon'\,v_r'\,dn_1'\,dn_2'\,d\tau_r\,dt$$
$$= b\,db\,d\epsilon\,v_rf(\mathbf{v}_1',\mathbf{r},t)f(\mathbf{v}_2',\mathbf{r},t)\,d\tau_{v1}'\,d\tau_{v2}'\,d\tau_r\,dt \quad (11\text{-}81)$$

since the impact parameters and azimuths, and the magnitudes of the initial relative velocities are equal for an encounter and its inverse. In order to obtain the number of collisions which replenish the $\mathbf{v}_1$ group, it is necessary to transform from $d\tau_{v1}'\,d\tau_{v2}'$ to $d\tau_{v1}\,d\tau_{v2}$. Then

$$d\tau_{v1}'\,d\tau_{v2}' = |J|\,d\tau_{v1}\,d\tau_{v2} \quad (11\text{-}82)$$

where J is the Jacobian determinant. But, from Eqs. (5-21),

$$d\tau_{v1}\,d\tau_{v2} = dv_{cx}\,dv_{cy}\,dv_{cz}\,dv_{rx}\,dv_{ry}\,dv_{rz}$$
$$d\tau_{v1}'\,d\tau_{v2}' = dv_{cx}\,dv_{cy}\,dv_{cz}\,dv_{rx}'\,dv_{ry}'\,dv_{rz}'$$

and therefore
$$J = \frac{\partial(v_{rx}',v_{ry}',v_{rz}')}{\partial(v_{rx},v_{ry},v_{rz})} \quad (11\text{-}83)$$

wherein the partial differentiations are to be performed holding constant the impact parameter b and azimuth ϵ. Introducing polar coordinates v_r, θ_r and v_r', θ_r' in the collision plane in the C system and recalling that $v_r' = v_r$, we obtain $J = \partial\theta_r'/\partial\theta_r$ with v_r, b, and ϵ held constant. Since $\theta_r' = \theta_r + \chi(v_r,b)$ where χ is the angle of deflection, the result is that $J = 1$. This can also be seen by taking components of $\mathbf{v}_r$ and $\mathbf{v}_r'$ parallel and perpendicular to the apse line; the perpendicular components are equal and the parallel components differ only in sign.† Therefore $d\tau_{v1}'\,d\tau_{v2}' = d\tau_{v1}\,d\tau_{v2}$, and (11-81) can be rewritten as

$$b\,db\,d\epsilon\,v_rf(\mathbf{v}_1',\mathbf{r},t)f(\mathbf{v}_2',\mathbf{r},t)\,d\tau_{v1}\,d\tau_{v2}\,d\tau_r\,dt$$

The total number of encounters per unit volume per unit time in which one molecule enters the velocity range $\mathbf{v}_1$ to $\mathbf{v}_1 + d\mathbf{v}_1$ is then given by

$$d\tau_{v1}\int_{-\infty}^{\infty} d\tau_{v2}\int_0^{2\pi} d\epsilon\int_0^{\infty} db\,bv_rf(\mathbf{v}_1',\mathbf{r},t)f(\mathbf{v}_2',\mathbf{r},t)$$

* If another pair of initial velocities $\mathbf{v}_1''$ and $\mathbf{v}_2''$ were also to replenish the $\mathbf{v}_1$ group, we should have $(\mathbf{v}_1, \mathbf{v}_2 \rightarrow \mathbf{v}_1'', \mathbf{v}_2'')$ in addition to $(\mathbf{v}_1, \mathbf{v}_2 \rightarrow \mathbf{v}_1', \mathbf{v}_2')$. This is impossible because the dynamical equations have a unique solution.

† The determinant J of (11-83) corresponds to a transformation carrying $\mathbf{v}_r$ into $\mathbf{v}_r'$. Since this is a pure rotation, J is the determinant of an orthogonal transformation; hence $|J| = 1$.

whence

$$\left(\frac{\partial f(\mathbf{v_1},\mathbf{r},t)}{\partial t}\right)_{\text{coll}}^{+} = \int_{-\infty}^{\infty} d\tau_{v2} \int_0^{2\pi} d\epsilon \int_0^{\infty} db \ bv_r f(\mathbf{v}_1',\mathbf{r},t)f(\mathbf{v}_2',\mathbf{r},t) \quad (11\text{-}84)$$

and the right-hand side of Eq. (11-78) becomes

$$\left(\frac{\partial f(\mathbf{v_1})}{\partial t}\right)_{\text{coll}} = \int_{-\infty}^{\infty} d\tau_{v2} \int_0^{2\pi} d\epsilon \int_0^{\infty} db \ bv_r[f(\mathbf{v}_1')f(\mathbf{v}_2') - f(\mathbf{v}_1)f(\mathbf{v}_2)] \quad (11\text{-}85)$$

using (11-80) and (11-84). The arguments $\mathbf{r}$ and t, which are common[*] to the four distribution functions in the integrand, have been dropped for the sake of brevity. Inserting (11-85) in (11-78), we obtain *Boltzmann's integrodifferential equation* for the distribution function $f(\mathbf{v},\mathbf{r},t)$ of a pure gas

$$\frac{\partial f}{\partial t} + v_x \frac{\partial f}{\partial x} + v_y \frac{\partial f}{\partial y} + v_z \frac{\partial f}{\partial z} + a_x \frac{\partial f}{\partial v_x} + a_y \frac{\partial f}{\partial v_y} + a_z \frac{\partial f}{\partial v_z}$$
$$= \int_{-\infty}^{\infty} d\tau_{v2} \int_0^{2\pi} d\epsilon \int_0^{\infty} db \ bv_r[f(\mathbf{v}')f(\mathbf{v}_2') - f(\mathbf{v})f(\mathbf{v}_2)] \quad (11\text{-}86)$$

This can be readily generalized to the case of a gas mixture: the distribution function of the ith component gas $f_i(\mathbf{v}_i,\mathbf{r}_i,t)$ will satisfy the equation

$$\frac{\partial f_i}{\partial t} + v_{ix} \frac{\partial f_i}{\partial x_i} + v_{iy} \frac{\partial f_i}{\partial y_i} + v_{iz} \frac{\partial f_i}{\partial z_i} + a_{ix} \frac{\partial f_i}{\partial v_{ix}} + a_{iy} \frac{\partial f_i}{\partial v_{iy}} + a_{iz} \frac{\partial f_i}{\partial v_{iz}}$$
$$= \sum_j \int_{-\infty}^{\infty} d\tau_{vj} \int_0^{2\pi} d\epsilon \int_0^{\infty} db \ bv_r[f_i(\mathbf{v}_i')f_j(\mathbf{v}_j') - f_i(\mathbf{v}_i)f_j(\mathbf{v}_j)] \quad (11\text{-}87)$$

The right-hand member takes into account both like and unlike molecule encounters.

Integral Transformation Formulas and the Equation of Change. The equation of change for the molecular property $Q(\mathbf{v})$ can be obtained directly from Eq. (11-86) by multiplying both sides of the equation by $Q(\mathbf{v})$ and integrating over $\mathbf{v}$. Thus, in the absence of an external field,

$$\int_{-\infty}^{\infty} Q(\mathbf{v}) \left(\frac{\partial f}{\partial t} + v_x \frac{\partial f}{\partial x} + v_y \frac{\partial f}{\partial y} + v_z \frac{\partial f}{\partial z}\right) d\tau_v$$
$$= \int_{-\infty}^{\infty} \int_{-\infty}^{\infty} \int_0^{2\pi} \int_0^{\infty} Q(\mathbf{v_1})[f(\mathbf{v}_1')f(\mathbf{v}_2') - f(\mathbf{v}_1)f(\mathbf{v}_2)]v_r b \ db \ d\epsilon \ d\tau_{v1} \ d\tau_{v2}$$
$$(11\text{-}88)$$

where the integration variable $\mathbf{v}$ has been relabeled $\mathbf{v}_1$ in the integral on

---

[*] We have assumed that the distribution function does not vary appreciably over a distance of the order of the range of intermolecular forces or in a time interval comparable to the duration of an encounter.

the right side. Transforming the left side gives

$$\int_{-\infty}^{\infty} Q(\mathbf{v}) \frac{\partial f}{\partial t} \, d\tau_v = \frac{\partial}{\partial t} \int_{-\infty}^{\infty} Q(\mathbf{v}) f(\mathbf{v},\mathbf{r},t) \, d\tau_v = \frac{\partial}{\partial t} (n\langle Q \rangle) \qquad (11\text{-}89)$$

and
$$\int_{-\infty}^{\infty} Q(\mathbf{v}) v_x \frac{\partial f}{\partial x} \, d\tau_v = \frac{\partial}{\partial x} \int_{-\infty}^{\infty} v_x Q(\mathbf{v}) f(\mathbf{v},\mathbf{r},t) \, d\tau_v = \frac{\partial}{\partial x} (n\langle v_x Q \rangle)$$

where $f(\mathbf{v},\mathbf{r},t)$ has been replaced by $n(\mathbf{r},t)F(\mathbf{v},\mathbf{r},t)$ and the averages $\langle Q \rangle$ and $\langle v_x Q \rangle$ have been defined in Sec. 11-1. The right side of (11-88) can be rewritten as

$$
\begin{aligned}
R &= \iiiint Q(\mathbf{v}_1)[f(\mathbf{v}_1')f(\mathbf{v}_2') - f(\mathbf{v}_1)f(\mathbf{v}_2)]v_r b \, db \, d\epsilon \, d\tau_{v1} \, d\tau_{v2} \\
&= \iiiint Q(\mathbf{v}_2)[f(\mathbf{v}_1')f(\mathbf{v}_2') - f(\mathbf{v}_1)f(\mathbf{v}_2)]v_r b \, db \, d\epsilon \, d\tau_{v1} \, d\tau_{v2} \qquad (11\text{-}90) \\
&= \tfrac{1}{2} \iiiint [Q(\mathbf{v}_1) + Q(\mathbf{v}_2)][f(\mathbf{v}_1')f(\mathbf{v}_2') - f(\mathbf{v}_1)f(\mathbf{v}_2)] \, v_r b \, db \, d\epsilon \, d\tau_{v1} \, d\tau_{v2}
\end{aligned}
$$

since an interchange of the subscripts 1 and 2 does not alter the value of the integral. Furthermore

$$
\begin{aligned}
\iiiint &[Q(\mathbf{v}_1) + Q(\mathbf{v}_2)]f(\mathbf{v}_1')f(\mathbf{v}_2')v_r b \, db \, d\epsilon \, d\tau_{v1} \, d\tau_{v2} \\
&= \iiiint [Q(\mathbf{v}_1') + Q(\mathbf{v}_2')]f(\mathbf{v}_1)f(\mathbf{v}_2)v_r' b' \, db' \, d\epsilon' \, d\tau_{v1}' \, d\tau_{v2}' \\
&= \iiiint [Q(\mathbf{v}_1') + Q(\mathbf{v}_2')]f(\mathbf{v}_1)f(\mathbf{v}_2)v_r b \, db \, d\epsilon \, d\tau_{v1} \, d\tau_{v2}
\end{aligned}
\qquad (11\text{-}91)
$$

where the second expression has been obtained from the first by noting that, since every collision has an inverse, summing over all possible collisions is equivalent to summing over their inverses. Thus the value of the integral is unchanged by "inverting" the integrand, replacing primed by unprimed quantities, and vice versa. In the third expression, we have used $|J| = 1$ and other results for the inverse encounters discussed above. Substitution of (11-91) in (11-90) now gives

$$
\begin{aligned}
R &= \tfrac{1}{2} \iiiint [Q(\mathbf{v}_1') + Q(\mathbf{v}_2') - Q(\mathbf{v}_1) - Q(\mathbf{v}_2)]f(\mathbf{v}_1)f(\mathbf{v}_2)v_r b \, db \, d\epsilon \, d\tau_{v1} \, d\tau_{v2} \\
&= \tfrac{1}{2}n^2(\mathbf{r},t) \iiiint \delta Q \, F(\mathbf{v}_1,\mathbf{r},t)F(\mathbf{v}_2,\mathbf{r},t)v_r b \, db \, d\epsilon \, d\tau_{v1} \, d\tau_{v2} \\
&= \pi n^2(\mathbf{r},t) \iiint \overline{\delta Q} \, F(\mathbf{v}_1,\mathbf{r},t)F(\mathbf{v}_2,\mathbf{r},t)v_r b \, db \, d\tau_{v1} \, d\tau_{v2}
\end{aligned}
\qquad (11\text{-}92)
$$

where δQ has been defined in Eq. (11-9) and $\overline{\delta Q}$ is given by

$$\overline{\delta Q} = (2\pi)^{-1} \int_0^{2\pi} \delta Q \, d\epsilon$$

Comparison of (11-92) with (11-10) shows that they are identical; also, the left-hand side of (11-88) is seen with the aid of (11-89) to be identical with the left-hand member of (11-11). The result is again Maxwell's equation of change. The integral transformations in (11-90) and (11-91) will be found useful later. It is not difficult to generalize the derivation just given to the case of a molecular property which depends explicitly on position and time as well as on velocity. The resulting equation for $Q(\mathbf{v},\mathbf{r},t)$ is referred to as *Enskog's equation of change.* *

The Boltzmann equation (11-87) is the starting point for many important classical investigations of the nonequilibrium properties of gases. Enskog's method of treating the transport phenomena is based on a solution of this equation by successive approximations. Details of these elaborate calculations can be found elsewhere.†

11-4. THE H THEOREM AND THE MAXWELL-BOLTZMANN DISTRIBUTION LAW

The Boltzmann equation is used in this section to give a rigorous derivation of the Maxwell-Boltzmann distribution law for a gas in equilibrium. An equilibrium state of a gas has been defined in Sec. 11-2 as one in which the distribution of molecular velocities is independent of position and time and thus is necessarily unaffected by molecular encounters. Then, for an equilibrium state of a pure gas in the absence of an external field, the entire left-hand member of Eq. (11-86) must vanish. The last three terms vanish when the field is zero. The first term vanishes for any steady state as well as for the state of equilibrium. The second, third, and fourth terms involve gradients of the density n and velocity distribution function F. In the equilibrium state there can be no gradients of physical properties such as the temperature or the velocity of mass motion, which would necessitate a dependence of the distribution function F on position. The density n must be uniform in the absence of an external field if molecular chaos prevails. Hence the second, third, and fourth terms also vanish.‡ Then Boltzmann's equation (11-86) reduces to

$$\int_{-\infty}^{\infty} d\tau_{v2} \int_{0}^{2\pi} d\epsilon \int_{0}^{\infty} db\ bv_r[f(\mathbf{v}_1')f(\mathbf{v}_2') - f(\mathbf{v}_1)f(\mathbf{v}_2)] = 0 \quad (11\text{-}93)$$

One possible solution of (11-93) is that

$$f(\mathbf{v}_1')f(\mathbf{v}_2') = f(\mathbf{v}_1)f(\mathbf{v}_2) \quad (11\text{-}94)$$

for all values of $\mathbf{v}_1$ and $\mathbf{v}_2$. This can also be written as

$$F(\mathbf{v}_1')F(\mathbf{v}_2') = F(\mathbf{v}_1)F(\mathbf{v}_2) \quad (11\text{-}95)$$

---

* Cf. Chapman and Cowling, *op. cit.*, p. 48.

† Chapman and Cowling, *op. cit.;* and Hirschfelder, Curtiss, and Bird, *op. cit.*

‡ If there is a gradient of mass velocity or of temperature in the z direction, the fourth term will not vanish. In the former case, the left-hand side of (11-86) reduces to $nv_z\ \partial F/\partial z$.

Since the integrand of (11-93) can have either sign, the vanishing of the integral does not require the vanishing of the integrand but merely the mutual cancellation of positive and negative contributions to the value of the integral from different parts of the region of integration. Thus (11-94) is a *sufficient* condition for equilibrium, but we cannot conclude, without further analysis, that it is a necessary condition. The necessity was first established by Boltzmann through the proof of the so-called *H* theorem. We shall now give this proof for the case of a pure gas in the absence of a force field, assuming that the states to be considered are all uniform so that f depends on $\mathbf{v}$ and t but not on $\mathbf{r}$. The Boltzmann equation (11-86) then reduces to

$$\frac{\partial f}{\partial t} = \int_{-\infty}^{\infty} d\tau_{v2} \int_{0}^{2\pi} d\epsilon \int_{0}^{\infty} db \, bv_r[f(\mathbf{v}')f(\mathbf{v}_2') - f(\mathbf{v})f(\mathbf{v}_2)] \quad (11\text{-}96)$$

The Boltzmann *H* function, defined by

$$H(t) = \int_{-\infty}^{\infty} d\tau_v \, f(\mathbf{v},t) \log f(\mathbf{v},t) \quad (11\text{-}97)$$

is a function only of t. Since f is independent of t in an equilibrium state, a necessary condition for equilibrium is that $dH/dt = 0$. Time differentiation of (11-97) gives

$$dH/dt = \int_{-\infty}^{\infty} d\tau_v \, (\partial f/\partial t)(\log f + 1) \quad (11\text{-}98)$$

and, on substituting $\partial f/\partial t$ from (11-96), this becomes

$$\frac{dH}{dt} = \int_{-\infty}^{\infty} \int_{-\infty}^{\infty} \int_{0}^{2\pi} \int_{0}^{\infty} [\log f(\mathbf{v}_1) + 1]$$
$$\cdot [f(\mathbf{v}_1')f(\mathbf{v}_2') - f(\mathbf{v}_1)f(\mathbf{v}_2)]v_r b \, db \, d\epsilon \, d\tau_{v1} \, d\tau_{v2} \quad (11\text{-}99)$$

where the integration variable $\mathbf{v}$ has been relabeled $\mathbf{v}_1$. On comparing Eq. (11-99) with Eq. (11-88), it is seen that their right-hand members become identical if we set $Q(\mathbf{v}_1) = \log f(\mathbf{v}_1) + 1$. The transformations of Eqs. (11-90) and (11-91) then give

$$\frac{dH}{dt} = \tfrac{1}{2} \iiiint [Q(\mathbf{v}_1') + Q(\mathbf{v}_2') - Q(\mathbf{v}_1) - Q(\mathbf{v}_2)]$$
$$\cdot f(\mathbf{v}_1)f(\mathbf{v}_2)v_r b \, db \, d\epsilon \, d\tau_{v1} \, d\tau_{v2}$$
$$= \tfrac{1}{2} \iiiint \{\log [f(\mathbf{v}_1')f(\mathbf{v}_2')] - \log [f(\mathbf{v}_1)f(\mathbf{v}_2)]\}$$
$$\cdot f(\mathbf{v}_1)f(\mathbf{v}_2)v_r b \, db \, d\epsilon \, d\tau_{v1} \, d\tau_{v2} \quad (11\text{-}100)$$
$$= \tfrac{1}{2} \iiiint \{\log [f(\mathbf{v}_1)f(\mathbf{v}_2)] - \log [f(\mathbf{v}_1')f(\mathbf{v}_2')]\}$$
$$\cdot f(\mathbf{v}_1')f(\mathbf{v}_2')v_r b \, db \, d\epsilon \, d\tau_{v1} \, d\tau_{v2}$$

Adding the last two expressions and dividing by two, we have, finally,

$$\frac{dH}{dt} = -\frac{1}{4} \iiiint \{\log [f(\mathbf{v}_1')f(\mathbf{v}_2')] - \log [f(\mathbf{v}_1)f(\mathbf{v}_2)]\}$$
$$\cdot [f(\mathbf{v}_1')f(\mathbf{v}_2') - f(\mathbf{v}_1)f(\mathbf{v}_2)]v_r b\, db\, d\epsilon\, d\tau_{v1}\, d\tau_{v2} \quad (11\text{-}101)$$

The integrand of (11-101) is nonnegative for all values of the variables of integration.* Hence $dH/dt \leq 0$, and the equality can only hold if the integrand vanishes everywhere over the range of integration. The integral vanishes only if, for all values of $\mathbf{v}_1$ and $\mathbf{v}_2$,

$$f(\mathbf{v}_1')f(\mathbf{v}_2') = f(\mathbf{v}_1)f(\mathbf{v}_2) \quad (11\text{-}102)$$

Thus (11-102) is a *necessary* as well as a sufficient condition for equilibrium. The physical significance of Eq. (11-102) can be seen by rewriting it as

$$b\, db\, d\epsilon\, v_r f(\mathbf{v}_1)f(\mathbf{v}_2)\, d\tau_{v1}\, d\tau_{v2} = b\, db\, d\epsilon\, v_r f(\mathbf{v}_1')f(\mathbf{v}_2')\, d\tau_{v1}\, d\tau_{v2}$$
$$= b'\, db'\, d\epsilon'\, v_r' f(\mathbf{v}_1')f(\mathbf{v}_2')\, d\tau_{v1}'\, d\tau_{v2}' \quad (11\text{-}103)$$

since $|J| = 1$ and b', ϵ', and v_r' are equal to b, ϵ, and v_r, respectively. Equation (11-103) shows that the differential rate at which encounters specified by (infinitesimal ranges about) $\mathbf{v}_1$, $\mathbf{v}_2$, b, and ϵ take place is exactly equal to the rate at which the inverse encounters occur. Thus, in a state of equilibrium, not only do the encounters as a whole have no effect on the distribution but the effect of each particular encounter is compensated by the encounter that is its inverse. This is a particular instance of the more general principle of *detailed balancing*, which is treated in statistical mechanics.† Boltzmann's H theorem shows, under the assumptions that have been stated, that (a) $dH/dt \leq 0$ and (b) the preservation of an equilibrium state requires detailed balancing.‡

Derivation of the Equilibrium Distribution Function. The equilibrium distribution function for molecular velocities can be derived from the detailed balancing condition. Taking the logarithm of both sides of Eq. (11-95) yields

$$\log F(\mathbf{v}_1') + \log F(\mathbf{v}_2') = \log F(\mathbf{v}_1) + \log F(\mathbf{v}_2) \quad (11\text{-}104)$$

Equation (11-104) shows that $\log F$ is a collisional invariant. It has been

---

* We note that $\log x$ increases monotonically with increasing x.

† See R. H. Fowler, "Statistical Mechanics," Cambridge University Press, London, 1936.

‡ The H theorem can be readily extended to gas mixtures. It can also be extended to take into account ternary and higher-order molecular encounters. In the case of nonspherical molecules for which a collision does not in general possess an inverse, it is still possible to show that $dH/dt \leq 0$ by considering a closed cycle of collisions. See Tolman, *op. cit.*

shown on page 208 that, in the case of molecules possessing no internal degrees of freedom, there are four and only four velocity-dependent quantities that are collisional invariants, and these are the three components of linear momentum and the kinetic energy. Hence $\log F$ must be a linear combination of these quantities with constant coefficients, i.e., coefficients that are independent of $\mathbf{r}$ and t, since the equilibrium state is a uniform, steady one. Thus

$$\log F(\mathbf{v}) = \alpha_1 + \alpha_2 m v_x + \alpha_3 m v_y + \alpha_4 m v_z + \alpha_5 \tfrac{1}{2} m v^2 \quad (11\text{-}105)$$

and
$$F(\mathbf{v}) = A e^{-(\beta m/2)[(v_x-a)^2+(v_y-b)^2+(v_z-c)^2]} \quad (11\text{-}106)$$

where $\alpha_1, \alpha_2, \ldots, \alpha_5$ are constants and A, β, a, b, and c are an equivalent set of constants. Formula (11-106) is the Maxwell distribution function for a gas in uniform mass motion with components of mass velocity equal to a, b, and c. The values of β and A have already been obtained in Sec. 5-1; they are determined by the kinetic-theory definition of temperature. This completes the derivation of Maxwell's famous law.

If an external field of force is present, the distribution function for an equilibrium state can again be obtained from the Boltzmann equation. Denoting the potential energy of a molecule at the point $\mathbf{r}$ by $V(\mathbf{r})$, the field-produced acceleration has components

$$a_x = -(1/m)\,\partial V/\partial x \qquad \text{etc.} \quad (11\text{-}107)$$

which are substituted in Eq. (11-86). Instead of deriving the complete solution,* we shall simply verify that the Maxwell-Boltzmann distribution function (5-2) satisfies the Boltzmann equation. Rewriting (5-2) as

$$f(\mathbf{v},\mathbf{r}) = A e^{-(1/kT)[(m/2)(v_x{}^2+v_y{}^2+v_z{}^2)+V(x,y,z)]} \quad (11\text{-}108)$$

it is immediately obvious that the detailed balancing condition (11-94) is satisfied because of energy conservation and that the right-hand member of (11-86) reduces to zero. Since $\partial f/\partial t = 0$, the remaining terms of (11-86) give

$$v_x \frac{\partial f}{\partial x} + v_y \frac{\partial f}{\partial y} + v_z \frac{\partial f}{\partial z} - \frac{1}{m}\left(\frac{\partial V}{\partial x}\frac{\partial f}{\partial v_x} + \frac{\partial V}{\partial y}\frac{\partial f}{\partial v_y} + \frac{\partial V}{\partial z}\frac{\partial f}{\partial v_z}\right) = 0 \quad (11\text{-}109)$$

and, on substituting (11-108), this is identically zero.

Extensions of the H Theorem and the Relation of the H Function to the Statistical-mechanical Probability of a Macrostate. The proof of the H theorem has been given above for the restricted case of uniform states. It has been shown that H decreases with time until equilibrium is reached and that thereafter H ceases to change. Thus the approach toward equilibrium is characterized by a decrease in the value of H. We now extend our considerations to include the possibility of nonuniform

* See Fowler, *op. cit.*, p. 672.

states in which f depends on $\mathbf{r}$ as well as on $\mathbf{v}$ and t. It is necessary to generalize the definition of H by integrating over position coordinates as well as velocity components. The generalized H function is given by

$$\mathcal{H}(t) = \int_V d\tau_r \int_{-\infty}^{\infty} d\tau_v \, f(\mathbf{v},\mathbf{r},t) \log f(\mathbf{v},\mathbf{r},t) \qquad (11\text{-}110)$$

Considering a nonuniform spatial distribution in the absence of an external field, it will now be shown that changes in the direction of increased uniformity are accompanied by a decrease in the value of $\mathcal{H}$. Time differentiation of (11-110) gives

$$\frac{d\mathcal{H}}{dt} = \int_V d\tau_r \int_{-\infty}^{\infty} d\tau_v \left[\frac{\partial f}{\partial t} \log f + \frac{\partial f}{\partial t} \right] \qquad (11\text{-}111)$$

The second term vanishes since, for a fixed number of molecules N in the gas sample,

$$\int d\tau_r \int d\tau_v \, \partial f/\partial t = \partial/\partial t \int d\tau_r \int d\tau_v f = \partial N/\partial t = 0 \qquad (11\text{-}112)$$

Then
$$d\mathcal{H}/dt = \int d\tau_r \int d\tau_v \, (\partial f/\partial t) \log f \qquad (11\text{-}113)$$

Since, according to Eq. (11-112), the summation of $\partial f/\partial t$ over the entire position and velocity space is equal to zero, we can pair off elements with equal and opposite values of $\partial f/\partial t$. If changes take place in the direction of increased uniformity in the spatial distribution, the negative value of $\partial f/\partial t$ will go with a larger-than-average value of f and the positive value of $\partial f/\partial t$ with a smaller than average value of f. Since the integrand of (11-113) weights the negative value of $\partial f/\partial t$ more heavily than the positive value, it follows that $d\mathcal{H}/dt$ will be negative for changes that tend to increase spatial uniformity in the absence of an external field.* In the approach to equilibrium, the changes in the velocity distribution take place much more rapidly than in the spatial distribution, so that the Maxwellian velocity distribution is established locally long before the equilibrium spatial distribution is attained. It can be shown from the equations of change that the "relaxation time" for establishing the local velocity distribution is of the order of a few collision times and is thus about 10^{-9} seconds under standard conditions.†

* A formal proof of the H theorem for the case of nonuniform states can be given in close analogy to the previous proof of the theorem for uniform states. On substituting into Eq. (11-111) the value of $\partial f/\partial t$ from Boltzmann's equation (11-86), one obtains, in addition to the collision integral of the previous proof, a further integral arising from the second, third, and fourth terms on the left side of (11-86). With the aid of the divergence theorem, this new volume integral can be transformed into a surface integral over the walls of the container and can be shown to vanish if the walls reflect specularly or diffusely. The remainder of the proof that $d\mathcal{H}/dt \leqq 0$ follows exactly as before. See Prob. 11-8.
† See Kennard, *op. cit.*, p. 177.

It has now been demonstrated that $\mathfrak{IC}$ will decrease as the gas approaches its equilibrium state.* There remains, however, the theoretical possibility that $\mathfrak{IC}$ might decrease indefinitely and that the equilibrium state might never be attained. We shall now show that this cannot be the case. The proof will consist in showing that $\mathfrak{IC}$ has a minimum and that the distribution at the minimum is given by the Maxwell-Boltzmann law. In order to take advantage of results previously derived in Appendix 5-2, we rewrite Eq. (11-110), replacing the integral by a sum:

$$\mathfrak{IC} = \sum_i f_i \log f_i \, \Delta\tau \tag{11-114}$$

where $\Delta\tau = \Delta\tau_r \, \Delta\tau_v$. In accordance with the terminology introduced in Appendix 5-2, we may interpret (11-114) as a sum over small cells in the phase space† of equal "volume" $\Delta\tau$. Let $N_i = f_i \, \Delta\tau$ be the number of molecules with representative points in the ith cell. Then (11-114) becomes

$$\begin{aligned}
\mathfrak{IC} &= \sum_i N_i \log \, (N_i/\Delta\tau) \\
&= \sum_i N_i \log N_i - \log \Delta\tau \sum_i N_i \\
&= \sum_i N_i \log N_i - N \log \Delta\tau
\end{aligned} \tag{11-115}$$

where N is the total number of molecules in the gas. In minimizing $\mathfrak{IC}$ we can drop the second term of (11-115), which is merely a constant. The variables of the problem are the N_i, which are not independent because, in a gas at rest, there are two conservation relations: one for the total number of molecules N and the other for the total energy E. We have now to minimize the function

$$F(N_1, N_2, \ldots) = \sum_i N_i \log N_i \tag{11-116}$$

subject to the conditions

$$\sum_i N_i = N \qquad \text{and} \qquad \sum_i N_i \varepsilon_i = E$$

where ε_i is the energy of a molecule in the ith cell. This is exactly the same problem that was previously stated in Eqs. (5-73) and solved by the Lagrange multiplier method. The result for N_i is given in Eq. (5-74) and for $f(\mathbf{v},\mathbf{r},t)$ in (5-77); the latter is the equation for the nor-

---

* In uniform states it is immaterial whether H or $\mathfrak{IC}$ is used, since $\mathfrak{IC} = \int H \, d\tau_r = VH$ where V is the volume of the container.

† This is not quite the phase space of Appendix 5-2, since velocity components are now used as coordinates in place of the momentum components used previously.

malized Maxwell-Boltzmann distribution function.* We have therefore shown, with due regard for the conservation laws, that $\mathcal{3C}$ is minimized by the Maxwell-Boltzmann function.

The preceding argument establishes an important connection between the kinetic-theoretical and statistical-mechanical treatments of equilibrium. Comparison of Eq. (11-115) with Eq. (5-72) reveals that the Boltzmann $\mathcal{3C}$ function is related to the statistical-mechanical probability of a macrostate W by the equation

$$\mathcal{3C} = -\log W + \text{const.} \tag{11-117}$$

where the constant term is fixed for any given specimen of gas and does not depend on the state of motion of the molecules. The kinetic-theory definition of the equilibrium state as one in which the velocity distribution is independent of position and time has been seen to require the vanishing of $d\mathcal{3C}/dt$. The H theorem shows that $\mathcal{3C}$ continually decreases, and we have found that $\mathcal{3C}$ reaches a minimum at equilibrium. The statistical-mechanical definition of the equilibrium state is that it is the state of maximum probability. Equation (11-117) shows that the two definitions are consistent. Both $\mathcal{3C}$ and W measure the extent to which the state of a gas differs from the equilibrium state. The approach to equilibrium is marked by a decrease in $\mathcal{3C}$ toward its minimum value and an increase in W toward its maximum value.

Reversibility, Irreversibility, and Entropy. The reversibility of dynamical processes raises an interesting question with regard to the validity of the H theorem. The classical equations of motion are invariant to time reversal, i.e., to the transformation $t' = -t$. Corresponding to any solution in which the particle trajectories are specified by

$$\mathbf{r}_i = \mathbf{R}_i(t)$$

there will then be an alternative solution to the equations of motion given by $\mathbf{r}_i^* = \mathbf{R}_i(-t)$. Consider two identical systems, S and S^*, in which the particles, at $t = 0$, have identical positions or configurations and equal but opposite velocities: $\mathbf{r}_i^*(0) = \mathbf{r}_i(0)$ and $\dot{\mathbf{r}}_i^*(0) = -\dot{\mathbf{r}}_i(0)$. At any later time t we must have: $\mathbf{r}_i^*(t) = \mathbf{r}_i(-t)$ and $\dot{\mathbf{r}}_i^*(t) = -\dot{\mathbf{r}}_i(-t)$. Thus the configuration of S^* at the time t is the same as that of S at time $-t$, and the velocities of the particles are oppositely directed. The particles of S^* retrace the paths previously followed by the particles of S in the opposite sense, and the past configurations of S become the future configurations of S^*. By the *reversibility* of dynamical processes, one means that for every particular solution of a dynamical problem represented by a system S of moving particles, there is another possible

---

* The distribution function Φ of (5-77) differs slightly from f in that it refers to momentum instead of velocity components and is normalized to unity.

solution represented by the system S^* in which the motions of the particles are reversed.

An objection to the H theorem (Loschmidt's *Umkehreinwand*) arises as follows: Consider a particular state of motion of all the molecules in which $\mathcal{K}$ is decreasing; another possible state of motion is the reverse of the first, and, since the value of $\mathcal{K}$ is unchanged by a reversal of the velocities, the reversed state of motion is one in which $\mathcal{K}$ increases. Therefore, there are an infinite number of possible states of motion for any given value of $\mathcal{K}$ for which $d\mathcal{K}/dt > 0$ in apparent contradiction of the H theorem, which requires that $d\mathcal{K}/dt \leqq 0$. This legitimate objection is met by considering more carefully the meaning of the H theorem. The theorem is a statistical one, based on specific statistical assumptions that enter particularly in the calculation of the effects of molecular encounters. The H theorem does not assert that $\mathcal{K}$ can never increase; it does assert that the average, or most probable, behavior of a gas is characterized by a decreasing $\mathcal{K}$. We have still to explain why some states of motion obey the H theorem and others do not and why the former are enormously more probable than the latter. Before taking this up, we formulate a related objection, sometimes called the "reversibility paradox": Consider all possible states of motion corresponding to a given value of $\mathcal{K}$; for every state in which $\mathcal{K}$ is decreasing there is a reverse state in which $\mathcal{K}$ is increasing at the same rate. Picking states of motion at random, one is as likely to select a "reverse" state for which $\mathcal{K}$ is increasing as a "natural" state with $\mathcal{K}$ decreasing. Hence the average value of $d\mathcal{K}/dt$ should be zero, contradicting the H theorem except when the gas is in equilibrium.

The paradox is resolved by noting that the two averages of $d\mathcal{K}/dt$ are different and that one of them has nothing to do with reality. In the "dynamical" averaging, which was discussed immediately above, equal weights are attached to "natural" and "reverse" states; i.e., the assumption is made that they are equally probable, whereas in fact they are not. The initial states of molecular motion, which follow from any conceivable experimental arrangement, will be "natural" states rather than "reverse" states with overwhelming probability. The "natural" states are ones in which molecular chaos prevails and which change in the direction of increasing randomness and uniformity. The "reverse" states do not obey the principle of molecular chaos. Specific examples are provided by the mixing of two gases that are initially at different pressures, at different temperatures, or of different compositions. In all three cases, random, chaotic motions of the molecules lead to a reduction of $\mathcal{K}$. The "reverse" motions are organizing in character; in the case of interdiffusion, the molecules of different species would behave in a "reverse" motion as if they had received instructions to segregate on opposite sides of the container. No conceivable experimental arrangement could lead to an effect of this kind; it is, however, highly improbable rather than impossible.

The fundamental statistical assumption underlying the Boltzmann equation and the H theorem is the assumption of molecular chaos. It has been pointed out that the "reverse" states do not conform to this assumption, and it is therefore clear that the H theorem cannot apply to these states. *The validity of the H theorem rests on the overwhelming preponderance of molecularly chaotic states of motion (in which $\mathfrak{K}$ decreases) over the reverse, organizing states of motion (in which $\mathfrak{K}$ increases).* Only at equilibrium will the reverse of a molecularly chaotic motion be also a chaotic one; at equilibrium the "natural" and "reverse" motions occur with equal frequency. It can be shown that after equilibrium has been reached in an isolated system, the value of $\mathfrak{K}$ will not remain permanently at its minimum but will undergo small fluctuations in the course of time. Although large fluctuations are improbable, it is theoretically possible for the gas to return to its initial state even though this may be so far from equilibrium that a very large fluctuation is involved. For any ordinary gaseous process, e.g., an expansion into vacuo or an interdiffusion, a spontaneous return to the initial state is so fantastically improbable that it would not be expected to occur in practice at all. Only in the case of Brownian motion and a few related fluctuation phenomena is it possible to observe fluctuations from the most probable or equilibrium state.

The H theorem reflects the intrinsic irreversibility of natural processes as expressed by the second law of thermodynamics or the law of increasing entropy. Boltzmann's theorem provides a direct demonstration of the second law for the gaseous state of matter, in which the irreversibility and the tendency of the entropy to increase are shown to follow from the effects of molecular encounters. Evidently there is a close connection between $\mathfrak{K}$ and the entropy S, which we shall now deduce for the case of a monatomic perfect gas in a state of equilibrium. Using the Maxwell distribution function (5-11) for F, we find that

$$
\begin{aligned}
\mathfrak{K} &= \int_V d\tau_r \int_{-\infty}^{\infty} d\tau_v \, f \log f \\
&= Vn \int d\tau_v \, F \log (nF) \\
&= N(\log n + \langle \log F \rangle) \\
&= N \left(\log n + \tfrac{3}{2} \log \frac{m}{2\pi kT} - \frac{m\overline{v^2}}{2kT} \right) \\
&= N \left(\log n - \tfrac{3}{2} \log T + \tfrac{3}{2} \log \frac{m}{2\pi k} - \tfrac{3}{2} \right) \\
&= N(\log n - \tfrac{3}{2} \log T) + \text{const.}
\end{aligned}
\tag{11-118}
$$

where V is the volume of the container and N the total number of molecules. The entropy of a perfect gas, referred to an unspecified standard state, is given by the thermodynamic formula[*]

$$S = \nu \int C_v \frac{dT}{T} + \nu R \log V + S_0$$

where C_v is the specific heat per mole at constant volume and ν is the number of moles. It has been shown in Sec. 2-4 that $C_v = 3R/2$ for a monatomic perfect gas; hence

$$
\begin{aligned}
S &= \nu R(\log V + \tfrac{3}{2} \log T) + S_0 \\
&= kN[\log (N/n) + \tfrac{3}{2} \log T] + S_0 \\
&= -kN(\log n - \tfrac{3}{2} \log T) + kN \log N + S_0 \\
&= -kN(\log n - \tfrac{3}{2} \log T) + \text{const.}
\end{aligned}
\qquad (11\text{-}119)
$$

Comparison of Eqs. (11-118) and (11-119) then shows that

$$S = -k\mathfrak{H} + \text{const.} \qquad (11\text{-}120)$$

The thermodynamic definition of entropy is given only for equilibrium states; Eq. (11-120) can be used to define the entropy of a nonequilibrium state. The H theorem can then be restated as: $dS/dt \geqq 0$, and in an equilibrium state, $dS/dt = 0$. The remarks made above about the interpretation of the H theorem can be rephrased in terms of the entropy. Finally, by combining Eqs. (11-117) and (11-120), one obtains Boltzmann's well-known relation

$$S = k \log W + \text{const.} \qquad (11\text{-}121)$$

which, when extended to more complicated systems such as imperfect gases, liquids, and solids, is known as *Boltzmann's hypothesis*.[†]

Further developments along these lines appear to be outside the province of an introductory textbook in kinetic theory.[‡] We hope, in conclusion, that the reader has acquired some appreciation of the great, fundamental contributions to this subject that are associated with the names of James Clerk Maxwell and Ludwig Boltzmann.

[*] See, e.g., M. W. Zemansky, "Heat and Thermodynamics," 4th ed., McGraw-Hill Book Company, New York, 1957, p. 175.

[†] The density-fluctuation formula (9-24) was originally derived by Einstein and von Smoluchowski with the aid of Eq. (11-121).

[‡] The reader is referred to Chaps. 6 and 12 of Tolman's book and to Appendix I of D. ter Haar, "Elements of Statistical Mechanics," Rinehart & Company, Inc., New York, 1954.

PROBLEMS

(Probs. 11-7 and 11-8 require some familiarity with vector analysis.)

11-1. Show that the left side of Eq. (11-41) is obtained from a direct evaluation of the left side of Eq. (11-37), i.e., of $n \, d/dz \, \langle v_z{}^2 v_y \rangle$, with the first approximation function (11-31).

11-2. Using the result of Prob. 8-7 for the angle of deflection, show that the transport cross section for viscosity in Sutherland's model is given to first order by

$$\sigma_\eta = 2\pi d^2/3 + 2\pi c' j_2(q)/\varepsilon d^{q-2}$$

where

$$j_2(q) = 4 \int_0^1 dx_m \, x_m{}^{2-q}(2x_m{}^2 - 1)(1 - x_m{}^2)^{1/2} \int_0^{x_m} dx \, x^q(1 - x^2)^{-3/2}$$

Note: $j_2(q)$, which is a function of q only, is identical with the quantity $i_2(q + 1)$, which is tabulated on p. 184 of Chapman and Cowling's book.

11-3. Through substitution of σ_η from the preceding problem into the formula for Ω_η, show that

$$\Omega_\eta = \Omega_\eta{}^{r.s.}[1 + (S/T)]$$

and

$$\eta = \eta^{r.s.}/[1 + (S/T)]$$

where

$$S = c' j_2(q)/k d^q = j_2(q)|u(d)|/k$$

and r.s. denotes the rigid-sphere value. Obtain a formula for $\rho D_{11}/\eta$ on Sutherland's model.

11-4. Generalize the equation of change (11-11) to a mixture of two gases.

11-5. Evaluate the Jacobian determinant of Eq. (11-82) by choosing the x axis along the apse line of the relative orbit.

11-6. Generalize the H theorem to a binary mixture and prove that equilibrium exists if and only if three detailed balancing conditions are satisfied. Show that the two of these conditions which refer to like-molecule encounters lead to Maxwell's law as before and that the third equation, which refers to an unlike-molecule encounter, requires that both gases be at the same temperature and have the same mass motion.

11-7. Let $\mathbf{k}$ be a unit vector along the apse line of the relative orbit directed from the point of closest approach toward the center of force. Show that the initial velocities $\mathbf{v}_1$ and $\mathbf{v}_2$ before an encounter are related to the final velocities $\mathbf{v}_1'$ and $\mathbf{v}_2'$ after the encounter by the vector equations

$$\mathbf{v}_1' - \mathbf{v}_1 = - \frac{2m_2}{m_1 + m_2} \, (\mathbf{v}_r \cdot \mathbf{k})\mathbf{k}$$

$$\mathbf{v}_2' - \mathbf{v}_2 = \frac{2m_1}{m_1 + m_2} \, (\mathbf{v}_r \cdot \mathbf{k})\mathbf{k}$$

11-8. Prove the H theorem in the absence of an external field, taking into account the possibility of a nonuniform spatial distribution. Use the $\mathfrak{K}$ function defined in Eq. (11-110) and follow the procedure outlined in the footnote on page 236. The new terms give rise to the surface integral $\int n \langle v_\nu \log f \rangle \, dS$ where v_ν is the component of $\mathbf{v}$ along the outward normal to the element dS of the surface of the container. Note that the velocity distribution function F must be an even function of v_ν in the immediate neighborhood of a specularly or diffusely reflecting wall.

11-9. Apply the result of Prob. 11-4 for the equation of change of a binary mixture to the mutual-diffusion problem in first approximation. Show that the equation of change for a suitable choice of Q reduces to the basic equation of the momentum-transfer method.

CHAPTER 12

INTERMOLECULAR FORCES

One of the fundamental problems of molecular physics is the determination of the law of force between two molecules. The nature of the intermolecular forces has been touched on briefly in Chap. 1 and taken up in more detail in Chap. 6. Our previous discussion has been concerned less with the intermolecular forces per se than with the way in which certain properties of gases can be understood qualitatively and quantitatively with the aid of certain very simple models of the molecules and their force fields. In this chapter our attention is focused on the origin of the intermolecular forces; on the methods by which they can be most accurately determined, particularly those based on transport theory; and on the results of the most recent and accurate determinations.

12-1. THEORETICAL CLASSIFICATION OF INTERMOLECULAR FORCES

It has already been pointed out that the quantum theory of atomic and molecular structure provides, at least in principle, a method for calculating the interaction at any distance between any pair of molecules. Because of the prohibitively complicated and laborious nature of such computations, which is rapidly intensified with increasing complexity of the molecules involved, detailed quantum-mechanical calculations of reasonable accuracy have been made for only the simplest cases, namely, the interaction of H atoms, He atoms, and H_2 molecules.* In the case of interactions between neutral, nonpolar, spherical molecules, e.g., noble gas atoms, the quantum-theoretical interaction energy can be approximately decomposed into several parts, of which the two most important are the London *dispersion energy* and the *valence repulsion energy*. The London dispersion energy, which makes the principal contribution to the van der Waals attraction of nonpolar molecules, has already been discussed in Sec. 6-2, where it has been shown to vary inversely with the

---

* The most reliable and most extensively tested calculation of an intermolecular potential is for the case of two He atoms. The principal calculations were made by Slater and Kirkwood, *Phys. Rev.*, vol. 37, p. 682, 1931; H. Margenau, *Phys. Rev.*, vol. 56, p. 1000, 1939; and P. Rosen, *Jour. Chem. Phys.*, vol. 18, p. 1182, 1950.

sixth power of the distance.* The valence repulsion energy is associated with the short-range repulsion that sets in when the electron distributions of the two molecules begin to overlap; this has been briefly discussed in Sec. 6-3.† No simple general dependence of the valence repulsion energy on the distance r between centers has been found to exist; as a convenient approximation to the calculated expressions,‡ it has become customary to use the exponential potential $Ae^{-\alpha r}$.

If either one or both of the interacting molecules has a charge or a permanent electric moment, there will be electrostatic forces operating in addition to the forces discussed in the preceding paragraph. In the case of an interaction between two ions, between an ion and a polar molecule (i.e., one possessing a permanent dipole moment), or between two polar molecules, the mutual potential energy can be obtained from classical electrostatics. The interaction energy between an ion, represented by a point charge, and a polar molecule, represented by an ideal dipole, depends on the orientation of the dipole moment vector with respect to the line joining the centers; the interaction energy between two polar molecules, treated as ideal dipoles, is a function of the orientations of both dipoles, being positive (repulsive) for some angles and negative (attractive) for others. When both these interactions are averaged over all possible orientations,§ using the Maxwell-Boltzmann distribution function $e^{-u/kT}$ where u is the mutual potential energy, the resulting expressions give a temperature-dependent attractive interaction. The net attraction results from the distribution law, which statistically favors the orientations of low potential energy, corresponding to attractions, over the orientations of high potential energy, corresponding to repulsions. For large separations or high temperatures, the averaged dipole-dipole interaction energy is readily found to be

$$\bar{u}_K(r) = - \frac{2}{3kT} \frac{\mu_1{}^2 \mu_2{}^2}{r^6} \tag{12-1}$$

where μ_1 and μ_2 are the permanent dipole moments of the two molecules. This expression, which is known as the Keesom *alignment energy*,‖ has the same r^{-6} dependence as the dispersion energy but is much smaller

* The term "dispersion" energy is used because of the relationship between this type of interaction and the dispersion of light, both phenomena depending on the same "oscillator strengths" of the atomic oscillators. The dispersion forces were first calculated by F. London, *Z. Phys. Chem.*, vol. B11, p. 222, 1930.

† The term "valence" repulsion is used because these forces are similar in origin to the attractive forces of the covalent chemical bond.

‡ These are of the form: $P(r)e^{-\alpha r}$ where $P(r)$ is a polynomial with positive and negative powers of r.

§ For a similar calculation, see Prob. 5-7.

‖ W. H. Keesom, *Physik. Z.*, vol. 22, p. 129, 1921.

than the latter for most of the polar gases at ordinary temperatures, outstanding exceptions being the highly polar H_2O and NH_3 molecules.*

Even in the case of nonpolar gases such as H_2, N_2, and CH_4, it is possible to have an electrostatic contribution from the interaction of permanent quadrupole and higher multipole moments; however, these effects are always smaller than the dispersion effect and can usually be neglected. A different type of electrostatic effect arises from the induction of a moment in one molecule by the field due to a charge or permanent moment in the other molecule; the induced moment then interacts with the inducing charge or moment. The electrostatic derivation of the interaction between an inducing dipole and an induced dipole has been presented in simplified form at the end of Sec. 6-2. In the present application, the inducing dipole is a permanent rather than an instantaneous dipole, and the only average to be taken is over the orientations. The result, which is known as the Debye-Falkenhagen *induction energy*,† is

$$\bar{u}_{DF}(r) = -(\alpha_2\mu_1{}^2 + \alpha_1\mu_2{}^2)/r^6 \qquad (12\text{-}2)$$

where μ_1 and μ_2 are the permanent dipole moments and α_1 and α_2 are the polarizabilities of the two interacting molecules. The induction energy has the same r^{-6} dependence as the dispersion and alignment energies and is independent of the temperature. It is always much smaller than the sum of the dispersion and alignment energies. The induction effects associated with permanent quadrupole and higher multipole moments in nonpolar gases are negligible in comparison with the dispersion energy. In the case of noble gas atoms, which have exact spherical symmetry and therefore possess no permanent multipole moments, the alignment energy and the induction energy are both zero. We conclude that, *apart from a few polar gases with exceptionally large molecular dipole moments, the predominant contribution to the van der Waals attraction is from the London dispersion forces.* As has already been indicated, the dispersion forces have a quantum-mechanical basis, and the detailed treatment leads to complicated expressions that are difficult to evaluate. Nevertheless, there exist simple approximate formulas which make it possible to estimate the magnitude of the dispersion force from other known molecular properties. One such formula for the dispersion energy between like, spherical molecules is‡

$$u_L(r) = -\frac{3h\nu_0\alpha^2}{4r^6} \qquad (12\text{-}3)$$

---

* In the case of water, the alignment energy at 20°C is four times as large as the dispersion energy.

† P. Debye, *Physik. Z.*, vol. 21, p. 178, 1920; H. Falkenhagen, *Physik. Z.*, vol. 23, p. 87, 1922.

‡ F. London, *Z. Phys. Chem.*, vol. B11, p. 222, 1930.

where α is the molecular polarizability and ν_0 the predominant natural frequency obtained from the one-term dispersion equation for the refractive index of the gas* (h is Planck's constant).

12-2. SEMIEMPIRICAL DETERMINATION OF INTERMOLECULAR FORCES

Enough has been said to indicate that the nature of the intermolecular forces is qualitatively well understood but that accurate quantitative results cannot be obtained from the theory of these forces except in a few simple cases. The most detailed information about the actual magnitudes of intermolecular forces is obtained by the semiempirical procedure of (1) choosing an intermolecular force law, with one or more adjustable constants, on the grounds of physical plausibility and mathematical convenience, (2) selecting a macroscopic property that can be accurately measured and accurately calculated from the force law assumed, (3) using the results of measurements over a wide range of experimental conditions to fix the values of the adjustable parameters in the force law.† From the foregoing, it would appear that two of the simple models used previously—the model of rigid elastic spheres and the model of point centers of inverse power repulsion—must give entirely unrealistic potential curves. The van der Waals–Sutherland model with an inverse sixth-power attractive potential is more reasonable since, in fact, the valence repulsion energy does rise very steeply as the "outer shells" of electrons begin to interpenetrate. A more satisfactory representation is obtained through the use of the fourth model of Sec. 6-3, in which the intermolecular force, given by Eq. (6-36), is the sum of an inverse power repulsion and an inverse power attraction. The attractive potential is now known to have an inverse sixth-power dependence. The index of the repulsive potential is an adjustable parameter in some calculations; in others, especially of transport properties, it is taken equal to 12, primarily for mathematical convenience, but also because the

---

* See, for example, G. Joos, "Theoretical Physics" 2d ed., Hafner Publishing Company, New York, 1950, p. 450.

† An interesting analogy exists between the determination of intermolecular forces in kinetic theory and the determination of the forces between nuclear particles in nuclear physics. The intermolecular forces can be determined in principle by solving a complicated problem in the quantum theory of atomic and molecular structure, but this is not feasible in practice except in a few simple cases. The nuclear forces can be determined in principle from some form of mesonic field theory, but the correct form of this theory has not yet been ascertained, although some qualitative success has been achieved. The practical procedure in both cases has been to assume a simple, semiempirical force law and to use this force law to calculate the results of experiments, in particular experiments which involve two-particle encounters.

empirical indices are close to this value for many gases. We write the potential energy of interaction for this case in the standard form

$$u(r) = 4\varepsilon[(\sigma/r)^{12} - (\sigma/r)^6] \tag{12-4}$$

This is known as the *Lennard-Jones (12,6) potential*,* and it has been extensively used for calculating both the equilibrium and nonequilibrium properties of nonpolar gases. The parameters ε and σ characterize the particular pair of like or unlike molecules involved; σ is the value of r for which $u(r) = 0$ and ε is the value of $|u(r)|$ at the minimum of the potential curve, which occurs at $r = 2^{1/6}\sigma$. Evidently σ is the distance of closest approach when the relative kinetic energy is initially zero, and ε is the maximum potential energy of attraction.

A fifth model, which has been recently used to calculate equilibrium and transport properties of nonpolar gases, is the *modified expo-six* model,† in which the attractive potential is given by the usual inverse sixth-power law, but the repulsive potential has the exponential form suggested by quantum-theoretical calculations of the valence repulsion energy. This form of interaction, if unmodified, leads to an anomalous behavior of the potential for small separations: as r is decreased, the potential curve rises to a high maximum at r_{max} and then descends to $-\infty$ as $r \to 0$. The spurious maximum occurs at such high energies that it has but little effect on interactions taking place at ordinary temperatures; it is avoided in the modified form of the potential by introducing a rigid-sphere repulsion at $r = r_{max}$. The modified expo-six potential is given by

$$\begin{aligned} u(r) &= \alpha\varepsilon(\alpha - 6)^{-1} \{6\alpha^{-1}e^{\alpha[1-(r/r_m)]} - (r_m/r)^6\} & r \geq r_{max} \\ &= \infty & r < r_{max} \end{aligned} \tag{12-5}$$

where ε is the value of $|u(r)|$ at the minimum of the potential curve, which occurs at $r = r_m$, and α is a parameter measuring the steepness of the exponential repulsion. The three parameters ε, r_m, and α are adjusted to fit experimental data and their values depend on the specific types of molecules involved. Although other models for the intermolecular forces have been investigated, we shall consider in the following only those calculations that are based on the Lennard-Jones (12,6) and the modified expo-six potentials.

A particular functional representation of the intermolecular force can be considered satisfactory only if it is possible to secure agreement with all experimental data involving a particular pair of molecules with a single choice of the parameters that appear in the law of force. Considering that a variety of physical properties are available and that each

* J. E. Lennard-Jones, *Proc. Royal Soc.*, vol. A106, pp. 441, 463, 1924.

† The original expo-six model was extensively applied by R. A. Buckingham (see *Proc. Royal Soc.*, vol. A168, pp. 264, 378, 1938); references to the modified version are given below.

may be measured over a wide range of experimental conditions, one readily sees that this constitutes a severe test of the assumed laws of interaction, particularly in view of the small number of flexible parameters. We now consider some macroscopic properties that lend themselves to an accurate determination of the intermolecular law of force between neutral, nonpolar molecules.* The types of experimental data that can be used for this purpose may be classified in four categories: (1) equilibrium properties of solids, (2) equilibrium properties of gases, (3) nonequilibrium properties of gases, (4) molecular-beam scattering experiments. The last of these is the most direct method and will be considered first. A beam of neutral atoms or molecules of relatively high energy (several hundred electron volts) is scattered in a gas at room temperature $(kT = 0.025$ ev). The total collision cross section is measured for several values of the beam energy, which is well defined and so large that the motion of the target molecules can be neglected. The energy dependence of the cross section can be used to determine the intermolecular potential over part of its range; because of the high energies involved, this method gives information about the short-range repulsive region of interaction only.†

Determination of Force Constants from Equilibrium Properties. Fairly accurate information about intermolecular forces can be obtained in some cases from calculating the potential energy of the crystal lattice and using data on the low-temperature properties of the solid—e.g., density, compressibility, heat of sublimation, etc.—to fix the unknown force constants. A number of precise calculations have been made for neutral, nonpolar molecules such as the rare gases, N_2, and CH_4, all of which crystallize in the face-centered cubic form characteristic of close-packed spheres.‡ The total potential energy of the lattice is calculated from the assumed law of interaction and is minimized with respect to the lattice distance (distance between nearest neighbors) to obtain the lattice energy at absolute zero. The experimental values of the lattice distance and the heat of sublimation, both extrapolated to 0°K, can then be used to fix two of the force constants; the negative heat of sublimation at 0°K is equal to the potential energy of the lattice plus the zero-point energy.§ The

---

* The long-range forces between molecules having permanent dipole and quadrupole moments have recently been investigated by microwave methods that make use of the pressure-broadening of spectral lines (the broadening depends on the long-range forces). See C. H. Townes and A. L. Schawlow, "Microwave Spectroscopy," McGraw-Hill Book Company, Inc., New York, 1955.

† I. Amdur et al., *Jour. Chem. Phys.*, vol. 22, pp. 664, 670, 1071, 1954.

‡ Buckingham, *loc. cit.*; O. K. Rice, *Jour. Amer. Chem. Soc.*, vol. 63, p. 3, 1941; J. Corner, *Trans. Faraday Soc.*, vol. 44, p. 914, 1948; E. A. Mason and W. E. Rice, *Jour. Chem. Phys.*, vol. 22, p. 843, 1954.

§ The zero-point energy, previously mentioned on page 86, must be taken into account in accurate work and is large for H_2 and He. It can be expressed in terms of

solid-state data have commonly been used in conjunction with gas properties in the determination of the force-law parameters.

The equilibrium gas properties that provide the most useful information about intermolecular forces are the virial coefficients, especially the second virial coefficient $B(T)$, and the zero-pressure Joule-Thomson coefficient $\mu_0(T)$. The latter coefficient, which is defined as the rate of change of temperature with pressure in an isenthalpic expansion, can be evaluated in terms of the virial coefficients and their temperature derivatives. In the zero-pressure limit, the Joule-Thomson coefficient depends only on $B(T)$ and dB/dT. Measurements of Joule-Thomson coefficients can then be used to supplement p-V-T data on the temperature variation of $B(T)$. The second virial coefficient can be calculated from Eq. (6-26) when the intermolecular potential $u(r)$ has been specified. The Lennard-Jones (12,6) potential contains the two adjustable parameters ε and σ, which are varied to give the best fit to measured values of B or μ_0 over a range of temperatures (actually, values of B at two temperatures determine both parameters). Parameters determined from the second virial coefficients can be used to calculate the Joule-Thomson coefficients and the agreement with experiment is excellent. The observed temperature variation of B and of μ_0 is very satisfactorily represented by the (12,6) potential for many nonpolar gases over a wide temperature range; the good agreement holds not only for spherically symmetric molecules such as the rare-gas atoms but also for slightly asymmetric molecules such as N_2 and CO_2.* Similar results have been obtained for the modified expo-six potential.† The latter function contains three adjustable parameters and existing measurements of $B(T)$ over the widest available temperature range do not suffice to determine these parameters uniquely. If one parameter, say α, is fixed at a reasonable value, the $B(T)$ and $\mu_0(T)$ data can be used to obtain the other parameters ε and r_m quite precisely; however, another reasonable choice of α, together with revised values of ε and r_m, can give just as good agreement with the data. Since these data leave the value of one parameter flexible within rather wide limits, it is necessary to use some other physical property, e.g., a solid state or transport property, to fix the three constants. The crystal data have been used for this purpose and good agreement has been found with the measured virial coefficients of nonpolar spherical and nearly spherical molecules.† The parameter α of the expo-six potential corresponds to

---

the Debye characteristic temperature (see Fowler, *op. cit.*, p. 123). It is actually the sum of the potential and zero-point energies which is minimized to obtain the equilibrium lattice distance at 0°K.

* Detailed references to measurements and calculations of second virial coefficients may be found in Hirschfelder, Curtiss, and Bird, *op. cit.*, chap. 3.

† W. E. Rice and J. O. Hirschfelder, *Jour. Chem. Phys.*, vol. 22, p. 187, 1954; E. A. Mason and W. E. Rice, *Jour. Chem. Phys.*, vol. 22, p. 843, 1954.

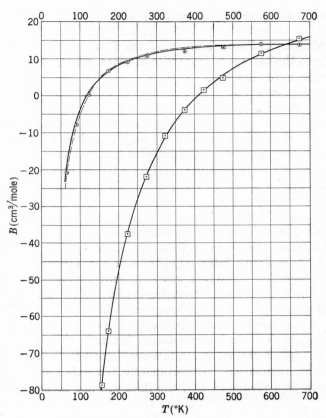

FIG. 12-1. The second virial coefficients of neon and argon as functions of the temperature (B in cm³/mole and T in °K). Experimental values for neon are represented by circles ⊙ and for argon by squares ⊡. The neon data are mainly due to Holborn and Otto, Z. Physik, vol. 33, p. 1, 1925; vol. 38, p. 359, 1926; the argon data are taken from Holborn and Otto, Z. Physik, vol. 23, p. 77, 1924, vol. 30, p. 320, 1924, vol. 33, p. 1, 1925, and from Michels, Wijker, and Wijker, Physica, vol. 15, p. 627, 1949. The full curve for neon is the theoretical curve for the (12,6) potential, using as parameters: $\varepsilon/k = 34.9$°K and $\sigma = 2.78$ Å. The dashed curve for neon is the theoretical curve for the expo-six potential with parameters $\alpha = 14.5$, $\varepsilon/k = 38.0$°K, and $r_m = 3.147$ Å. In the case of argon, the theoretical curves for the (12,6) and expo-six potentials are almost indistinguishable over the entire temperature range. The full curve shown for argon corresponds about equally well to a (12,6) potential with parameters: $\varepsilon/k = 119.5$°K, and $\sigma = 3.421$ Å, or to an expo-six potential with parameters $\alpha = 14$, $\varepsilon/k = 123.2$°K, and $r_m = 3.866$ Å.

the index of repulsion in the Lennard-Jones model; the inverse twelfth power gives good agreement with crystal data in general but a better fit to the combined data can be obtained in a few cases by using a different index of repulsion (from 9 to 14). In Fig. 12-1 we compare observed values of the second virial coefficients $B(T)$ with values calculated with the (12,6) and expo-six potentials. Reliable information about inter-molecular forces cannot as yet be obtained from third virial coefficients.

Determination of Force Constants from Transport Properties. Turning finally to the transport properties of gases, we observe that accurate determinations of the interaction potentials require the use of the advanced transport theory of Chapman and Enskog. The quite accurate first-approximation formulas for the mutual diffusion and viscosity coefficients in terms of a spherically symmetric interaction potential have been developed in detail in Secs. 8-3 and 11-2, respectively. Accurate formulas for the thermal conductivity of a monatomic gas and for the thermal-diffusion ratio of a gas mixture are also available.* Information about the force law between like molecules can be obtained from measuring the temperature dependences of the viscosity coefficient, the self-diffusion coefficient and the isotopic thermal diffusion ratio; in the case of monatomic gases, the thermal conductivity can also be used. At the present time, the viscosity data provide more accurate information about the like-molecule interaction than do measurements of the other transport properties. The best way in principle to determine the parameters of the unlike-molecule interaction is to measure the mutual-diffusion coefficient over a wide range of temperatures. The first-approximation formula for D_{12} has been found (in Sec. 8-3) to depend only on the unlike-molecule interaction; the forces between like molecules do not enter until the second approximation, which is a very small fraction (~ 1 per cent) of the first approximation. Unfortunately, few data are available on the temperature dependence of D_{12}, the data are not highly accurate, and uncertainty exists with regard to the value of the composition to which a particular measured value of D_{12} is to be assigned. The thermal-diffusion factor, although it depends on both like and unlike molecule interactions, has its temperature-dependence determined largely by the unlike interactions; hence, measurements of thermal diffusion at different temperatures can give some information about the forces between unlike molecules. The second virial coefficients, viscosities, and thermal conductivities of binary mixtures depend on both like- and unlike-molecule force laws; however, these properties are so insensitive to the unlike-molecule interaction that they are not useful in its determination. Some success has been attained through the use of semiempirical combining rules that relate the force constants between unlike molecules to those between like molecules. Thus, in the case of the (12,6) potential of Eq. (12-4), the unlike-molecule parameters σ_{12} and ε_{12} can be expressed in terms of the like-

---

* Chapman and Cowling, *op. cit.* An alternative method of obtaining higher approximations has been developed by T. Kihara; see Kihara, "Imperfect Gases," Asakusa, Tokyo, 1949 (in Japanese) and *Rev. Mod. Phys.*, vol. 25, p. 831, 1953.

molecule parameters σ_1, ε_1, and σ_2, ε_2 by the simple rules

$$\sigma_{12} = \tfrac{1}{2}(\sigma_1 + \sigma_2) \qquad \varepsilon_{12} = (\varepsilon_1\varepsilon_2)^{\frac{1}{2}} \qquad (12\text{-}6)$$

which are found to give fairly good results when applied to the calculation of the second virial coefficients, viscosities, and thermal conductivities of binary mixtures as well as the mutual-diffusion coefficients and thermal-diffusion ratios.

The calculations of transport properties mentioned in the preceding paragraph are laborious for the cases of the (12,6) and expo-six potentials because of the large amount of numerical work involved. The angles of deflection χ have first to be determined by numerical integration of Eq. (8-21) for sets of values of the impact parameter b and the initial relative velocity v_r. The tabulated values of χ are then used to evaluate numerically the cross section integrals of Eqs. (8-48) and (8-49). The first-approximation formulas for D_{12} and η involve the transport integrals Ω_D and Ω_η, which have been defined in Eqs. (8-83) and (11-61), respectively. Numerical integration is again required to obtain the Ω integrals from the calculated cross sections. Other integrals similar to Ω_D and Ω_η need to be evaluated in order to obtain higher approximations to the transport coefficients. The necessary calculations and tabulations have been carried out for the (12,6) potential[*] and for the modified expo-six potential.[†] It is of interest to compare the parameters of the (12,6) potential derived from (a) crystal data, (b) second virial coefficients, and (c) viscosity coefficients; such a comparison is shown in Table 12-1 for the rare gases and

TABLE 12-1. PARAMETERS OF THE LENNARD-JONES (12,6) POTENTIAL

Substance	Crystal data		Virial coefficients		Viscosity coefficients	
	$\sigma(\text{Å})$	ε/k	$\sigma(\text{Å})$	ε/k	$\sigma(\text{Å})$	ε/k
Ne	2.82	36.5°	2.78	34.9°	2.79	35.7°
A	3.46	119°	3.41	120°	3.42	124°
Kr	3.60	165°	3.60	171°	3.61	190°
Xe	3.98	229°	4.10	221°	4.06	229°
N_2	3.64	108°	3.70	95.1°	3.68	91.5°

N_2. The agreement is seen to be good but the discrepancies in some cases are too large to be attributed to experimental error. The values of the

* Kihara and Kotani, *Proc. Phys. Math. Soc. Japan*, vol. 24, p. 76, 1942, vol. 25, p. 602, 1943; de Boer and van Kranendonk, *Physica*, vol. 14, p. 442, 1948; J. Rowlinson, *Jour. Chem. Phys.*, vol. 17, p. 101, 1949; Hirschfelder, Bird, and Spotz, *Jour. Chem. Phys.*, vol. 16, p. 968, 1948; *Chem. Rev.*, vol. 44, p. 205, 1949; Hirschfelder, Curtiss, and Bird, *op. cit.*

† E. A. Mason, *Jour. Chem. Phys.*, vol. 22, p. 169, 1954.

parameters depend slightly on the temperature range of the $B(T)$ or $\eta(T)$ data used to determine them. Since the equilibrium and non-equilibrium properties emphasize different regions of the potential curve, the use of an unrealistic or oversimplified potential can lead to discrepancies in that the force constants that purchase accuracy in one region of the potential curve will forfeit accuracy in other regions. Even though the (12,6) potential is somewhat oversimplified and leads to slightly different parameters for virial-coefficient and viscosity data, one can expect that the parameters obtained from the $B(T)$ data will reproduce other equilibrium properties accurately and that the parameters adjusted to the $\eta(T)$ data will be suitable for calculating nonequilibrium (transport) properties. Thus the virial-coefficient force constants have been found to give accurate Joule-Thomson coefficients, and the viscosity force constants lead to accurate predictions of the self-diffusion coefficient. As an example, we compare the accurately measured value* of D_{11} for xenon at 27.3°C extrapolated to 1 atm with the value calculated using the (12,6) potential and force constants from viscosity data: the calculated value is 0.0571 and the measured value 0.0576 $\pm$ 0.0009 cm²/sec. For argon at 0°C and 1 atm the calculated value is 0.154 and the measured values† 0.156 $\pm$ 0.002 and 0.158 $\pm$ 0.002 cm²/sec.

The modified expo-six potential has also been extensively used for transport calculations.‡ The three adjustable parameters are fixed by supplementing measurements of $B(T)$ with crystal data in the manner indicated above. In the case of the rare gases, it has been found that the potential parameters that fit the equilibrium properties also give fairly good agreement in most cases with the transport properties, including the temperature variation of the viscosity, the thermal conductivity, the self-diffusion coefficient, and the isotopic thermal-diffusion ratio. The agreement appears to be slightly better for the expo-six potential than for the (12,6) potential. In Fig. 12-2 we compare observed values of the viscosity coefficient $\eta(T)$ with values calculated with these two potentials. It has been pointed out that both potentials reproduce the measurements of $B(T)$ satisfactorily for nearly spherical molecules such as N_2. Satisfactory agreement with the experimental data for $\eta(T)$ in the case of nearly spherical molecules can also be obtained with both potentials; however, the parameters that fit the equilibrium properties do not give

* S. Visner, Report K-688, K-25 Plant, Carbide and Carbon Chemicals Corporation, Oak Ridge, 1951; *Phys. Rev.*, vol. 82, p. 297, 1951.

† E. B. Winn, *Phys. Rev.*, vol. 80, p. 1024, 1950; F. Hutchinson, *Jour. Chem. Phys.*, vol. 17, p. 1081, 1949.

‡ Mason and Rice, *Jour. Chem. Phys.*, vol. 22, p. 843, 1954; E. A. Mason, *Jour. Chem. Phys.*, vol. 23, p. 49, 1955; K. P. Srivastava, *Jour. Chem. Phys.*, vol. 26, p. 579, 1957.

a good fit to the transport properties, and vice versa. The general result for nonspherical, nonpolar molecules is that, whereas the temperature variation of one or more properties may be satisfactorily reproduced, different sets of potential parameters are needed to fit different properties of the same substance. This behavior, which is found to hold for both the (12,6) and expo-six potentials, appears to indicate that a nonspherical

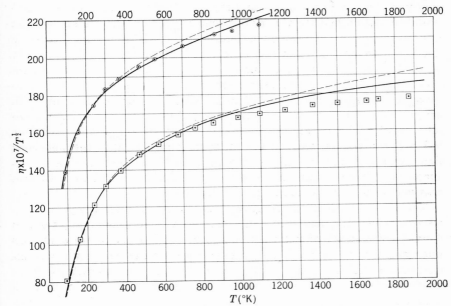

FIG. 12-2. The viscosity coefficients of neon and argon as functions of the temperature (the ordinate is $\eta \times 10^7$ gm cm^{-1} sec^{-1} divided by $T^{1/2}$). Experimental values for neon are represented by circles ⊙ and those for argon by squares ⊡. The experimental data are listed in Table A of the General Appendix, where references are given to the original sources. The full curves are theoretical curves for the (12,6) potential, and the dashed curves have been calculated with the expo-six potential. The values of the (12,6) potential parameters used for neon are $\varepsilon/k = 35.7°$K and $\sigma = 2.789$ Å; for argon, $\varepsilon/k = 124°$K and $\sigma = 3.418$ Å. The parameters of the expo-six potential for both neon and argon are taken to be the same as in Fig. 12-1. Note that according to the rigid-elastic-sphere model the graph would show a straight line of zero slope. The high-temperature discrepancies have not yet been explained.

molecule cannot be adequately represented by a spherically symmetric intermolecular potential, as is assumed for mathematical convenience in the calculations of advanced transport theory. The second virial coefficients of nonspherical, nonpolar molecules have been calculated on the basis of several simplified nonspherical models, e.g., rigid ellipsoids of revolution ("elliptical billiard balls"!), but transport calculations have not been made.* Virial coefficients of polar gases have been calculated by adding to the (12,6) potential an extra term representing the angle-dependent electrostatic interaction of two ideal dipoles, but no transport calculations have been made with this potential.†

The Special Cases of H_2 and He. The lightest gases, H_2 and He, require special attention because one is not justified in neglecting quantum effects for these gases, even at room temperature. The quantum theory of the virial coefficients and the quantum reformulation of Boltzmann's equation and the theory of transport phenomena are beyond the scope of this book. The modifications introduced by quantum theory are of two sorts: (*a*) the *diffraction effects*, already briefly discussed in Sec. 1-3, which arise from the wave nature of the molecule, and (*b*) the *indistinguishability effects*, previously mentioned on page 92, which characterize the quantum statistics. The use of classical mechanics and the classical Maxwell-Boltzmann statistics is justified when these effects are both small. The diffraction effects are small if the mean molecular de Broglie wave length $\overline{\Lambda}$ (see p. 7) is short compared with the molecular dimensions or the "range" of the intermolecular forces. The indistinguishability effects are small if $\overline{\Lambda} \ll n^{-\frac{1}{3}}$, i.e., if the mean de Broglie wave length is much less than the average distance between neighboring molecules in the gas. Since $\overline{\Lambda} \approx h/(mkT)^{\frac{1}{2}}$, the quantum effects are largest for low temperatures and light gases. The indistinguishability effects, which depend on both temperature and density, are evidently much smaller than the diffraction effects and can be entirely neglected except for H_2 and He in the neighborhood of 1°K. The diffraction effects are negligible at room temperature for all gases except H_2 and He but must be taken into account at low temperatures. The cases of H_2 and He are of particular interest because they are the only gases for which quantum-mechanical calculations of reasonable accuracy have been made. The intermolecular potential, deduced approximately from these calculations, is somewhat too complicated to use in transport computations. The approximate theoretical potential curve may, however, be compared with the empirical potential curves obtained by fitting the Lennard-Jones (12,6) and modified expo-six potentials to measured gas properties in the manner described above (taking quantum deviations into account). The

---

* Of interest are Kihara's calculations of $B(T)$ with the ellipsoidal model and a model of cylinders capped by hemispheres (capsule-shaped and pill-shaped) in which the (12,6) potential is assumed and the interaction distance taken to be the shortest distance between suitably defined molecular "cores." See T. Kihara, *Jour. Phys. Soc. Japan*, vol. 6, p. 289, 1951. A different type of nonspherical potential has been used by J. Corner, *Proc. Royal Soc.*, vol. A192, p. 275, 1948.

† W. H. Stockmayer, *Jour. Chem. Phys.*, vol. 9, p. 398, 1941; Margenau and Myers, *Phys. Rev.*, vol. 66, p. 307, 1944; J. S. Rowlinson, *Trans. Faraday Soc.*, vol. 45, p. 974, 1949, vol. 47, p. 120. 1951.

agreement between the theoretical curves for helium and the empirical curves obtained by applying the (12,6) potential* and the expo-six potential† to virial-coefficient and viscosity data is satisfactory in that the empirical curves differ from each other by about as much as they deviate from the theoretical curves.   This concludes our review of this important subject, which extends far outside the boundaries of the conventionally defined kinetic theory of gases.‡

* De Boer and Michels, *Physica*, vol. 5, p. 945, 1938; De Boer and Lunbeck, *Physica*, vol. 14, p. 510, 1948; De Boer and van Kranendonk, *Physica*, vol. 14, p. 442, 1948.

† Mason and Rice, *Jour. Chem. Phys.*, vol. 22, p. 522, 1954.

‡ The most comprehensive reference work is the treatise by Hirschfelder, Curtiss, and Bird, *op. cit.*   A briefer account is given by Beattie and Stockmayer in Taylor and Glasstone, "A Treatise on Physical Chemistry: States of Matter," D. Van Nostrand Company, Inc., Princeton, N.J., 1951.

GENERAL APPENDIX

TABLES OF TRANSPORT COEFFICIENTS FOR A FEW SIMPLE GASES

Table A. Viscosity Coefficients

Gas	$T(°K)$	$\eta \cdot 10^7$ gm cm^{-1} sec^{-1}	Ref.	Gas	$T(°K)$	$\eta \cdot 10^7$ gm cm^{-1} sec^{-1}	Ref.
Ne	90	1311	g	N$_2$	90.2	651	k
	90	1320	i		90	630	h
	160	2026	i		160	1068	h
	240	2708	i		240	1505	h
	300	3173	i		300	1786	h
	373	3646	a		300	1781	b
	473	4248	a		400	2191	b
	558	4708	c		500	2559	b
	702	5454	c		572	2797	c
	867	6230	c		681	3141	c
	959	6626	c		763	3374	c
	1100	7210	c		873	3664	c
A	90	763	i		986	3930	c
	160	1298	i		1098	4192	c
	240	1878	i		1259	4585	j
	300	2270	i		1321	4720	j
	373	2695	a		1564	5195	j
	473	3223	a		1691	5425	j
	575	3685	c	O$_2$	90	691	h
	674	4115	c		160	1202	h
	766	4484	c		240	1728	h
	857	4815	c		300	2071	h
	987	5257	c		400	2568	b
	1100	5632	c		500	3017	b
	1230	6015	j		556	3233	c
	1372	6435	j		675	3693	c
	1503	6785	j		769	4013	c
	1650	7148	j		881	4370	c
	1709	7315	j		963	4612	c
	1868	7685	j		1102	5012	c

TABLE A. VISCOSITY COEFFICIENTS (*Continued*)

Gas	$T(°K)$	$\eta \cdot 10^7$ gm cm^{-1} sec^{-1}	Ref.	Gas	$T(°K)$	$\eta \cdot 10^7$ gm cm^{-1} sec^{-1}	Ref.
CO$_2$	190	966	*h*	CH$_4$	90	365	*h*
	240	1209	*h*		160	629	*h*
	300	1495	*h*		240	919	*h*
	300	1493	*d*		300	1116	*h*
	400	1944	*d*		373	1331	*e*
	500	2354	*d*		474	1605	*e*
	572	2637	*c*		557	1813	*c*
	682	3021	*c*		653	2026	*c*
	765	3283	*c*		772	2264	*c*
	885	3639	*c*	Xe	293	2260	*f*
	985	3906	*c*		400	3009	*f*
	1097	4191	*c*		450	3351	*f*
	1231	4540	*j*		550	3954	*f*
	1351	4815	*j*				
	1553	5254	*j*				
	1686	5537	*j*				

a. Trautz and Binkele, *Ann. d. Physik*, vol. 5, p. 561, 1930.
b. Trautz and Melster, *ibid.*, vol. 7, p. 409, 1930.
c. Trautz and Zink, *ibid.*, vol. 7, p. 427, 1930.
d. Trautz and Kurz, *ibid.*, vol. 9, p. 981, 1931.
e. Trautz and Sorg, *ibid.*, vol. 10, p. 81, 1931.
f. Trautz and Heberling, *ibid.*, vol. 20, p. 118, 1934.
g. Trautz and Zimmermann, *ibid.*, vol. 22, p. 189, 1935.
h. Johnston and McCloskey, *Jour. Phys. Chem.*, vol. 44, p. 1038, 1939.
i. Johnston and Grilly, *Jour. Phys. Chem.*, vol. 46, p. 948, 1942.
j. V. Vasilesco, *Ann. d. Physique*, vol. 20, p. 292, 1945.
k. Van Itterbeek, van Paemel, and van Lierde, *Physica*, vol. 13, p. 88, 1947.

TABLE B. THERMAL CONDUCTIVITIES

Gas	$T(°K)$	$K \cdot 10^7$ cal cm^{-1} sec^{-1} °K^{-1}	Ref.	Gas	$T(°K)$	$K \cdot 10^7$ cal cm^{-1} sec^{-1} °K^{-1}	Ref.
Ne	90.2	489	b	Xe	194.7	91	b
	194.7	876	b		273.2	123	b
	273.2	1110	b		373.2	168	b
	373.2	1357	b		491.2	208	b
	491.2	1595	b		579.1	237	b
	579.1	1789	b	CH_4	90	227	a
A	90.2	141	b		180	467	a
	194.7	293	b		280	755	a
	273.2	394	b		380	1122	a
	373.2	506	b	O_2	80	170	a
	491.2	614	b		180	395	a
	579.1	685	b		280	597	a
Kr	194.7	152	b		380	803	a
	273.2	208	b	CO_2	180	198	a
	373.2	272	b		280	361	a
	491.2	340	b		380	563	a
	579.1	388	b				

a. H. Johnston and E. Grilly, *Jour. Chem. Phys.*, vol. 14, p. 233, 1946.
b. W. Kannuluik and E. Carman, *Proc. Phys. Soc.* (London), vol. 65B, p. 701, 1952.

TABLE C. SELF-DIFFUSION COEFFICIENTS
All data are for 1 atm pressure

Gas	$T(°K)$	D_{11} cm²/sec	Ref.	Gas	$T(°K)$	D_{11} cm²/sec	Ref.
Ne	77.7	0.0492	c	N₂	77.7	0.0168	c
	194.7	0.255	c		194.7	0.104	c
	273.2	0.452	c		273.2	0.185	c
	353.2	0.703	c		273.2	0.172	e
	77.7	0.0134	c		353.2	0.287	c
	194.7	0.0830	c	O₂	77.7	0.0153	c
	273.2	0.157	b, c		194.7	0.104	c
	353.2	0.249	c		273.2	0.187	c
Kr	293	0.093	a		273.2	0.175	e
Xe	194.7	0.0257	g		353.2	0.301	c
	300.5	0.0576	d	CO₂	194.8	0.0516	f
	378	0.0900	g		273.2	0.0970	f
CH₄	90.2	0.0266	c		273.2	0.0974	c
	194.7	0.0992	c		312.8	0.1248	f
	273.2	0.206	c		362.6	0.1644	f
	353.2	0.318	c				

a. W. Groth and P. Harteck, *Z. Elektrochem.*, vol. 47, p. 167, 1941.
b. F. Hutchinson, *Jour. Chem. Phys.*, vol. 17, p. 1081, 1949.
c. E. B. Winn, *Phys. Rev.*, vol. 80, p. 1024, 1950.
d. S. Visner, *Phys. Rev.*, vol. 82, p. 297, 1951.
e. E. R. S. Winter, *Trans. Faraday Soc.*, vol. 47, p. 342, 1951.
f. Amdur, Irvine, Mason, and Ross, *Jour. Chem. Phys.* vol. 20, p. 436, 1952.
g. I. Amdur and T. F. Schatzki, *Jour. Chem. Phys.*, vol. 27, p. 1049, 1957.

TABLE D. MUTUAL-DIFFUSION COEFFICIENTS

All data are for 1 atm pressure. The composition of the mixture has not been given, since the variation with concentration is of the order of the experimental error ($\sim$1 per cent).

Gas pair	T(°K)	D_{12} cm²/sec	Ref.	Gas pair	T(°K)	D_{12} cm²/sec	Ref.
H_2-A	287.9	0.828	d	N_2-CO_2	273	0.144	a
	354.2	1.111	d		288	0.158	b
	418.0	1.714	d		298	0.165	c
He-A	273.2	0.641	a	H_2-N_2	273	0.674	a
	287.9	0.697	d		288	0.743	b
	354.2	0.979	d	H_2-CH_4	273	0.625	a
	418.0	1.398	d		298	0.726	c
A-Xe	194.7	0.0508	e	H_2-O_2	273	0.697	a
	273.2	0.0962	e	N_2-O_2	273	0.181	a
	329.9	0.137	e	O_2-CO_2	273	0.139	a
	378.0	0.176	e	CO_2-CH_4	273	0.153	a
H_2-CO_2	273	0.550	a				
	288	0.619	b				
	298	0.646	c				

a. "International Critical Tables," vol. V.

b. L. Boardman and N. Wild, *Proc. Royal Soc.*, vol. A162, p. 511, 1937.

c. Boyd, Stein, Steingrimsson, and Rumpel, *Jour. Chem. Phys.*, vol. 19, p. 548, 1951.

d. R. A. Strehlow, *Jour. Chem. Phys.*, vol. 21, p. 2101, 1953.

e. I. Amdur and T. F. Schatzki, *Jour. Chem. Phys.*, vol. 27, p. 1049, 1957, and vol. 29, p. 1425, 1958.

TABLE E. THERMAL-DIFFUSION FACTORS

All nonisotopic data refer to mixtures of equal proportions. The temperature ranges given for the isotopic mixtures are appropriate to the two bulbs of the diffusion apparatus (T and T' are the temperatures of the cold and hot bulbs, respectively). A single temperature is given for the nonisotopic mixtures listed, since the experimental method, including a special graphical analysis of the data, made possible a point determination of α for a specific temperature. This method is not available for isotopic mixtures because of the small separations. The observed value of α for an isotopic mixture, which is a mean value over the range $T \to T'$, can be identified with an unaveraged value of α at an appropriate intermediate temperature T_r. An approximate formula for T_r, due to H. Brown, is: $T_r = [TT'/(T' - T)] \log (T'/T)$.

Gas pair	$T(°\mathrm{K})$	α	Ref.	Gas pair	$T \to T'(°\mathrm{K})$	α	Ref.
He-A	185	0.36	d	Ne^{20}-Ne^{22}	90–195	0.0162	b
	293	0.38			90–296	0.0187	
	369	0.39			195–296	0.0233	
	465	0.39			195–490	0.0254	
He-Kr	185	0.43	d		302–645	0.0302	
	293	0.45			460–638	0.0318	
	369	0.45			621–819	0.0346	
	465	0.45		A^{36}-A^{40}	90–195	0.00315	b
He-Xe	233	0.43	d		90–296	0.00709	
	293	0.43			195–296	0.0116	
	369	0.43			195–495	0.0146	
	465	0.43			273–623	0.0182	
Ne-A	185	0.148	d		455–685	0.0218	
	293	0.174			638–833	0.0250	
	369	0.190		O_2^{16}-$O_2^{16,18}$	195–373	0.0099	f
	465	0.191			295–528	0.0128	f
Ne-Kr	185	0.21	d		296–703	0.0145	f
	293	0.29		N_2^{14}-$N_2^{14,15}$	195–429	0.0071	g
	369	0.31			294–678	0.0091	g
	465	0.32			195–623	0.0051	e
Ne-Xe	185	0.26	d	$C^{12}H_4$-$C^{13}H_4$	296–573	0.0074	a
	293	0.30			296–728	0.0080	a
	369	0.33			195–433	0.0072	g
	465	0.37			295–708	0.011	g
A-Kr	185	0.038	d	$N^{14}H_3$-$N^{15}H_3$	197–298	−0.010	c
	294	0.075			197–373	−0.004	c
	370	0.104			298–457	+0.010	c
	465	0.149					
A-Xe	185	0.063	d				
	294	0.087					
	369	0.139					
	465	0.176					

a. A. O. Nier, *Phys. Rev.*, vol. 56, p. 1009, 1939.
b. L. G. Stier, *Phys. Rev.*, vol. 62, p. 548, 1942.
c. Watson and Woernley, *Phys. Rev.*, vol. 63, p. 181, 1943.
d. K. E. Grew, *Proc. Royal Soc.*, vol. A189, p. 402, 1947.
e. A. K. Mann, *Phys. Rev.*, vol. 73, p. 412, 1948.
f. Whalley, Winter, and Briscoe, *Trans. Faraday Soc.*, vol. 45, p. 1085, 1949.
g. Davenport and Winter, *Trans. Faraday Soc.*, vol. 47, p. 1160, 1951.

TABLE OF FUNDAMENTAL CONSTANTS

Gas constant per mole: $R = 8.3166 \times 10^7$ erg mole^{-1} °C^{-1}
Avogadro's number: $L = 6.0247 \times 10^{23}$ mole^{-1}
Boltzmann's constant: $k = 1.3804 \times 10^{-16}$ erg °C^{-1}
Standard molar volume: $V_0 = 22{,}421$ cm^3 mole^{-1}
Standard number density: $n_0 = 2.6871 \times 10^{19}$ cm^{-3}
Absolute temperature of ice point: $T_0 = 273.16$°K
Atomic mass unit: $m(O^{16})/16 = 1.6598 \times 10^{-24}$ gm
Electronic charge: $e = 4.8029 \times 10^{-10}$ esu
Faraday's constant: $F = Le = 2.8936 \times 10^{14}$ esu mole^{-1}
Planck's constant: $h = 6.6252 \times 10^{-27}$ erg sec
Velocity of light: $c = 2.99793 \times 10^{10}$ cm sec^{-1}
Electron rest mass: $m_e = 9.1085 \times 10^{-28}$ gm
Proton rest mass: $m_p = 1.6724 \times 10^{-24}$ gm

SOME INTEGRAL FORMULAS

One of the commonest reasons for the vanishing of a definite integral is that the integrand is an odd function of the variable and the limits are symmetric about zero. The function $f(x)$ is called *even* if $f(-x) = f(x)$ and *odd* if $f(-x) = -f(x)$. It is easily shown that

$$\int_{-a}^{a} f(x)\, dx = 2 \int_0^a f(x)\, dx \qquad \text{if } f(x) \text{ is even}$$

$$\int_{-a}^{a} f(x)\, dx = 0 \qquad \text{if } f(x) \text{ is odd}$$

An important form of definite integral, appearing frequently in kinetic theory calculations, is the following:

$$I_n(a) = \int_0^\infty x^n e^{-ax^2}\, dx \qquad a > 0$$

where n is a nonnegative integer. Elementary methods give

$$I_1(a) = \int_0^\infty x e^{-ax^2}\, dx = \frac{1}{2a}$$

In order to evaluate I_0, we form

$$I_0^2(a) = \int_0^\infty e^{-ax^2}\, dx \int_0^\infty e^{-ay^2}\, dy$$
$$= \int_0^\infty dx \int_0^\infty dy\, e^{-a(x^2+y^2)}$$
$$= \int_0^{\pi/2} d\phi \int_0^\infty dr\, r e^{-ar^2}$$
$$= \tfrac{1}{2}\pi I_1(a) = \frac{\pi}{4a}$$

where the double integral over the first quadrant of the (x,y) plane has been transformed from cartesian to plane-polar coordinates. Hence

$$I_0(a) = \int_0^\infty e^{-ax^2}\, dx = \frac{1}{2}\left(\frac{\pi}{a}\right)^{\frac{1}{2}}$$

The integrals I_2, I_3, I_4, . . . can now be obtained by differentiating under the integral sign with respect to the parameter a. Thus

$$I_2(a) = -\frac{dI_0}{da} = \frac{1}{4a}\left(\frac{\pi}{a}\right)^{\frac{1}{2}}$$

$$I_3(a) = -\frac{dI_1}{da} = \frac{1}{2a^2}$$

$$I_4(a) = -\frac{dI_2}{da} = \frac{3}{8a^2}\left(\frac{\pi}{a}\right)^{\frac{1}{2}}$$

$$\cdot$$
$$\cdot$$
$$\cdot$$

$$I_{n+2}(a) = -\frac{dI_n}{da}$$

BIBLIOGRAPHY

This bibliography is a compilation of books referred to in the text, plus a few additional references that are briefly described. Complete periodical references are given in footnotes to the text and are not repeated here.

BOOKS ON KINETIC THEORY

Boltzmann, L.: "Vorlesungen über Gastheorie." Leipzig: J. A. Barth, 1923.

Chapman, S., and T. G. Cowling: "The Mathematical Theory of Nonuniform Gases." London: Cambridge University Press, 1939. Addendum, 1952.

Cowling, T. G.: "Molecules in Motion." London: Hutchinson & Co., Ltd., 1950.
A concise, elementary, and very readable introduction to kinetic theory with a minimum of mathematics.

Grew, K. E., and T. L. Ibbs: "Thermal Diffusion in Gases." London: Cambridge University Press, 1952.

Herzfeld, K. F.: "Kinetische Theorie der Wärme," Müller-Pouillet's "Lehrbuch der Physik." Brunswick, Germany: Vieweg-Verlag, 1925.

Herzfeld, K. F., and H. M. Smallwood: Chap. 1 of "A Treatise on Physical Chemistry," vol. 2, "States of Matter" (ed. by H. S. Taylor and S. Glasstone). Princeton, N.J.: D. Van Nostrand Company, Inc., 1951.
An English translation of part of Herzfeld's "Kinetische Theorie der Wärme" with added material (e.g., on thermal diffusion) to take account of subsequent developments.

Hirschfelder, J. O., C. F. Curtiss, and R. B. Bird: "Molecular Theory of Gases and Liquids." New York: John Wiley & Son, Inc., 1954.

Jeans, J. H.: "An Introduction to the Kinetic Theory of Gases." London: Cambridge University Press, 1946.

Kennard, E. H.: "Kinetic Theory of Gases." New York: McGraw-Hill Book Company, Inc., 1938.

Kihara, T.: "Imperfect Gases." Tokyo: Asakusa Bookstore, 1949. Translated by U.S. Office of Air Research, Wright-Patterson Air Force Base, Dayton, Ohio.

Knudsen, M.: "The Kinetic Theory of Gases." London: Methuen & Co., Ltd.; New York: John Wiley & Sons, Inc., 1950.

Loeb, L. B.: "The Kinetic Theory of Gases," 2d ed. New York: McGraw-Hill Book Company, Inc., 1934.

Maxwell, J. C.: "Scientific Papers" (ed. by W. Niven). Paris: Hermann & Cie, 1927; New York: Dover Publications, 1952. Referred to as "Collected Works" throughout the text.

Patterson, G. N.: "Molecular Flow of Gases." New York: John Wiley & Sons, Inc., 1956. Contains applications of kinetic theory to problems in aerodynamics.

Perrin, J.: "Brownian Movement and Molecular Reality." London: Taylor and Francis, 1910.

BOOKS ON STATISTICAL MECHANICS AND THERMODYNAMICS

Beattie, J. A., and W. H. Stockmayer: Chap. 2 of "A Treatise on Physical Chemistry," vol. 2, "States of Matter" (ed. by H. S. Taylor and S. Glasstone). Princeton, N.J.: D. Van Nostrand Company, Inc., 1951.

Chandrasekhar, S.; M. C. Wang and G. E. Uhlenbeck; M. Kac: "Selected Papers on Noise and Stochastic Processes" (ed. by N. Wax). New York: Dover Publications, 1954.

Fowler, R. H.: "Statistical Mechanics," 2d ed. London: Cambridge University Press, 1936.

Hill, T. L.: "Statistical Mechanics." New York: McGraw-Hill Book Company, Inc., 1956.

Landau, L. D., and E. M. Lifschitz: "Statistical Physics." London: Oxford University Press, 1938.

Sears, F. W.: "Thermodynamics, the Kinetic Theory of Gases, and Statistical Mechanics," 2d ed. Reading, Mass.: Addison-Wesley Publishing Company, 1953.

Slater, J. C.: "Introduction to Chemical Physics." New York: McGraw-Hill Book Company, Inc., 1939.

ter Haar, D.: "Elements of Statistical Mechanics." New York: Rinehart & Company, Inc., 1954.

Tolman, R. C.: "The Principles of Statistical Mechanics." London: Oxford University Press, 1938.

Zemansky, M. W.: "Heat and Thermodynamics," 4th ed. New York: McGraw-Hill Book Company, Inc., 1957.

BOOKS ON MISCELLANEOUS SUBJECTS

Bhagavantam, S.: "Scattering of Light and the Raman Effect." New York: Chemical Publishing Company, Inc., 1942.

Born, M.: "Optik." Berlin: J. Springer, 1933; Ann Arbor, Mich.: J. W. Edwards, Publisher, 1943.

Courant, R.: "Differential and Integral Calculus." New York: Interscience Publishers, Inc., 1937.

Glasstone, S., K. Laidler, and H. Eyring: "The Theory of Rate Processes." New York: McGraw-Hill Book Company, Inc., 1941.

Goldstein, H.: "Classical Mechanics." Reading, Mass.: Addison-Wesley Publishing Company, 1950. Chapter 3, on the two-body central-force problem, is recommended to supplement Sec. 8-1.

Hinshelwood, C. N.: "The Kinetics of Chemical Change." London: Oxford University Press, 1941.

Jeffreys, H. and B.: "Methods of Mathematical Physics." London: Cambridge University Press, 1956.

Joos, G.: "Theoretical Physics," 2d ed. New York: Hafner Publishing Company, 1950.

Massey, H. S. W., and E. H. S. Burhop: "Electronic and Ionic Impact Phenomena." London: Oxford University Press, 1952.

Maxwell, J. C.: "A Treatise on Electricity and Magnetism," 3d ed. London: Oxford University Press, 1892; New York: Dover Publications, 1954.

Millikan, R. A.: "Electrons, Protons, Photons, Neutrons, Mesotrons, and Cosmic Rays." Chicago: University of Chicago Press, 1947.

Page, L.: "Introduction to Theoretical Physics," 2d ed. Princeton, N.J.: D. Van Nostrand Company, Inc., 1935.

Partington, J. R.: "An Advanced Treatise on Physical Chemistry," vol. 1. London: Longmans, Green & Co., Ltd., 1949.

Perrin, J.: "Atoms," 2d ed. London: Constable & Co., Ltd., 1923.

Lord Rayleigh: "The Theory of Sound," 2d ed. London: Macmillan & Co., Ltd., 1894–1896; New York: Dover Publications, 1945.

Rosenfeld, L.: "The Theory of Electrons." New York: Interscience Publishers, Inc., 1951.

Smith, K. F.: "Molecular Beams." London: Methuen & Co., Ltd.; New York: John Wiley & Sons, Inc., 1955.

Smyth, H. de W.: "Atomic Energy for Military Purposes." Princeton, N.J.: Princeton University Press, 1945.

Soodak, H., and E. C. Campbell: "Elementary Pile Theory." New York: John Wiley & Sons, Inc., 1950.

Townes, C. H., and A. L. Schawlow: "Microwave Spectroscopy." New York: McGraw-Hill Book Company, Inc., 1955.

Uspensky, J. V.: "Introduction to Mathematical Probability." New York: McGraw-Hill Book Company, Inc., 1937.

NAME INDEX

SUBJECT INDEX